*INTERNATIONAL SERIES OF MONOGRAPHS ON
PURE AND APPLIED BIOLOGY*

Division: **ZOOLOGY**

GENERAL EDITOR: G. A. KERKUT

VOLUME 17

THE PHYSIOLOGY OF
MOSQUITOES

A

OTHER TITLES IN THE ZOOLOGY DIVISION

General Editor: G. A. KERKUT

OTHER DIVISIONS IN THE SERIES ON PURE AND APPLIED BIOLOGY

BIOCHEMISTRY

BOTANY

MODERN TRENDS IN PHYSIOLOGICAL SCIENCES

PLANT PHYSIOLOGY

THE PHYSIOLOGY OF
MOSQUITOES

BY

A. N. CLEMENTS

Department of Physiology and Biochemistry
University of Southampton

A Pergamon Press Book

THE MACMILLAN COMPANY
NEW YORK
1963

THE MACMILLAN COMPANY

60 Fifth Avenue

New York 11, N.Y.

This book is distributed by

THE MACMILLAN COMPANY — NEW YORK

pursuant to a special arrangement with

PERGAMON PRESS LIMITED

Oxford, England

Copyright © 1963

PERGAMON PRESS LTD.

Library of Congress Card Number 62–19280

Printed in Great Britain by

THE BAY TREE PRESS, STEVENAGE, HERTS

CONTENTS

ACKNOWLEDGEMENTS

ONE of the pleasures of writing this book has been the contact with the many people who have helped me during its preparation. To name only a few, J. D. Gillett, J. C. Jones and J. J. Laarman have made a most valuable contribution by reading and criticizing parts of the manuscript, and A. W. A. Brown, A. J. Haddow, A. O. Lea, P. F. Mattingly and E. T. Nielsen have helped me in a variety of ways. To these and the many others I express my gratitude. I am also greatly indebted to Miss Barbara Trott, Librarian of the Commonwealth Institute of Entomology, for much assistance. Thanks are due to D. S. Bertram and R. G. Bird and to the Editors of the Transactions of the Royal Society of Tropical Medicine and Hygiene for permission to reproduce electron micrographs, which form a valuable addition to the book.

I am grateful to the following publishers for permission to reproduce illustrations: Akademie-Verlag G.m.b.H. (*Deutsche Entomologische Zeitschrift*); Akademische Verlagsgesellschaft Geest und Portig K.-G. (*Zoologisches Anzeiger*); American Entomological Society (*Entomological News*); American Institute of Biological Sciences (*Entomological Review*); British Museum (Natural History) (Edwards, *Mosquitoes of the Ethiopian Region;* Lang, *A Handbook of British Mosquitoes;* Marshall, *The British Mosquitoes*); Cambridge University Press (*Journal of Experimental Biology; Parasitology;* Christophers, *Aëdes aegypti*); Clarendon Press, Oxford (*Quarterly Journal of Microscopical Science*); Commonwealth Institute of Entomology (*Bulletin of Entomological Research*); Ecological Society of America and Duke University Press (*Ecology*); Ejnar Munksgaard Ltd (*Oikos*); Elsevier Publishing Company (*Tropical and Geographical Medicine*); Entomological Society of America (*Annals of the Entomological Society of America*); VEB Gustav Fischer Verlag (*Zoologische Jahrbucher*); S. Hirzel-Verlag (*Acustica*); Imprimerie Albert Kundig (*Revue Suisse de Zoologie*); *Indian Journal of Medical Research;* Macmillan & Co., Ltd. (*Nature*); Ohio State University and Ohio Academy of Science (*Ohio Journal of Science*); Presses Universitaires de France (*Bulletin Biologique de la France et de la Belgique*); Royal Entomological Society of London (*Proceedings and Transactions of the Royal Entomological Society of London*); W. B. Saunders Co., Ltd. (Boyd, *Malariology*); Smithsonian Institution (*Smithsonian Miscellaneous Collection*); Springer-Verlag (*Osterreichische Zoologische Zeitschrift, Wilhelm Roux' Archiv für Entwicklungsmechanik der Organismen, Zeitschrift für*

Morphologie und Okologie der Tiere, Zeitschrift für Vergleichende Physiologie); Stanford University (*Microentomology*); Tôhoku University (*Science Reports of Tôhoku University*); University Press of Liverpool (*Annals of Tropical Medicine and Parasitology*); University Press, Notre Dame, Indiana (*American Midland Naturalist*); Verlag Birkhäuser AG (von Buddenbrock, *Vergleichende Physiologie*); Verlag für Recht und Gesellschaft A.G. (*Acta Tropica*); Verlag der Zeitschrift für Naturforschung (*Zeitschrift für Naturforschung*); Wistar Institute of Anatomy and Biology (*Journal of Morphology*); World Health Organization (*Bulletin and Monograph of the World Health Organization*).

CHAPTER 1

THE EGG

Embryonic Development

Mosquito eggs are elongate and bilaterally symmetrical and bounded by a thick shell which is pierced at the anterior pole by the micropyle. The newly-laid egg is filled with yolk granules separated from one another by a fine cytoplasmic network while a thin layer of cytoplasm free of yolk granules, the periplasm, is found under the shell, being thicker at the anterior and posterior poles. The bigger yolk granules are composed of protein (Nicholson, 1921) and between these are many small fat droplets associated with Golgi apparatus (Nath, 1929). At the posterior pole is a saucer-shaped heavily-staining region of pole plasm. Before fertilization the nucleus lies in a small volume of yolk-free cytoplasm, situated towards the anterior pole in *Anopheles maculipennis* (Ivanova-Kazas, 1949) and about the middle of the egg and near the surface in *Culex pipiens* (Idris, 1960a).

Sperm are thought to pass through the micropyle as the egg traverses the genital chamber at oviposition. Polyspermy is normal in *Culex pipiens*, many sperm penetrating the egg but only one fertilizing it. The eggs of *Culex pipiens* are usually laid during the first maturation division of the oocyte nucleus, sometimes during the second. After the second maturation division the female pronucleus migrates to the centre of the egg, and the polar bodies, consisting of the other daughter nuclei of the meiosis, remain in the periplasm and later degenerate. At 21°C fusion of male and female pronuclei occurs 30–45 min after oviposition (Idris, 1960a).

Five divisions convert the zygote nucleus to a group of 32 cleavage energids in the centre of the egg, each consisting of a nucleus embedded in a small volume of cytoplasm (Fig. 1). The following 2 divisions yield a sphere of 64 and then 128 energids which migrate with their cytoplasm towards the surface. At the 128-nuclei stage in *Culex pipiens* a small number of cleavage energids penetrate the pole plasm, absorbing some of its basophilic material, and continue their migration to the posterior pole. After the next division the ooplasm withdraws from the posterior pole leaving a liquid-filled space into which pass those cleavage energids which

1

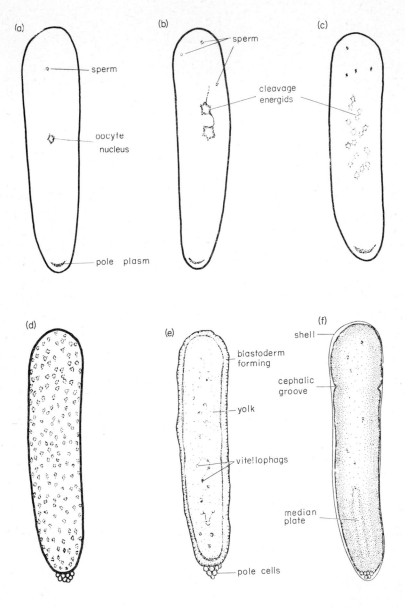

FIG. 1a–f. Cleavage and blastoderm formation in *Culex pipiens*.

(a) Egg before cleavage; (b–d) certain stages from 1st to 8th cleavages; (e) preblastoderm stage (cf. Fig. 2a); (f) blastoderm at start of differentiation (cf. Fig. 2c). (From Idris, 1960a).

have penetrated the pole plasm, now visibly differentiated as spherical pole cells. These by division form a group of approximately 12 pole cells (Fig. 1d) (Idris, 1960a). In *Anopheles maculipennis* 4 cleavage energids normally penetrate the pole plasm and by division form a group of 20–30 pole cells (Ivanova-Kazas, 1949). The 8th division, which occurs shortly after the mass of cleavage energids have penetrated the periplasm, should theoretically yield 256 nuclei but in *Culex pipiens* approximately 16 nuclei remain dispersed in the yolk becoming vitellophags and these do not divide simultaneously with the others. The periplasm doubles in thickness during the early cleavages.

Owing to the position of the fusion nucleus cleavage starts near the anterior pole in *Anopheles maculipennis* (Ivanova-Kazas, 1949) and near the middle of the egg in *Culex pipiens* (Idris, 1960a). In *Culex pipiens* eggs at 18°C the number of nuclei increases logarithmically during the first 3 hr with a division every 20 min but after that time, when blastoderm formation starts, the rate of cleavage falls off (Christophers, 1960). Development proceeds at a similar rate in *Anopheles maculipennis* (Ivanova-Kazas, 1949). Blastoderm formation starts after the 9th division when furrows in the egg surface begin to separate the nuclei, starting near the middle of the egg where the energids first reach the edge of the yolk. A further division occurs and the furrows penetrate deeper into the periplasm soon forming complete cell walls so that a blastoderm of columnar cells surrounds the yolk and cuts off the group of pole cells (Fig. 2). At this time the egg of *Culex pipiens* contains 35–50 vitellophags and rather fewer than 1000 blastoderm cells (Idris, 1960a).

The blastoderm next thickens ventrally forming the germ band (Fig. 2c), a condition which is reached in *Culex pipiens* after 5 hr development at 21°C (Idris, 1960a). Considerable changes take place between 5 and 20 hr development in the dimensions and form of the germ band. It grows to the anterior pole and also grows backwards past the posterior pole to extend upwards and along the dorsal surface so that it almost encircles the egg (Fig. 3a–e). Idris (1960b) considers that this extension results from growth of the whole germ band and not simply of the caudal region, and this is confirmed by the fact that momentary irradiation of the posterior end of the egg during extension damages different segments between the front and tip of the abdomen depending on the time of irradiation (Oelhafen, 1961). Elsewhere the blastoderm becomes reduced to a delicate nucleated membrane but as the germ band is wide this thin region consists only of 2 narrow lateral bands linked by an area on the dorsal surface where the caudal end of the germ band fails to reach the head (Fig. 5) (Christophers, 1960). The embryo as a whole does not sink into the yolk at any stage. After 10 hr development the germ band

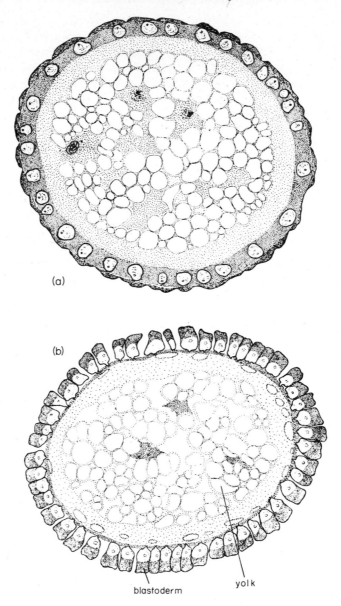

(a)

(b)

blastoderm   yolk

FIG. 2a–d. Blastoderm formation and gastrulation in *Culex pipiens*.

(a) T.S. through middle of embryo in preblastoderm stage; (b) T.S. through middle of embryo in uniform-blastoderm stage; (c) T.S. towards posterior end of embryo at start of differentiation; (d) T.S. through middle of embryo during elongation of germ band (cf. Fig. 3c). (From Idris, 1960a).

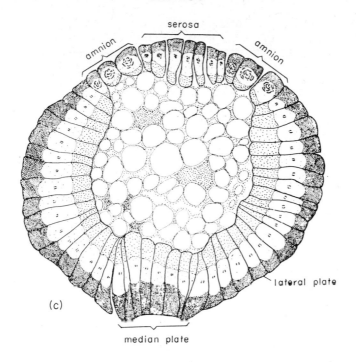

(c)

median plate

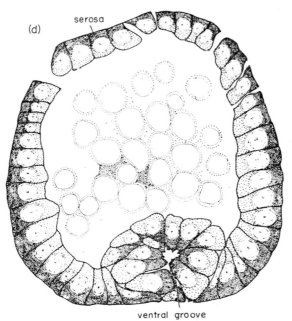

ventral groove

starts to shorten, probably through redistribution of egg material (Ivanova-Kazas, 1949) and simultaneously blastokinesis occurs, the embryo rotating clockwise on its longitudinal axis through 180° (Idris, 1960a). Blastokinesis occurs in a similar manner in *Anopheles* (Ivanova-Kazas, 1949), *Culiseta* and *Aedes* (Rosay, 1959). After 20 hr development at 21°C the caudal end of the germ band has retracted to the posterior pole of the egg; contraction of the embryo now stops and by lateral growth the germ band starts to encircle the yolk (Fig. 3).

The formation, elongation and contraction of the germ band provide useful time guides when considering the other changes which occur during this period. A short time after the formation of the germ band in *Culex pipiens* a transverse furrow, the cephalic (or cervical) groove, appears about one-third of the length of the egg behind the anterior pole (Fig. 1f). Shortly afterwards another furrow has developed anterior to the cephalic groove and 7 more posterior to it giving the appearance of segmentation (Fig. 3b). Most of the furrows are transient, however, and during the extension of the germ band all but the cephalic groove disappear (Fig. 3c–e). Shortly afterwards segmentation of the embryo begins affecting both the ectoderm and mesoderm, and several segments are delimited within the space of 10 min. The cervical groove is thought by Idris (1960a) to become the boundary between the mandibular and maxillary segments, by Christophers (1960) to separate head and thorax. By damaging the areas before and behind the cervical groove with ultraviolet radiation Oelhafen (1961) confirmed that it separates the prospective mandibular and maxillary segments. By the time the embryo has finished contracting, 3 thoracic segments, 8 abdominal segments and a terminal cell mass have been delimited posteriorly while the head comprises an anterior lobe which later shows the labral, antennal, intercalary, mandibular, maxillary and labial segments (Fig. 3f). Only the germ band is segmented at this time and the dorsal surface is not segmented until the embryo is 36 hr old. The respiratory siphon develops later from part of the 8th abdominal segment, and the anal segment of the larva, which is probably composite, develops from the terminal mass (Christophers, 1950; Idris, 1960a). Segmentation is said to occur before germ band formation in *Anopheles maculipennis* (Ivanova-Kazas, 1949) but it seems likely that the segment boundaries are merely transient grooves.

Gastrulation, or germ-layer formation, starts in *Culex pipiens* after 5 hr development at 21°C with the differentiation of a median plate 9–12 cells wide near the posterior end of the germ band, distinguishable through the centripetal movement of nuclei (Fig. 2c). The blastoderm cells which will form amnion and serosa are also discernable at this time. The median plate sinks inwards forming a groove at the posterior end of

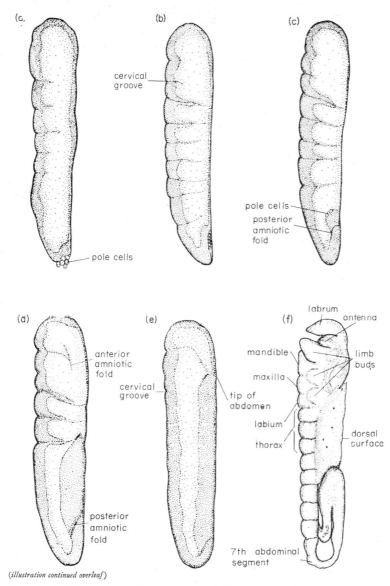

(a,

(b)

cervical
groove

(c)

pole cells

pole cells
posterior
amniotic
fold

(d)

anterior
amniotic
fold

cervical
groove

(e)

tip of
abdomen

labrum
antenna

(f)

mandible

maxilla

labium

thorax

limb
buds

dorsal
surface

posterior
amniotic
fold

7th abdominal
segment

(illustration continued overleaf)

FIG. 3a–i. Elongation and contraction of the germ band, segmentation, and organ formation in *Culex pipiens*.

(a–e) Lateral aspect showing progressive elongation of germ band, formation and disappearance of furrows; (f) lateral aspect at 16 hr, germ band shortening, segmentation apparent; (g) dorsal aspect at 20 hr, growth of mesenteron; (h) lateral aspect at 22 hr; (i) lateral aspect at 36 hr, completion of organ formation. (From Idris, 1960a).

B

(illustration continued from previous page)

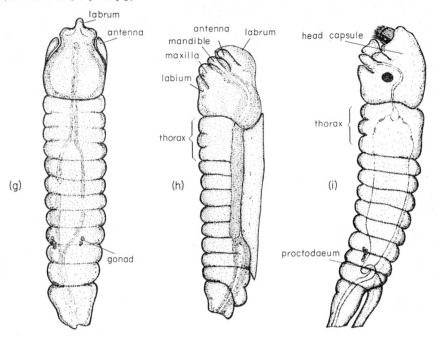

the germ band (Fig. 1f); this ventral groove extends forwards and 2 lateral plates which flank it, each 14–17 cells wide, move medially to cover the median plate and fuse in the midline (Fig. 2d). The lateral plates fuse first near the middle of the egg about 20 min after the germ band starts to lengthen. The cells of the median plate spread out to form mesoderm, or possibly mesendoderm, and the lateral plates form ventral ectoderm (Fig. 4b). Owing to the anterior extension of the caudal region of the germ band, sections through the posterior part of the embryo during the period of extension show 2 plates of ectoderm and 2 groups of mesoderm cells (Figs. 4a, 5). A similar process of gastrulation occurs in *Anopheles maculipennis* (Ivanova-Kazas, 1949).

Shallow invaginations at the edge of the germ band produce double-layered folds which grow over the germ band enclosing it in a double envelope (Fig. 4a, b). The thin outer layer or serosa is continuous with the extra-embryonic blastoderm; the inner layer or amnion, which is considered to be an extension of the germ band, is at first composed of cubical cells (Fig. 4a) but these later become flattened (Fig. 5). The posterior amniotic fold is the first part to arise and forms a hood-shaped fold over the caudal end of the germ band shortly after the germ band has started to extend over the dorsal surface of the egg (Fig. 3c). Its growth keeps pace

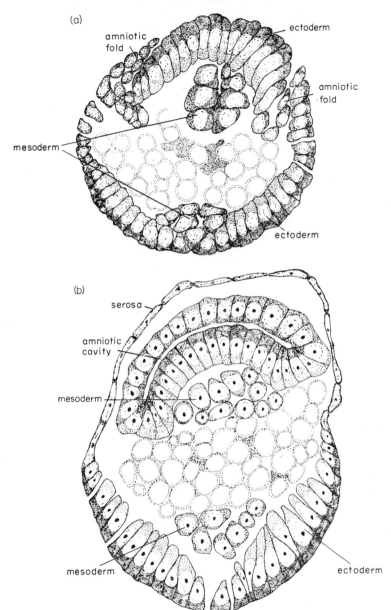

FIG. 4a–b. T.S. through the posterior region of a *Culex pipiens* embryo during elongation of the germ band, showing stages in development of the embryonic membranes and mesoderm formation.

(a) At about the stage shown in Fig. 3a; (b) at about the stage shown in Fig. 3e. (From Idris, 1960a).

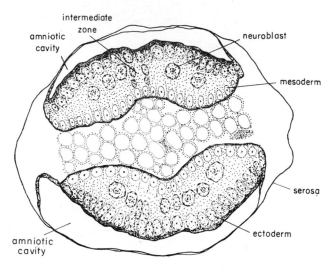

FIG. 5.   T.S. through the middle of a *Culex pipiens* embryo after completion
of segmentation. (From Idris, 1960a).

with the forward movement of the caudal region so that when the germ
band has reached its full length the edge of the posterior amniotic fold is
in approximately the same position as that in which it arose, although
amnion and serosa now cover the elongate tail region of the embryo
(Fig. 3e).   The anterior amniotic fold arises later and has only covered a
small length of the head region by the time the germ band has reached its
maximum length.   The anterior and posterior amniotic folds eventually
meet and fuse, enclosing the embryo in the amniotic cavity.   Contraction of
the embryo leaves the dorsal surface of the egg covered only by membrane,
but within 24 hr development (at 21°C) the lateral edges of the embryo
have started to grow over the yolk and will later enclose it completely, a
process called dorsal closure.   The serosa secretes a serosal cuticle in the
form of a thick hard chitinous sac around the embryo (p. 26) (Idris,
1960a; Christophers, 1960).

    The foregut and hindgut develop from the stomodaeum and procto-
daeum respectively, invaginations which arise before the germ band
shortens, in the head region and in a pocket formed by the caudal amniotic fold at the posterior end of the germ band.   Cells carried at the
tip of the stomodaeum grow backwards in the form of two ribbons which
meet and fuse with similar ribbons of cells growing forwards from the
proctodaeum (Fig. 7) to form the mesenteron region of the midgut around
the yolk. Idris (1960a) considers that parts of the invaginated median plate
caught up by the stomodaeum and proctodaeum form the mesenteron.

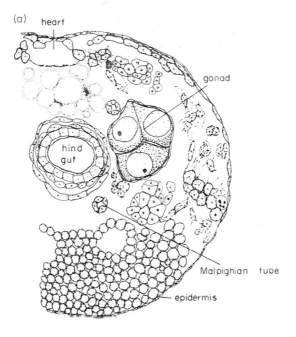

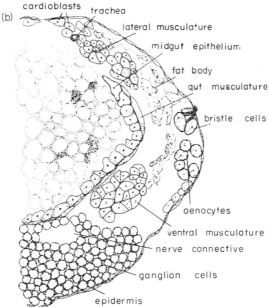

Fig. 6a–b. T.S. through a 36-hr embryo of *Culex pipiens* (cf. Fig. 3i). (a) 7th abdominal segment; (b) 4th abdominal segment. (From Idris, 1960a).

Ivanova-Kazas (1949) thinks that the median plate is a highly-elongated blastopore with endoderm at its ends and that this endoderm is carried inwards by invagination of the stomodaeum and proctodaeum. Christophers (1960) states that 2 visibly-differentiated groups of cells, the anterior and posterior polar (or mesenteron) rudiments are carried inwards by the stomodaeum and proctodaeum to form the mesenteron. Whatever may be the origin of the mesenteron cells the manner of mesenteron formation is agreed by all authors. It is thought that vitellophags play no part in mesenteron formation in *Culex pipiens* because no mesenteron appears when endoderm is prevented from forming by ligation, the vitellophags remaining in the yolk (Idris, 1960b).

In later development the end of the stomodaeum, which is closed by a membrane, invaginates into the mesenteron and forms the oesophageal invagination (Fig. 8). The end of the proctodaeum is also closed by a membrane but both membranes later disappear and the cavities of the stomodaeum, mesenteron and proctodaeum become continuous. The mesenteron remoulds itself anteriorly to form 8 caeca while 5 Malpighian tubes, at first solid, arise from the anterior end of the proctodaeum. The anal papillae arise within the proctodaeum as solid outgrowths of its wall and only later become situated externally (Ivanova-Kazas, 1949; Christophers, 1960).

The pole cells are pushed forward ahead of the caudal region as the germ band elongates and come to lie in the yolk near the blind end of the proctodaeum. At this time the pole cells assume the form of primary sex cells, very large cells with big nuclei and rather sparse cytoplasm, and they retain this form throughout embryonic development. After contraction of the embryo the pole cells are found to be divided into 2 sexual rudiments on either side of the posterior mesenteron rudiments (Fig. 7) and they come to lie in their final position in the 5th or 6th abdominal segment. The sexual rudiments are later covered by a thin layer of mesoderm cells which form the gonad sheaths and proximal genital ducts.

Certain organs start to form before contraction of the germ band is complete, notably the gut and the head appendages, but most organs develop after contraction. Transient protuberances in the thoracic region of *Anopheles maculipennis* have been interpreted as legs by Ivanova-Kazas (1949) but these appendages were not described in *Culex pipiens* by Idris (1960a) or Christophers (1960). The ectoderm gives rise to the epidermis and oenocytes, and the salivary glands and tracheae develop from ectodermal invaginations. The origin of nervous tissue has not been described in detail but according to Christophers (1960) a neural groove appears in the ventral midline and the ventral nerve cord develops from neuroblasts associated with it: the head blastoderm, originally single

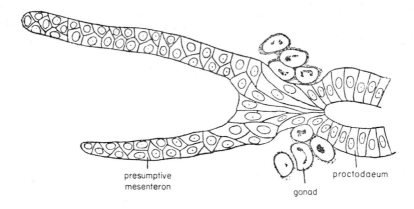

FIG. 7. Section through the tip of the proctodaeum of an *Anopheles maculipennis* embryo at the extended germ band stage, showing the posterior mesenteron rudiments and pole cells. (From Ivanova-Kazas, 1949).

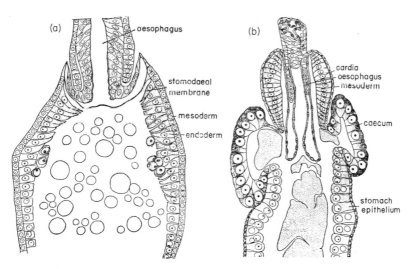

FIG. 8a–b. Stages in the development of the oesophageal invagination and midgut in *Anopheles maculipennis*.

(a) Horizontal section through the gut of an embryo after contraction of the germ band; (b) horizontal section through the gut of a larva before hatching. (From Ivanova-Kazas, 1949).

layered, gives rise to cell masses which fuse to form the proto-, deuto- and tritocerebral lobes of the brain, and 3 other masses fuse to form the suboesophageal ganglion. Three thoracic and 8 abdominal ganglia develop in the ventral nerve cord. The lateral ocelli become pigmented after 24 hr development at 21°C (Idris, 1960a). The mesoderm starts to differentiate later than the ectoderm. Coelomic pouches have not been seen by any author. The main mass of mesoderm forms the somatic musculature and a thin layer of mesoderm covers the gut forming the visceral musculature. The fat body develops from mesoderm cells loosely arranged in the body cavity and other mesoderm cells form nephrocytes. The heart appears after the dorsal closure as a straight tube with ostia. During the 12 hr before hatching in *Culex pipiens* histological differentiation occurs and the organs become capable of functioning, as seen in the beating of the heart.

Experimental Embryology

Idris (1960b) has investigated the organization of the eggs of *Culex pipiens* by freeing eggs of their chorions and then transversely ligaturing them with fine nylon fibres tied in different positions and at different stages of development. In describing the positions of ligatures Idris considered the length of the egg to be 100 per cent, the posterior pole being 0 per cent and the anterior pole 100 per cent; an egg ligatured in the middle would therefore be ligatured at 50 per cent. Oelhafen (1961) has added a few further observations on the organization of the *Culex pipiens* egg by following development after destroying small areas of the embryo at different stages of embryogenesis by means of ultraviolet irradiation.

Eggs ligatured during maturation all died shortly afterwards. When eggs were ligatured during the first 5 cleavage divisions, blastoderm would subsequently form in front of ligatures tied at 30 per cent of the egg length and behind ligatures tied at 70 per cent but not in the small isolated regions at either end which lacked cleavage nuclei unless the ligatures were loose and permitted nuclei to pass; development never went further than the blastoderm even with loose ligatures. When ligatures were tied between 30 per cent and 70 per cent blastoderm developed in both anterior and posterior regions.

Other eggs were ligatured during the 6th to the 8th divisions, the period of migration when there were 64 to 256 nuclei. With ligatures situated below 30 per cent of the egg length no development took place in the posterior isolate but in the anterior isolate tissue developed which was unidentifiable except for a differentiated brain and ocelli. Endoderm and mesoderm were lacking and segmentation had not occurred. With ligature positions between 45 per cent and 65 per cent, a differentiated brain and ocelli developed in the anterior isolates as before and unidentifiable tissue developed in the posterior isolates, but there was no germ-layer formation or segmentation (Fig. 9a). It appears that as in other insects (Counce, 1961) ectoderm is a self-differentiating system. When eggs were constricted to half their diameter with loose ligatures

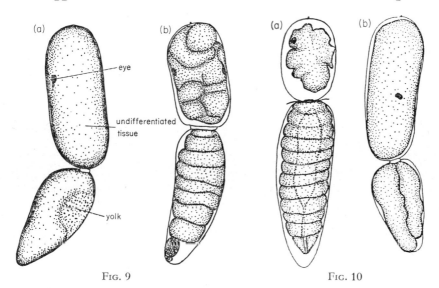

FIG. 9   FIG. 10

FIG. 9a–b. Development of *Culex pipiens* embryos after ligation at the stage of 256 nuclei.

(a) Condition at normal time of hatching after ligation at 45 per cent of the egg length showing development of undifferentiated tissue in both isolates and differentiation of brain and ocelli in the anterior isolate; (b) development of anterior and posterior partial embryos after a loose ligature had been applied at 60 per cent of the egg length. (From Idris, 1960b).

FIG. 10a–b. Development of *Culex pipiens* embryos after ligation in the preblastoderm stage.

(a) Partial embryo in the posterior isolate and head piece without segmentation in the anterior isolate after ligation at 75 per cent of the egg length; (b) anterior and posterior isolates without segmentation or germ-layer formation after ligation at 40 per cent of the egg length. (From Idris, 1960b).

during the later stages of cleavage, partial embryos consisting of head and thorax and a few or no abdominal segments subsequently formed in front of the ligature and partial embryos consisting of abdominal segments formed behind (Fig. 9b).

It is clear that blastoderm can form in front of and behind a tight ligature tied near the middle of the egg during the early stages of cleavage but development goes no further. Ligation during later cleavage stages permits development of tissue and differentiation of brain and ocelli but no germ-layer formation or segmentation takes place. Loose ligatures permit the formation of partial embryos in front of and behind the ligature, leading Idris (1960b) to conclude that a segmented embryo could form only when the anterior part of the embryo remained connected to the posterior part.

Idris performed operations on blastoderms of 3 different ages, i.e. during the 'preblastoderm stage' when approximately 512 nuclei were situated at the egg surface and before cell wall formation (Fig. 2a); during the 'uniform-blastoderm stage' when all cells were of the same size (Fig. 2b); and during the 'differentiated-blastoderm stage' when the middle plate had started to form (Fig. 2c).

Ligations performed during the preblastoderm stage which produced anterior or posterior isolates containing about two-thirds of the egg permitted the subsequent formation of anterior and posterior partial embryos in the large isolates but normally only unsegmented tissue formed in the other third of the egg. For example, ligatures at 10 per cent and 18 per cent led to the formation of anterior partial embryos complete as far back as the 4th abdominal segment and ligatures at 60–75 per cent led to the formation of posterior partial embryos consisting of thorax and abdomen or abdomen alone (Fig. 10a). In contrast, eggs ligatured near the middle, i.e. from 20 per cent to 55 per cent, developed at most unsegmented tissue with differentiated brain and ocelli but without germ-layer formation, the type of development which had occurred after operations during cleavage (Fig. 10b). Idris concluded that the egg contained 2 centres, anterior and posterior, both of which were necessary for full development and which were both contained in the big isolates made in the preblastoderm stage but which were separated by ligatures near the middle of the egg. Further ligature experiments revealed that the posterior centre lay between the posterior pole and 30 per cent of the egg length, the position of the activation centre in other insects, and that the anterior centre lay at about 65 per cent of the egg length in the region of the presumptive thorax, the characteristic position of the differentiation centre in other insects (Bodenstein, 1953). *Culex* eggs appear unusual in that the cleavage centre, the position of early cleavages, lies behind the differentiation centre in the middle of the egg; in most insects the cleavage centre lies in front of the differentiation centre (Bodenstein, 1953) as it does in *Anopheles maculipennis* in which the cleavage centre is near the anterior pole (Ivanova-Kazas, 1949).

Operations performed during the uniform- and differentiated-blastoderm stages confirmed the existence of the activation and differentiation centres and the need for both for full development, and also revealed the forward diffusion of a factor from the activation centre and the backward spread of the differentiation centre. Ligations made in the preblastoderm stage had shown that the factor from the activation centre had not diffused further forward than about 18 per cent since anterior partial embryos did not form when a ligature was tied anterior to this; however, anterior partial embryos formed after ligaturing in the uniform-blastoderm stage as far forward as the 65 per cent position (Fig. 11) and after ligaturing in the differentiated-blastoderm stage up to the 70 per cent position. Posterior partial embryos did not form if eggs in the preblastoderm and uniform-blastoderm stages had been ligated behind the 60 per cent position but

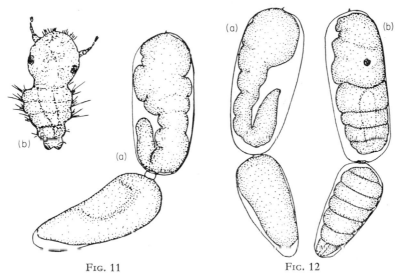

FIG. 11   FIG. 12

FIG. 11a–b. Stages in the development of a *Culex pipiens* embryo after ligation in the uniform-blastoderm stage at 50 per cent of the egg length. (a) Germ band has formed in both isolates but gastrulation has not occurred in the posterior isolate; (b) hatched anterior isolates. (From Idris, 1960b).

FIG. 12a–b. Stages in the development of a *Culex pipiens* embryo after ligation in the differentiated blastoderm stage at 40 per cent of the egg length. (a) Germ-band stage; (b) segmented partial embryos in anterior and posterior isolates. (From Idris, 1960b).

such embryos would develop after eggs in the differentiated blastoderm stage had been ligated as far back as 40 per cent indicating that the differentiation centre, or its influence, had spread from the thorax into the abdomen (Fig. 12).

Operations were also performed during elongation of the germ band when the posterior region of the embryo moved forward over the dorsal surface. Unfortunately these operations interfered with the movements of the embryonic material and probably for that reason frequently hindered development. Ligatures tied while the tip of the embryo advanced over the posterior third of the egg normally resulted in the formation of a germ band whose segments could not be identified, but in a few cases partial embryos formed. Ligatures tied at the time of maximum extension of the germ band, such that the anterior isolate contained the anterior- and posterior-most portions of the germ band and the posterior isolate contained the middle portion, led to formation in the anterior isolates of partial embryos consisting of head, anterior thoracic and terminal abdominal segments and in the posterior isolates of partial embryos consisting of posterior thoracic and anterior abdominal segments (Fig. 13). In general the anterior isolates developed better than the posterior isolates.

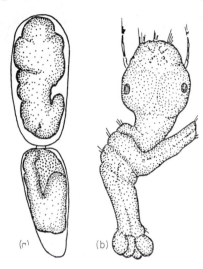

FIG. 13a–b. Stages in the development of a *Culex pipiens* embryo after ligation at 48 per cent of the egg length at the extended germ-band stage when the tip of the abdomen was at 73 per cent of the egg length.

(a) Germ-band stage; (b) hatched anterior partial embryo consisting of head, prothorax and 7th abdominal and following segments. (From Idris, 1960b).

If the pole cells were isolated by ligature from the rest of the embryo, gonad sheaths developed but they contained no sex cells. Gonad sheaths formed only when the 6th and 7th abdominal segments were present (Idris, 1960b). Irradiation of the pole plasm before cleavage nuclei had penetrated it, i.e. before formation of pole cells, led to sterility, the adult males containing empty testes and the adult females empty ovaries (Oelhafen, 1961). There is no evidence to show whether some pole cells normally contribute to midgut formation as in higher Diptera.

Dwarf embryos did not form after ligation at any stage of development. Determination had clearly taken place by the preblastoderm stage since only anterior segments developed in front of a ligature and only posterior segments behind it. Such partial embryos contained fully-developed internal organs, and anterior partial embryos could hatch if they contained a few abdominal segments. Embryos irradiated over restricted areas early in cleavage developed to larvae with visible defects, indicating that determination had occurred by that early stage. The egg of *Culex pipiens* is thus of the determinate or mosaic type and in common with other determinate eggs has a long germ band and abundant cytoplasm. Certain observations, however, show a slight capacity for regulation. Of 2 eggs ligated at the 5 per cent position during the preblastoderm stage one formed an externally-complete embryo and the other an embryo with a very small last segment. An egg ligated at 84 per cent during the differentiated-blastoderm stage developed an embryo which differed from normal only in the position of the ocelli and in the size of the antennae and labrum. Moreover, anterior or posterior mesenteron rudiments alone would suffice to form a normal midgut, and the embryonic material near a ligature would form an ectodermal cap to seal the partial embryo.

In a number of insects development is partly controlled by diffusion forward of some substance from the activation centre; incomplete ligatures do not prevent its passage. The differentiation centre, on the other hand, acts by producing movements of yolk which cause cells to accumulate in certain places, and loose ligatures prevent the spread of these movements (Bodenstein, 1953). Three *Culex* eggs which appeared to have been tightly ligatured during late cleavage were later found to have faulty ligatures. Partial embryos formed in the anterior isolates and unsegmented or weakly-segmented tissue in the posterior isolates of these eggs showed that the factor produced by the activation centre can diffuse through a very narrow gap, for anterior partial embryos do not form after complete ligation during cleavage. Certain *Culex* eggs fairly-tightly but not completely ligatured between 28 per cent and 52 per cent of their length during the uniform-blastoderm stage developed both anterior and posterior partial embryos although complete ligation in that position permits only anterior partial embryos to form. This suggests that the backward movement of the influence of the differentiation centre is not restricted by loose ligatures as in some other insects but can pass through a fairly small gap. Idris considers that the yolk is so reduced by the blastoderm stage that it cannot control movements of cells.

The results obtained by Idris (1960b) and Oelhafen (1961) may be summarised in the following manner. After ligation at any position during early cleavage the *Culex* egg does not develop beyond the blastoderm whereas after ligation during late cleavage mostly unidentifiable tissue forms and the brain and ocelli are the only organs capable of differentiation. It is not known what stimulates this tissue formation or the differentiation of the brain and ocelli. Ligature experiments have demonstrated an activation centre in the posterior third of the egg and a differentiation centre in the presumptive prothorax at about 65 per cent of the egg length. It is not known whether the activation centre is activated by cleavage nuclei as in certain other insects. A factor diffuses forward from the activation centre and is thought to activate the differentiation centre, and both centres must exert their influence before germ-layer formation or segmentation can occur so that ligatures which separate the 2 centres prevent further development. The activity of the differentiation centre moves backward into the abdomen during the late blastoderm stage and this movement is not prevented by loose ligatures suggesting that it is not a movement of yolk. Hormones from the brain and the corpus allatum-thoracic gland complex are not required for the later stages of embryogenesis. The egg is of the determinate type, the fate of the egg being determined at least by early cleavage and possibly earlier. A small degree of regulation is seen in the embryo's forming small but otherwise complete terminal segments after the anterior or posterior tip of the egg has been removed by ligation and in its forming midgut from the anterior or posterior mesenteron rudiment alone.

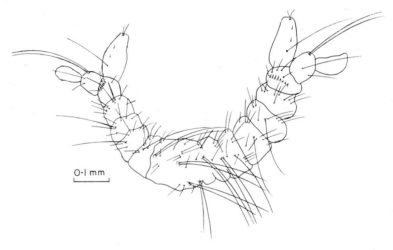

0·1 mm

FIG. 14.   Monster embryo of *Wyeomyia smithii* freed from its egg, composed of 2 complete abdomens fused at the 1st abdominal segments. (From Price, 1958a).

Examination of unhatched eggs in a colony of *Wyeomyia smithii* revealed 15 embryos unique in the abnormality of their structure (Price, 1958a). Each consisted of 2 abdomens fused at their 1st abdominal segments (Fig. 14). In every case the abdomens were morphologically complete and normal except for a ventral displacement of bristles on the two 1st abdominal segments and a slight obscuring of segmentation near the junction; there was no sign of head or thorax. The midguts of each pair were joined and had a continuous lumen and the ganglia of the two 1st abdominal segments were fused. The monsters were inverted in their eggs compared to normal embryos, each egg with 1 abdomen doubled on itself in the anterior third and the other abdomen stretched out straight in the posterior two-thirds. The monsters were alive when removed from the eggs and made typical thrashing movements. One remained alive for 24 hr before being killed. According to Price (1958a) this type of abnormality has not been described in any other insect. It is impossible to account for these remarkable embryos from what is known of the organization of mosquito eggs.

Genetic Control of Development

Chromosome studies on mosquitoes have revealed in every case a diploid number of 6 (Breland, 1961). Large, banded, polytene chromosomes occur in several tissues including the salivary glands and Malpighian tubes. Heterochromosomes have been described in *Anopheles* where they are equal in females and unequal in males, showing a variety of forms among different species (Frizzi, 1947a, b; Breland, 1961). They are thought to be concerned in sex determination (Frizzi, 1947b). Heterochromosomes have not been found in any other genera (Breland, 1961) and detailed studies such as that by Sutton (1942) on chromosome structure in *Culex pipiens* have revealed no differences at all between males and females. Polyploidy occurs in the nuclei of several tissues during larval growth, and the significance of this in development and metamorphosis is described in Chapter 4.

While investigating inheritance in a white-eyed strain of *Culex pipiens* var. *molestus*, Gilchrist and Haldane (1947) found that white eye (*w*), which was recessive to its normal allelomorph (+) and gave normal Mendelian ratios with 6·3 per cent crossing over, was sex-linked. Analysis of many crosses made with the mutant revealed that maleness could be explained as due to a single dominant gene (*M*) so that males were always heterozygous *Mm* and females always homozygous recessive *mm*. This accords with the sex ratio which is 1 : 1 in *Culex pipiens* var. *molestus* (Gilchrist and Haldane, 1947; Laven, 1955) and in *Culex pipiens fatigans* (Qutubuddin, 1953). Gilchrist and Haldane (1947) suggested that the overwhelming proportion of males which is occasionally found in cultures of *Culex pipiens* (Roubaud, 1933; Tate and Vincent, 1936), and which was given the name spanogyny by Roubaud (1933), could be caused by somatic crossing over producing mosquitoes or testes of genotype *MM* whose progeny would be entirely male. This would depend upon *M* not being lethal when homozygous.

Two non-allelic recessive genes in *Aedes aegypti*, red and rust, which affect eye colour show partial sex linkage of the type found in *Culex pipiens* by Gilchrist and Haldane (1947), leading McClelland (1962) to conclude that sex determination takes place in *Aedes aegypti* in the same unusual manner as in *Culex pipiens*. An inherited factor has been found in *Aedes aegypti* which causes a predominance of males. This factor is transmitted only by males and its frequency can be increased by selection. The excess of males is not due to differential mortality (Craig, Hickey and VandeHey, 1960). Similar results were obtained by McClelland (1960b) who also found a correlation between extent of white scaling on the male parent and proportion of males in the progeny. The variability of sex ratio in *Aedes aegypti* suggests that the male-producing factor must be present in different strengths in different populations. In 19 strains analysed by Craig, VandeHey and Hickey (1961) the proportion of females ranged from 18·6 per cent to 51·5 per cent although sex ratio within strains was constant over several generations. Ford (1961) has emphasized that sex is a case of balanced polymorphism and that selective forces will oppose departure from the optimum proportion of males and females which is generally, but by no means always, near equality.

Exposure of larvae of *Aedes stimulans*, a mosquito of northern N. America, to a continuous temperature of 29°C causes the determiners of maleness to fail to express themselves so that all the larvae give rise to adult females. The "genetically-intended" males are like females in all respects except for slight differences in the palps; internally, they have ovaries, oviducts and spermathecae and lack male reproductive organs. Male larvae exposed to 29°C for only the last 6 days of larval life give rise to adults showing a mixture of male and female characters. Female larvae are not affected by a temperature of 29°C (Horsfall and Anderson, 1961).

Gynandromorphs have been described in mosquitoes of several genera, some individuals showing bilateral differentiation with predominantly male structures on one side and predominantly female structures on the other, and other individuals showing an anterior-posterior organization in which the head is one sex and the genitalia the other, with legs, wings and body structure intermediate or mixed male and female (Kitzmiller, 1953). Gilchrist and Haldane (1947) discovered gynandromorphs among white-eyed mutants of *Culex pipiens* var. *molestus* in which one side of the body was mostly male and the other side mostly female and in which one eye was largely or completely pigmented and the other partly or entirely white. They considered that these gynandromorphs could have arisen in a number of ways. The female pronucleus and a polar body might have been fertilized by 2 spermatozoa and each might have provided nuclei for half the body. A single diploid nucleus, which would have been $m+/Mw$, since the parentage was known to be $m+/mw\,♀ \times mw/Mw\,♂$, might by somatic crossing over have given rise to $m+/m+$ and Mw/Mw regions, or the 2 daughters of 1 chromosome might have gone to 1 pole at an early mitosis and those of its homologue to the other. Laven (1957a) has described a recessive, autosomal factor in *Culex pipiens* var. *molestus* which causes formation of gynandromorphs.

Intersexes have been described in *Culex pipiens* var. *molestus* in which both the gonads and such secondary sexual characters as the antennae, palps and genitalia were intermediate in structure between male and female. Breeding experiments revealed that this condition was inherited and that it was due to a recessive, autosomal gene (*zwi*). The gene was ineffective in the female milieu but showed complete penetrance in homozygous males. The intersexes were sterile (Laven, 1955, 1957a).

Laven (1957b, 1959) has given an account of the variable interfertility of populations of *Culex pipiens* from different localities. Crossing experiments revealed that certain pairs of populations were completely interfertile, other pairs were interfertile in 1 direction only, i.e. when males of 1 population were mated with females from the other but not vice versa, and yet other pairs of populations were infertile in both directions although insemination and oviposition were normal. The infertile crosses not infrequently gave rise to a fairly high percentage of eggs which developed to a late embryonic stage but then died, and to a very low percentage of adults, all female and, as was shown with marker genes, all originating from the female genome. The few viable progeny were parthenogenetic and contained no genes from the father. Using classical methods to investigate crossing type, the system determining fertility in crosses between populations, Laven (1959) showed that crossing type in *Culex pipiens* was controlled by the cytoplasm and not by the genome. When populations from Oggelshausen and Hamburg were mated the cross $Og♀ \times Ha♂$ gave partial development but dying embryos in 71 per cent of the eggs and 0·17 per cent hatch, whereas the cross $Ha♀ \times Og♂$ gave an average hatch of 87·3 per cent yielding viable, fertile offspring. Hybrid females obtained from the fertile cross were backcrossed to $Og♂$ in successive generations ($Ha♀ \times Og♂ \times Og♂ \times Og♂ \ldots$) so that the cytoplasm of the progeny would be obtained from the egg of the Hamburg female while the chromosomes of the female parent *Ha* would be progressively replaced by chromosomes of the male parent strain *Og*. After continuous backcrossing for 60 generations both male and female hybrids retained the crossing characteristic of the maternal strain showing that replacement of chromosomes, which was proved to have taken place by marking the chromosomes with mutant genes, had no influence on crossing type, thus giving a clear demonstration of cytoplasmic inheritance. In crosses between *Aedes scutellaris* and *Aedes scutellaris katherinensis* the combination of the hybrid genome with *katherinensis* cytoplasm is non-viable (Smith-White and Woodhill, 1954) and this appears to be another case of cytoplasmic control of crossing type.

Laven (1956, 1957a) investigated the progeny which arose parthenogenetically from incompatible crosses in *Culex pipiens*. Females heterozygous for the mutant gene *Kuf* gave rise to parthenogenetic offspring of genotypes $+/+$, *Kuf*/$+$ and *Kuf*/*Kuf* which could only have occurred through fusion of the oocyte nucleus with a polar body or fusion of two polar bodies, a type of parthenogenesis called automixis (Suomalainen, 1950) or meiotic parthenogenesis (White, 1954). Laven (1956) considered that the sperm stimulated the egg to develop without fusing with the female pronucleus, presumably because of the high percentage of eggs which showed some development, but it is interesting that 3 larvae developed parthenogenetically from 85,851 eggs laid by virgin females of *Culex pipiens fatigans* (Kitzmiller, 1959) and eleven individuals, all males, developed parthenogenetically from eggs laid by virgin *Aedes aegypti* (Craig, 1957).

Infertility in crosses between certain palaearctic species of the *Anopheles maculipennis* complex is thought to be due to different rearrangements of chromosomes occurring in different species. In natural populations inversions were always found to be homozygous and heterozygous inversions rarely appeared in laboratory crosses, suggesting that they were inviable. Heterozygous inversions are fairly common in nearctic *Anopheles,* however, and they are particularly common in *Anopheles punctipennis*, a member of the *Anopheles maculipennis* complex (Frizzi and Kitzmiller, 1959). Heterozygous inversions also occur commonly in the S. American species *Anopheles albitarsis* and *A. evansae*, both of which form species complexes (Schreiber and Guedes, 1961).

Structure and Properties of the Egg Shell

At oviposition and for some hours afterwards the egg shell is a two - layered structure consisting of exochorion and endochorion secreted by the follicular epithelium of the mother (p. 170). Later the serosa of the embryo secretes the serosal cuticle below the endochorion (Fig. 15). These layers are largely uniform in structure around the egg but they show small modifications in the micropyle apparatus and, in *Anopheles*, in the 'floats'. The embryo depends upon the structure and properties of the shell for penetration of sperm, mechanical protection, passage of respiratory gases and resistance to water loss.

The exochorion which is always very thin and easily damaged is responsible for the fine sculpturing of the egg surface. Electron micrographs show that in *Aedes aegypti* and *Psorophora ferox* it is composed of 2 membranes with knobs or bosses between them. The outer membrane in these species is made of roughly parallel but intermeshed fibrils orientated at right angles to the long axis of the egg, while the inner membrane has no obvious structural orientation (Harwood, 1958). In *Anopheles labranchiae atroparvus* (Nicholson, 1921), *Culex pipiens* and *Culiseta annulata* (Christophers, 1945) the exochorion again forms an open meshwork but in the 2 last species the bosses project through the outer membrane (Figs. 15a, b). In *Aedes aegypti* the exochorion can repeatedly dry out and take up water from a saturated atmosphere (Harwood and Horsfall, 1959), but in *Culex pipiens* it is strongly hydrophobic and shrinks to a structureless mass when treated with ether (Christophers, 1945).

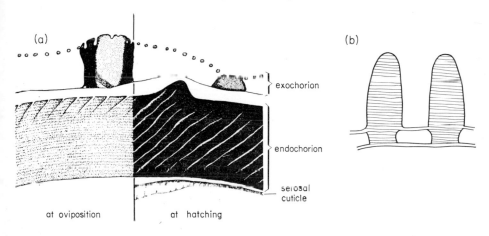

(a)   (b)

exochorion

endochorion

serosal
cuticle

at oviposition   at hatching

FIG. 15a–b.   Appearance of egg shells in section.

(a) Section through the shell of an aedine egg shortly after oviposition and at the time of hatching (from Harwood and Horsfall, 1959); (b) section through the exochorion of a *Culex pipiens* egg. (From Christophers, 1945).

The endochorion is a much stouter layer, $1·3\,\mu$ thick in fully-developed eggs of *Culex fatigans,* $2·2\,\mu$ in *Aedes aegypti* and $6·4\,\mu$ in *Psorophora ciliata*, and it provides the principal mechanical protection for the egg (Harwood and Horsfall, 1959). Within an hour or two of laying the endochorion of *Aedes aegypti* changes from a soft, white layer to a hard and dark one, at the same time becoming relatively impermeable to water (Gander, 1951; Beckel, 1958a). Electron micrographs show that the endochorion of *Aedes aegypti* is composed of a homogeneous material, stratified when first laid down but the stratification being replaced after oviposition by tightly-packed longitudinal fibrils, resembling flat needles, which spiral round the egg. The X-ray diffraction pattern of endochorion from these eggs is not unlike that of the protein arthropodin from the larval cuticle of *Sarcophaga* (Harwood, 1958). Both exochorion and endochorion of mosquito eggs are soluble in 5 per cent sodium hypochlorite solution (Mortenson, 1950).

The serosal cuticle of *Aedes aegypti* is secreted by the serosa of the

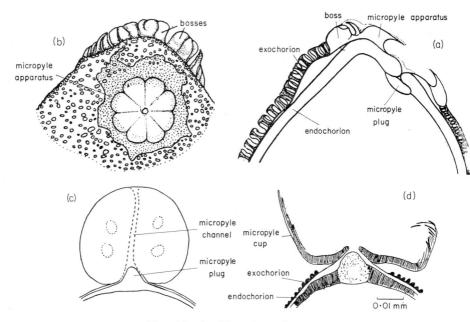

FIG. 16a–d.   The micropyle apparatus.

(a) L.S. through the micropyle apparatus of an *Anopheles labranchiae* egg; (b) surface view of the micropyle apparatus of an *Anopheles labranchiae* egg (from Marshall, 1938, after Nicholson, 1921); (c) L.S. through the micropyle apparatus of a *Culex pipiens* egg before oviposition; (d) L.S. through the micropyle apparatus of a *Culex pipiens* egg after oviposition (from Christophers, 1945).

embryo some 16–17 hr after oviposition (Harwood, and Horsfall, 1959), that of *Aedes hexodontus* after about 48 hr (Beckel, 1958a). In *Aedes aegypti* it consists of 2 membranes with a matrix between them. The outer membrane is composed of flat, overlapping, hexagonal micelles, and the inner membrane consists of fibrillar micelles running at right angles to the long axis of the egg. At the line of dehiscence of the egg cap the fibrils of the inner layer lose their parallel arrangement and become intermeshed

(Harwood, 1958). The X-ray diffraction pattern of the inner and outer membranes of the serosal cuticle of *Aedes aegypti* closely matches that of chitin (Harwood, 1958) and in *Aedes hexodontus* the serosal cuticle gives a positive response to histochemical tests for chitin (Beckel, 1958). It is insoluble in hypochlorite solution (Harwood, 1958).

At the anterior pole of mosquito eggs is a micropyle apparatus secreted by cells of the follicular epithelium at the time that the rest of the exochorion is laid down. In *Anopheles labranchiae atroparvus* it consists of a scalloped, disc-like membrane bounded by a thick ring (Figs. 16a, b). The membrane is produced into a funnel which passes through the endochorion, the cavity of the funnel being the micropyle. The micropyle is separated from the cytoplasm of the egg by a modified region of endochorion, the micropyle plug, which is secreted by specialized cells of the follicular epithelium (Nicholson, 1921). It is considered that sperm penetrate the micropyle during oviposition and that the micropyle plug is traversable by sperm at that time. In species of *Psorophora* the micropyle appears to be a relatively wide gap in the exochorion filled by a micropyle plug (Harwood and Horsfall, 1957). In the unlaid egg of *Culex pipiens* the micropyle apparatus is in the form of a large, closed sac which contains the remnants of the nurse cells and which is traversed in the midline by a delicate membranous channel, the micropyle funnel, which extends through the exochorion to open over the micropyle plug (Fig. 16c). The plug has a spongy texture in the recently-laid egg. During oviposition the apical region of the sac and most of the micropyle funnel are lost and in the laid egg the micropyle apparatus is seen as a cup (Fig. 16d) (Nath, 1924; Christophers, 1945).

Mosquito eggs are heavier than water. Those laid on water are supported by the surface film and usually bear structures which make them lie in a particular position (Trensz, 1933). The micropyle cups of *Culex* eggs are hydrophylic, unlike the general surface of the exochorion, so that the eggs which are held together in rafts lie at right angles to the water surface. Eggs of the subgenus *Culiseta* are also laid in rafts and, although lacking micropyle cups, have hydrophylic anterior poles and become orientated like *Culex* eggs (Christophers, 1945). In most species of *Anopheles* the exochorion balloons out on either side of the egg to form air-filled 'floats' which cause the egg to lie with its flattened ventral surface uppermost. If these are removed the egg floats on its side (Trensz, 1933; Newkirk, 1955). The eggs of certain species of *Anopheles,* including *Anopheles maculipennis* and *Anopheles punctipennis,* bear 5–6 minute exochorionic structures at either end, each cup-shaped and enclosing gelatinous material (Herms and Frost, 1932).

The eggs of *Anopheles quadrimaculatus* cannot resist drying if removed from water within 9 hr of laying but between 10 and 13 hr after laying they develop a resistance to drying, 27 per cent hatching after 12 hr exposure at 0 per cent R.H., 37 per cent hatching after 42 hr at 65 per cent R.H. and 25°C (Darrow, 1949). A change in permeability was also revealed by the observation that eggs of *Anopheles superpictus* and *Anopheles sergentii* transferred to 0·25M salt solution shortly after laying failed to hatch, but that eggs transferred 1 day after laying all hatched (Kligler and Theodor, 1925). Although anopheline eggs cannot resist prolonged drying they show a moderate resistance which may be of considerable importance in nature. Eggs of *Anopheles quadrimaculatus* exposed on the surface of soil drying out at 26°C and 35–65 per cent R.H. gave a 53 per cent hatch after 96 hr and a 16 per cent hatch after 120 hr desiccation (Kartman and Repass, 1952). Eggs of *Anopheles gambiae* gave an 8 per cent hatch after 72 hr exposure on a dry surface in bright sunlight (Gebert, 1937). Eggs of *Anopheles gambiae* gave a moderate hatch (26 per cent) after 10 days in drying sand (Deane and Causey, 1943), and eggs of *Anopheles punctimacula* hatched after 4 weeks in drying soil (Stone and Reynolds, 1939). However, only eggs of *Aedes, Psorophora, Haemagogus, Heizmannia,* (subgenus) *Armigeres* (Macdonald & Traub, 1960) and (subgenus) *Culicella* (Shute, 1933a) can withstand prolonged drying in air. *Anopheles quadrimaculatus* eggs removed from water exactly half way through their embryonic development, $23\frac{1}{2}$ hr after laying, and exposed to the air for 12, 24 or 36 hr all hatched approximately $23\frac{1}{2}$ hr after being returned to water, suggesting that embryonic development ceases during desiccation (Darrow, 1949). A similar observation was made on eggs of this species by Herms and Freeborn (1920).

Simple experiments and observations have revealed quite a lot about the nature of the waterproofing of the egg shell. As will become clear, the egg shell of *Aedes* becomes relatively impermeable to water when the endochorion hardens but it does not become fully resistant to desiccation until the serosal cuticle is formed. The endochorion turns from white to black within approximately 2 hr of oviposition but this change does not take place in *Aedes* eggs killed in various ways (Gander, 1951; Beckel, 1958a) nor in *Anopheles* eggs removed from water (Nicholson, 1921) or *Aedes* eggs in unsaturated air (Gander, 1951). The darkening and hardening suggest that the proteins of the chorion become tanned. The endochorion is thicker and becomes darker, perhaps therefore more highly tanned, in the eggs of *Aedes* and *Psorophora* which resist desiccation than in the non-resistant eggs of *Culex, Culiseta* and *Mansonia* (Harwood and Horsfall, 1959). Newly-laid eggs of *Aedes hexodontus* are readily permeable to water since they collapse almost immediately after being placed in a desiccator and rapidly regain their shape when returned to water. When placed in hypertonic salt solution slightly-darkened eggs of *Aedes hexodontus* collapse as though water were being extracted from them, and when returned to distilled water regain their turgor but more slowly than it was lost, leading Beckel (1958a) to conclude that their permeability to water had decreased. The chorion is clearly impermeable to salts from the time of oviposition for *Aedes aegypti* eggs laid on 0·1 per cent copper sulphate solution will hatch although the larvae soon die (Buxton and Hopkins, 1927).

When eggs of *Aedes dorsalis* are incubated at 26°C a strong resistance to desiccation develops gradually from 20 to 27 hr after oviposition in fertile but not in infertile eggs. The serosal cuticle appears and grows thicker over the same period (Telford, 1957). *Aedes aegypti* eggs become resistant to the dehydrating effects of hypertonic saline 16–17 hr after being laid when the serosal cuticle has just been formed (Harwood and Horsfall, 1959) and in *Aedes hexodontus* resistance to desiccation also develops with the appearance of the serosal cuticle (Beckel, 1958a). The serosal cuticle is composed of chitin but there is evidence that lipid is secreted into the egg shell at the time the serosal cuticle is laid down. The surface of the endochorion in *Aedes aegypti* eggs becomes hydrophobic about the 17th hr of incubation (Harwood and Horsfall, 1959) and mature eggs of *Aedes hexodontus* from which the chorion has been removed with hypochlorite rupture 1–5 hr after being placed in distilled water thus showing a low permeability, but treatment of dechorionated eggs with lipid solvents causes a great increase in permeability (Beckel, 1958a). It is not clear from this experiment whether the chorion must be present for full permeability or whether treatment with hypochlorite damages the remaining layers. Layers of wax or grease are known to be present in the egg shells of various insects and these layers have transition temperatures, characteristic for each species, at which the ordered arrangement of lipid molecules which is necessary for impermeability breaks down (Beament, 1961). Harwood and Horsfall (1959) found that eggs of *Aedes aegypti* collapsed in hypertonic saline at 61°C but not at lower temperatures, and Christophers (1960) using the same method, found the transition temperature of this species to lie between 50° and 55·5°C. It seems certain that the shells of mosquito eggs contain a continuous lipid layer, possibly secreted by the embryo, which plays a major role in preventing water loss.

Nothing is known of the mechanism of gas exchange in mosquito eggs. An air space is found within the exochorion in eggs of *Anopheles, Culex, Culiseta, Aedes* and *Psorophora* (Fig. 15), and in *Aedes*, at least, the space is already filled with air at oviposition (de Buck, 1938). This space resists penetration of water in *Anopheles* (Nicholson, 1921) and of oil in *Aedes*

(Powers and Headlee, 1939), and apparently is not open to the atmosphere at any point. It may be presumed that the fibrillar structure of the endochorion permits movement of gas molecules.

In *Culex pipiens* and *Culiseta annulata* eggs the posterior poles which point away from the water are hydrophilic and on the posterior pole of each egg a droplet of water is found (Christophers, 1945). If a raft of *Culex restuans* eggs is placed on methylene blue solution the drops at the posterior poles turn blue, whereas if a raft is inverted and placed on water a drop appears over the micropyle apparatus of each egg, suggesting that there is a point at either end of the egg at which water can enter and leave (Newkirk, 1955). Iltis and Zweig (1962) analysed droplets from a number of species of *Culex* and *Culiseta* and found that they were composed mainly of a lipid material which was slightly soluble in water and which contained an ester linkage and fatty acids (principally palmitic, stearic, linolenic); phosphorus was absent. The lipid was strongly surface active, lowering the surface tension when added to water, and it was thought that the droplets may play a part in restoring overturned egg rafts to their normal position which is essential for hatching.

Eggs of *Anopheles* (Downs, 1951), *Aedes* and *Culex* (Gander, 1951) increase in length up to 25 per cent during the day following deposition. This growth is dependent on the uptake of water since it can be prevented, in *Anopheles*, by placing the eggs in hypertonic saline. The additional water is not essential for development in *Anopheles* for eggs hatch in 0·2N-sodium chloride which have not increased in length at all (Downs, 1951).

Hatching

In *Aedes aegypti* the first indication of hatching is the appearance of a slowly-widening transverse crack in the dorsal surface of the egg shell towards the anterior end. The crack appears over the hatching spine, a short and very sharp spine arising from a small sclerite on the dorsal surface of the head, and extends fairly quickly around the egg. Pulsatile movements are seen within the head as this begins to be exposed. Larvae killed while hatching in cochineal solution are found to have the intestine distended with coloured solution, showing that the pulsations are swallowing movements of the pharynx and suggesting that distension of the intestine produces the turgor required to detach the cap from the remainder of the shell. As the cap breaks from the shell the anterior part of the larva is rapidly extruded and a quick movement of the larva, which is now greatly elongated, finally liberates it from the shell (Christophers, 1960).

Application of slight pressure at the anterior end of aedine eggs causes the shell to crack along the normal line of dehiscence. Caps cannot be separated from the posterior end in this manner; indeed, they can only be separated from the anterior end after the completion of embryonic development, before that time pressure causes irregular fractures (Gander, 1951; Horsfall, Henderson and Lum, 1957; Harwood and Horsfall, 1959). Gander (1951) concluded that the unhatched larva must weaken the shell with its hatching spine along the line of dehiscence by turning movements of the head, but such movements have never been seen and Beckel (1958a) found that on placing dechorionated eggs of *Aedes hexodontus* in trypan blue solution a small coloured spot appeared over the hatching spine as though it had pierced the serosal cuticle at that point alone. Harwood (1958) has described a modification in the fine structure of the serosal cuticle at the line of dehiscence (p. 26) which might account for weakness at that point, and this line may appear before the hatching spine is well formed (Harwood and Horsfall, 1959). Harwood (1958) was unable to ascertain whether the endochorion also changes in structure at the line of dehiscence, but it seems unlikely that weakness in the serosal cuticle which is relatively thin would lead to fracture in the same position in an unmodified chorion. There is some evidence that a part of the egg shell must be in a hydrated condition for normal hatching to occur: eggs of *Aedes aegypti* hatch in greater numbers and in a shorter period when previously held at high humidities (Harwood and Horsfall, 1959) and the exposure of eggs of *Aedes vexans* to dry air for 4 hr prevents half of them from responding to a hatching stimulus (Horsfall, 1956). It may be concluded that the hatching spine transmits turgor pressure to the preformed line of weakness in the serosal cuticle at hatching but why the chorion cracks in that position is not known. Two large muscles run between the sclerite bearing the hatching spine and the labral feeding brushes but their function is probably movement of the brushes rather than protrusion or retraction of the hatching spine (Christophers, 1960). After eggs of *Aedes aegypti* had been held at 100 per cent R.H. for 24 hr the shells in many cases were cracked along the normal line of dehiscence although the caps were not detached (Harwood and Horsfall, 1959) suggesting that the embryo can provide sufficient turgor pressure to crack the shell but must imbibe water to extend itself and push off the cap.

Slight variations are found in the mechanism of hatching. In *Anopheles claviger* (Bresslau, 1920) and *Culex pipiens* (Rosay, 1959) the cap remains attached to the shell by a small hinge on the surface opposite the hatching spine. In *Opifex fuscus* a flap of shell is burst open and the larva apparently emerges tail first (Kirk, 1923). In *Aedes* the hatching spine is always pointed, but it is chisel shaped in many other mosquitoes (Marshall, 1938).

After hatching the larva of *Aedes aegypti* immediately swims to the surface exposing its spiracles to the air and within 15–30 min the fluid which fills the tracheal system is completely replaced by air (Wigglesworth, 1938b). Beament (1961) has pointed out that the hydrofuge nature of the inner surface of insect tracheae is important for the penetration of air at hatching for without it the water could hardly be removed against a capillary pressure of hundreds of atmospheres. At hatching the larval head is wrinkled, triangular and no wider than the thorax, and the labral feeding brushes are tucked into the preoral cavity. The larva soon swallows water and, contracting its thorax and abdomen, drives haemolymph into the head which grows wider than the thorax, extension occurring mainly in the frontal region. The head later becomes hard and dark. The feeding brushes are extended and soon start to function (Wigglesworth, 1938b; Beckel, 1958; Christophers, 1960).

Hatching normally follows the completion of embryonic development but in *Anopheles* it can be delayed for some days in the absence of free water (Brumpt, 1935). Under adverse conditions aedine eggs enter a state of quiescence and some aedine mosquitoes undergo diapause in the egg stage. The conditions under which aedine eggs hatch after quiescence or diapause are described in Chapter 12.

CHAPTER 2

LARVAL NUTRITION, EXCRETION AND RESPIRATION

Food

Examination of gut contents reveals that larvae of most species feed indiscriminately upon the microplankton of their habitat, including algae, rotifers, protozoa, bacteria and fungal spores (Metz, 1919; Coggeshall, 1926; Senior-White, 1928a; Kühlhorn, 1958). A few species are predatory, feeding on other insect larvae. The major part of the gut contents often consists of amorphous organic matter, presumably ingested either as detritus or as colloidal particles (Hinman, 1930; Senior-White, 1928a; Shipitsina, 1930; van Thiel, 1928). *Culex bitaeniorhynchus* and related species almost invariably live within masses of *Spirogyra* or other filamentous algae and feed predominantly upon them (Laird, 1956; Senior-White, 1926), but such specificity is very rare.

Several authors consider that colloid particles are an important constituent of larval food, possibly forming a large part of the amorphous organic matter found in the gut (Hinman, 1932; Shipitsina, 1935; van Thiel, 1928). *Anopheles maculipennis* larvae are said to concentrate colloidal particles of silver (20 mμ) and gold (26–31 mμ) but not those of haemoglobin (2–4 mμ) or starch (4 mμ) (Shipitsina, 1930, 1935).[*] The colloidal particles which are retained are not only the larger but also the more highly charged ones, and it is possible that the motion of the labral brushes produces a sheer component along the length of the hairs generating a potential gradient in that direction which causes adsorption and clumping of charged particles. Mosquito larvae can sometimes develop to maturity on the non-living organic matter contained in natural waters which is fine enough to pass through Berkefeld filters (Hinman, 1930) but this is not always present in sufficient concentration to sustain life (Beklemishev, 1930). Larvae can develop in the laboratory when nutrients are supplied in true solution (Singh and Brown, 1957) but there is no evidence that growth can occur on solutes alone in nature.

Micro-organisms are the principal constituent of the larval diet in most species and although non-living organic matter may also be important the

[*] The units given by Shipitsina (1930, 1935) are $\mu\mu$ but should be mμ.

extent to which it can supplement or replace micro-organisms is not known.

Feeding Mechanism

Mosquito larvae feed in a number of ways. The most common method is filter feeding but larvae may also feed by gnawing large objects, by browsing on filamentous algae or on the slimes of algae, fungi and bacteria which cover submerged surfaces, by ingesting the film of living and non-living matter found at the water surface or by crushing and swallowing small Crustacea and other plankton. A few species are predatory and feed on insect larvae up to their own size. The modifications of the mouthparts which are found in larvae with specialized feeding habits have been described by Surtees (1959).

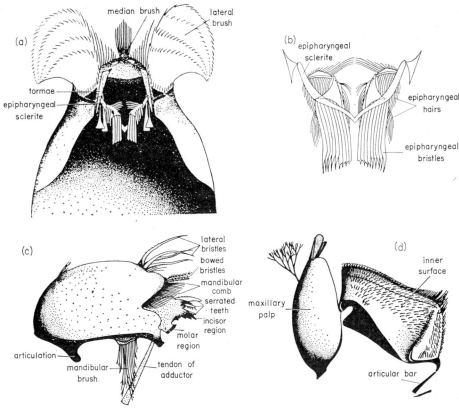

Fig. 17a–d. Mouthparts of *Anopheles maculipennis* larva.
(a) Ventral aspect of labrum and clypeus showing labral brushes and epipharynx apparatus; (b) dorsal aspect of epipharynx apparatus; (c) dorsal aspect of left mandible; (d) dorsal aspect of left maxilla. (From Schremmer, 1950).

The filter-feeding mechanism of *Anopheles maculipennis* has been described by Schremmer (1950) who has also given a detailed account of the structure and function of the various mouthparts. The preoral cavity is bounded dorsally by the epipharyngeal surface, anteriorly by the labral brushes, and laterally and ventro-laterally by the mandibles and maxillae, but owing to the shortness of the labium and hypopharynx it is open ventrally to a greater or lesser extent, especially when the mandibles and maxillae are abducted.

The labrum (Fig. 17a) bears a pair of large *lateral brushes* and a single small *median brush*. On each mandible (Fig. 17c) can be distinguished *incisor* and *molar regions;* 4 curved *lateral bristles,* which catch large food particles and draw them into the preoral cavity; 3 *serrated teeth* which clean the maxillae; a row of fine hairs, the *mandibular comb,* which clean the labral brushes; a number of movable *bowed bristles* whose function is not certain but which possibly help to close the preoral cavity when the mandibles are adducted; and a group of long hairs, the *mandibular brush,* which sweep food lying on the epipharynx into the pharynx. The mandibles move in the transverse plane and do not strike one another but hammer on the hypopharynx and labium which lie between them.

The maxillae (Fig. 17d) are greatly reduced but bear on their inner surfaces a number of short hairs which trap food particles. They also beat in the transverse plane. The labium is greatly reduced and is fused with the hypopharynx to provide a body on which the mandibles strike to break up large food particles. The epipharynx apparatus (Fig. 17a, b) is situated on the dorsal surface of the preoral cavity and comprises a pair of large sclerites bearing numerous long *epipharyngeal bristles* and 2 pairs of small plates bearing *epipharyngeal hairs.* The epipharynx apparatus can be protruded by muscles into the preoral cavity so that the *epipharyngeal bristles* lie in the path of the *mandibular combs.*

During feeding the mouthparts all move at the same tempo, from 180 to 240 beats/min depending on the temperature, but with differences of phase. Thus the labral brushes are fully adducted before the mandibles start their inward movement and are half extended again as the mandibles complete their adduction. The epipharynx apparatus is protruded at this stage to lie in the path of the opening mandibles and is withdrawn during the following inward beat of the labral brushes. The maxillae move in phase with the mandibles.

According to Schremmer (1950) the fast rhythmic movements of the lateral labral brushes cause water to flow towards the head while the movements of the median brush direct this flow into the axis of the body. Food particles become trapped between the hairs of the labral brushes during their inward beat. On the outward movement these particles are transferred to the oral side of the inward-moving mandibular combs as they pass through the labral brushes. When the mandibles are next opened the epipharynx apparatus has been protruded so that the epipharyngeal bristles pass through the interstices of the mandibular combs and remove the particles. The small epipharyngeal hairs are then moved so as to cast the food particles from the epipharyngeal bristles against the wall of the epipharynx. When the mandibles are next closed the mandibular brushes scrape the particles into the pharynx.

Small food particles are also caught between the bristles on the inner surface of each maxilla during its beat. The excursion of the maxillae is normally less than that of the mandibles so that the mandibles continue moving inwards after the maxillae have stopped and the serrated teeth of the mandibles pass through the bristles on the inner surfaces of the maxillae, depositing the particles on the front of the hypopharynx. These particles are pushed into the pharynx from time to time by occasional deep inward movements of the maxillae.

Large food particles which have not been caught by the labrum or maxillae are drawn into the preoral cavity by the lateral bristles of the mandibles. They are then crushed between the incisor and molar regions of the mandibles and the labiohypopharynx and brushed into the pharynx by the maxillae.

The pharynx (Fig. 18a) is roughly bell shaped and is separated from the preoral cavity by the mouth. Extrinsic muscles open the mouth and draw the dorsal and ventral surfaces of the pharynx apart so that water is sucked in, and intrinsic muscles close the mouth and press the roof and floor of the pharynx together, forcing the water into the lateral recesses and then out through gaps at the sides of the mouth into the preoral cavity. In this way water is pumped into and out of the pharynx during feeding. Running along each side of the roof of the pharynx are 2 rods from which long and very fine hairs, set only $1 \cdot 0 - 1 \cdot 5$ μ apart, project into the pharynx lumen (Fig. 18b, c). These 2 pairs of combs are thought to divide the middle part of the pharynx lumen from the lateral recesses during contractions of the pharynx so that water is forced between the hairs and any particles retained. In this way the pharyngeal combs strain from the water particles too fine to be trapped by the mouthparts. When Schremmer (1950) placed freshly-moulted, and therefore transparent, larvae of *Anopheles maculipennis* in a suspension of carmine, the carmine could be seen to accumulate in bow-shaped streaks in the lateral recesses of the pharynx. The contractions of the pharynx are synchronous with the beats of the mouthparts, and after a period of pumping particles trapped on the pharyngeal combs are deposited on the floor of the pharynx by a contraction of some sort and then passed into the oesophagus.

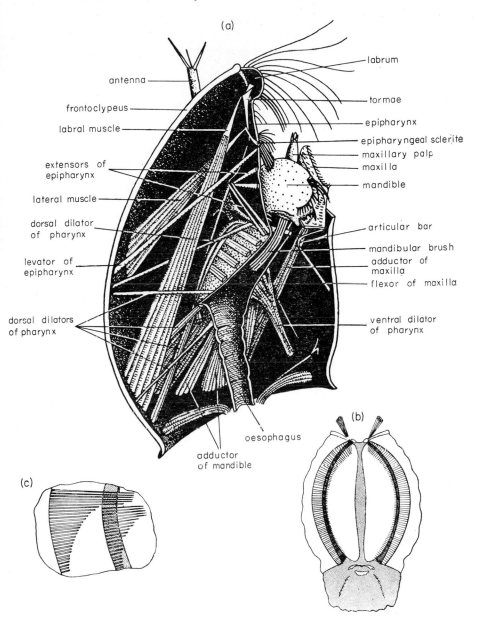

Fig. 18a–c.   Pharynx of the mosquito larva.

(a) Sagittal section through the head of *Anopheles maculipennis* (from Schremmer, 1950); (b) pharyngeal combs of *Culiseta incidens;* (c) detail of pharyngeal combs (from Cook, 1944).

In *Anopheles quadrimaculatus* food collected by the mouthparts is formed into a bolus which almost fills the pharynx. Contraction of pharyngeal muscles causes the sides of the pharynx to come together so that the bolus is forced back into the oesophagus where it is carried by rhythmical peristaltic contractions to the midgut (Farnsworth, 1947; Jones,1960). Food is said to be swallowed, by *Aedes aegypti*, without any noticeable amount of water (Wigglesworth, 1933b).

Christophers and Puri (1929) and Renn (1941) have described ways in which food is drawn towards the head of *Anopheles* larvae. The larvae feed while suspended from the surface membrane by non-wettable bristles on the dorsal surface of the thorax and abdomen and with the head rotated through 180° so that the mouthparts are directed towards the water surface. When the labral brushes vibrate below the surface they stir water near the head into 2 vortices which drive a common, converging food current towards the mouthparts while the surface membrane is hardly disturbed, if at all. When the labral brushes break the surface membrane and remove particles from it other particles on the surface move towards the head from all directions but there are no eddies below the surface and Protozoa can swim with impunity near the bases of the labral brushes. This type of feeding requires a surface tension of 60 dyne/cm or more. Natural bodies of water are often covered with a continuous bacterial mat and larvae can feed on this directly.

From the rate of disappearance of colloidal silver from water, 4th instar larvae of *Anopheles maculipennis* were considered to filter about 100 mm³ of water per day (Shipitsina, 1930). First instar larvae of *Anopheles subpictus* were found to clear 110–264 mm³ and 4th instar larvae 595–1229 mm³ of water of *Chlamydomonas* per day (Senior-White, 1928) and these seen to be more probable values. The area of surface that can be cleared of particles in a given time varies with size of larva, density of particles, and rate of filtration which is affected by temperature. Fourth instar larvae of *Anopheles maculipennis*, held at 25°C, cleared *Lycopodium* spores from 65, 30 and 9 mm² of surface per minute when there were 1–5, 21–30, and 31–40 spores per cm² respectively (Shipitsina, 1941). According to Renn (1941), 4th instar *Anopheles crucians* larvae clear 370 mm² of surface per minute and 4th instar *Anopheles quadrimaculatus* 520 mm²/min.

Structure of the Alimentary Canal

The structure of the alimentary canal of the larva (Fig. 19) has been described by Thompson (1905), Imms (1907), Schildmacher (1950), Christophers (1960) and Jones (1960). It starts with the preoral cavity between the mouthparts. This opens, through a slit-like mouth capable of considerable dilatation, into a short funnel-shaped pharynx which opens

ventrally into the oesophagus. The pharynx and oesophagus comprise
the foregut or stomodaeum. The pharynx wall consists of a flattened
epithelium lined with cuticle and bounded by circular and a few longitudinal muscle fibres. Related to its functions of filtering and swallowing
(p. 36) are 2 pairs of fine combs on the inner surface and a complicated
musculature. The pharynx and its muscles are well innervated, receiving
nerves from the brain and frontal ganglion.

The oesophagus is a narrow, muscular tube. Its flattened epithelium,

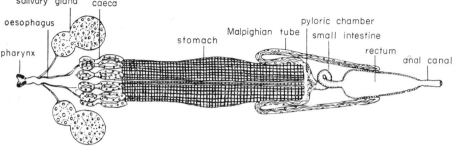

F<small>IG</small>. 19.   Alimentary canal and salivary glands of the larva of *Anopheles
quadrimaculatus*. (From Jones, 1960).

which is thrown into folds, is lined with a thin cuticle and bounded by
circular and occasional longitudinal muscle fibres. The posterior end of
the oesophagus telescopes into the lumen of the midgut forming the two-
layered oesophageal invagination (Fig. 20). At the anterior end of the
oesophageal invagination the circular muscle is very thick, forming the
cardiac sphincter, and behind that there is a prominent annular blood sinus.
The oesophageal invagination prevents regurgitation and on contraction
of the cardiac sphincter the sinus becomes distended, driving on the contents of the midgut.

The junction between foregut and midgut is marked by the anterior
imaginal ring, a band of columnar cells with characteristic staining properties situated at the anterior end of the recess formed by the oesophageal
invagination. These cells play an important part in the metamorphosis of
the alimentary canal (Thompson, 1905). Nerve cells situated on the surface of the alimentary canal in this region probably represent the stomachic
ganglia of the stomatogastric system (Jones, 1960).

The 3 main regions of the midgut—cardia, caeca and stomach—are
distinct in their gross structure but all have an epithelium of large cells
with polytene nuclei and striated border and between these cells lie small
regenerative cells. The cardia is a short section of midgut surrounding the
oesophageal invagination. Anteriorly its cells are columnar but posteriorly
they become cubical; there are no muscle fibres in its wall.

D

A chitinous peritrophic membrane extends from the cardia through the stomach in the form of a cylinder equal in diameter to the oesophageal invagination and uniform throughout. According to Wigglesworth (1930) the cells of the cardia can occasionally be seen to extrude globules which form the substance of the pericardial membrane and it is supposed that this secretion condenses into a solid sheet which issues from a mould formed by the oesophageal invagination and the cardia. In *Anopheles plumbeus* the cuticle on the outer face of the oesophageal invagination is greatly thickened to form a rigid ring covered with delicate, backward-pointing spines (Fig. 20). Longitudinal muscles are inserted into this ring and Wigglesworth suggests that contraction of the muscles will draw the ring forwards, pressing secretion out of the cardia cells, and that when the muscles relax and the cuticular ring moves backwards the spines on its surface will carry with them the newly-formed sheet of peritrophic

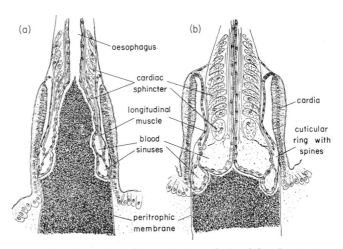

Fig. 20a–b. Oesophageal invagination of *Anopheles plumbeus* larva. (a) In position of relaxation; (b) following contraction and relaxation of the longitudinal muscle and with cardiac sphincter contracted and sinuses dilated. (From Wigglesworth, 1930).

membrane. Schildmacher (1950) supports Wigglesworth's account of peritrophic membrane formation but it is difficult to extend it to the Culicini in which both longitudinal muscles and spines are absent although a cuticular ring surrounds the oesophageal invagination. Most authors consider that the cardia secretes the substance of the peritrophic membrane but observations of Jones (1960) on *Anopheles quadrimaculatus* suggest that the peritrophic membrane may arise in the region of the anterior imaginal ring.

The 8 caeca are composed of very large, flattened cells with granular cytoplasm, and in *Anopheles* each caecum is constricted into anterior and posterior sections. If muscle fibres are present they are extremely difficult to see. On account of the peritrophic membrane, the caeca never contain undigested food particles but they are often filled with a thick brown or golden fluid and sometimes contain precipitated or crystalline solids. The stomach is a straight tube which is invested with a lattice-like arrangement of outer longitudinal muscles and inner circular muscles. Histologically it falls into 2, sharply-separated halves—an anterior half of clear, pale-staining cells and a posterior half in which the cells have a granular, deeply-staining cytoplasm and a more conspicuous brush border than elsewhere (Wigglesworth, 1942).

Five Malpighian tubes open into the alimentary canal behind the stomach. They run forward from this position, usually to the 5th or 6th abdominal segment, and then reverse their direction, ending blindly near the posterior end of the abdomen. The tubules are composed of large flat cells which have a brush border of the honeycomb type and contain large polytene nuclei. Behind the openings of the Malpighian tubes is found the posterior imaginal ring, a band of small, closely-packed, undifferentiated cells which become active at metamorphosis (Berger, 1938b) and which according to Henson (1946) form the boundary between mid- and hindgut.

The hindgut, or proctodaeum, consists of pyloric chamber, small intestine (or ileum), rectum (or colon) and anal canal. The pyloric chamber is a funnel-shaped layer of epithelium bearing numerous backward-pointing spines on its inner surface. It is naked in front but a layer of circular muscle surrounds the posterior part forming a somewhat indistinct pyloric sphincter. The epithelial cells are small and become increasingly small anteriorly until they resemble the undifferentiated cells of the posterior imaginal ring (Berger, 1938b; Trembley, 1951).

The small intestine, or ileum, is a narrow muscular tube lined with cuticle. Its epithelium is thrown into folds and consists of large thin cells containing polyploid nuclei. It is bounded by rings of circular muscle, each composed of three muscle cells united end to end, and by a few bands of longitudinal muscle. The rectum is a wider tube, sharply differentiated from the small intestine, and it is the most densely tracheated region of the alimentary canal. It is bounded by circular muscle. Its epithelium is composed of large, thick cells with polytene nuclei and with a striated border in place of the cuticular lining. There are no rectal papillae in the larva. The posterior end of the rectum tapers to join the anal canal which resembles the small intestine in structure, its epithelium being thin and folded, lined with cuticle and bounded by circular muscle.

The foregut and hindgut of *Anopheles quadrimaculatus* larvae exhibit only peristalsis but in the midgut a cycle is found in which frequent small antiperistaltic waves occur for a time, followed by quiescence and then by a powerful peristaltic wave which restarts the antiperistaltic waves. A cycle occurs every 1 or 2 min (Jones, 1960). This activity is apparently unrelated to the backward movement of the food column in the stomach but possibly serves to move fluid forward for absorption in the caeca (p. 64). The caeca themselves show vigorous waves of contraction. Most authors have found no sign of muscle fibres on the caeca but Schild-macher (1950) speaks of fine, ring muscles revealed by silver staining. The Malpighian tubes are immotile.

In *Aedes aegypti* most portions of an excised alimentary canal retain considerable activity. In *Anopheles quadrimaculatus* cauterization of indivi-dual ganglia of the ventral nerve cord causes only a small local reduction in the rate of contraction and although activity is profoundly depressed by ligaturing, some activity remains even in regions of the gut isolated from the stomachic ganglia (Jones, 1960). It appears that the contractions of the alimentary canal are partly, perhaps mainly, myogenic, automatic activity being strongest in the fore- and hindgut. Movements of the oesophagus in *Anopheles quadrimaculatus* are not directly stimulated by the presence of a bolus of food or by movements of the pharynx, although they are more frequent during feeding (Jones, 1960).

Each of the salivary glands of *Anopheles albimanus* consists of a spherical anterior portion of 12–15 cells, with large nuclei containing giant (poly-tene) chromosomes, and a larger terminal sac of 50–60 cells with smaller nuclei (Fig. 19). The salivary ducts lack taenidia and the common duct opens on the labiohypopharynx directly in front of the mouth. A chain of nephrocytes or pericardial cells extends between the 2 glands. In *Culex pipiens* the proximal part of each salivary gland is elongated and made up of small cells and the terminal sac globular and composed of much larger cells, whereas in *Aedes aegypti* the glands are cylindrical for most of their length but dilated towards the distal end (Jensen and Jones, 1957).

Digestion and Absorption

The *p*H of the different regions of the larval gut is known for several species (Table 1). In each case the caeca are slightly alkaline, the stomach contents fairly-strongly alkaline, and the Malpighian tubes and hindgut weakly alkaline or neutral. The stomach becomes more alkaline towards the posterior end and, in *Aedes aegypti* at least, the pyloric chamber is more alkaline than the rectum. *Toxorhynchites splendens*, which is entirely pre-datory, is similar in this respect to the other species (Senior-White, 1926; Ramsay, 1950).

Hinman (1933b) studied the enzymes of the digestive tract of mature larvae of *Culex pipiens fatigans* and *Aedes aegypti* by homogenizing whole intestine and adding substrate. The enzymes found were amylase, hydrolysing starch; invertase, hydrolysing sucrose; a protease which digested

TABLE 1. THE pH OF DIFFERENT REGIONS OF THE ALIMENTARY CANAL OF MOSQUITO LARVAE. (FROM SENIOR-WHITE (1926) AND RAMSAY (1950)).

Species	No. seen	Caeca	*Stomach	Malpighian tubes	Hindgut
Anopheles culicifacies	9	7·0–7·6	8·6–8·8	6·8–7·2	6·6–7·0
Uranotaenia campestris	10	7·2–7·8	9·0–9·6	7·0–7·6	6·4–7·4
Culex fuscocephalus	8	7·8–8·0	8·8–9·0	7·2–8·0	7·2–8·0
Toxorhynchites splendens	1	—	8·8	7·2	6·8
Aedes albopictus	25	7·4–8·8	9·0–9·4	6·6–7·8	7·6–7·8
Aedes aegypti	—	7·6–8·0	8·4	—	7·2–7·8

* Contents of peritrophic membrane

egg albumen and gelatine under alkaline conditions; a lipase; and an enzyme which attacked the pentose xylose. Negative results were obtained in tests for maltase, lactase and a protease active in an acid medium. Because of the method used one cannot be certain that the enzymes found were constituents of the digestive juice, and the enzyme which attacked xylose was quite possibly an intracellular enzyme.

The various products of digestion are absorbed in different regions of the gut. If deposition of substances within gut cells can be taken to indicate sites of absorption, the clear cells of the anterior half of the midgut in *Aedes aegypti* absorb fat and the granular cells of the posterior half absorb sugars and amino acids whereas the caeca absorb fat, sugars and amino acids (Fig. 21). There may be specialisation among caecal cells since only a proportion of them contain deposits after feeding one of these substances by itself. A sharp boundary divides the anterior region of the stomach which absorbs fat from the posterior region which absorbs sugars and amino acids (Wigglesworth, 1942). After feeding larvae of *Culex pipiens* on iron lactate, iron could be demonstrated histochemically in the cells of the posterior region of the stomach (de Boissezon, 1930b).

When dyes such as trypan blue are ingested by *Aedes aegypti* larvae the solid particles are confined within the peritrophic membrane but dye quickly appears in solution outside the peritrophic membrane. As no appreciable amount of water is swallowed the fluid must be secreted by the gut or the Malpighian tubes. Antiperistaltic waves pass forward over the midgut and carry the fluid to the caeca. The dye is not absorbed and the contents of the caeca gradually become darker until after 2 or 3 hr they consist of solid masses of dye. Since there is no solid dye elsewhere outside the peritrophic membrane it is evident that there must be a continuous absorption of fluid in the caeca (Wigglesworth, 1933b).

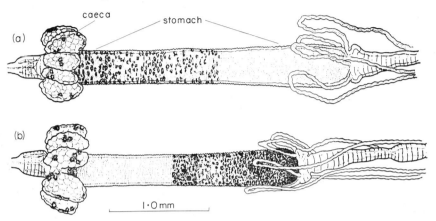

Fig. 21a–b. Alimentary canal of *Aedes aegypti* larva.

(a) After feeding on olive oil for 24 hr, stained with Sudan B to show distribution of lipid; (b) after feeding on starch for 48 hr, stained with iodine to show distribution of glycogen. (From Wigglesworth, 1942).

The rate of passage of food can be found by following distinctive particles through the gut. In 4th instar larvae of *Aedes aegypti* and *Culex pipiens* food reached the posterior end of the midgut 20–30 min after ingestion at 27°C and 50–60 min after ingestion at 20°C, whereas in the 2nd and 3rd instars only 15–20 min were required at 27°C. Fourth instar larvae of *Anopheles maculipennis* and *Anopheles superpictus* required about 60 min at 27°C. When food intake stops the food column remains stationary in the gut (Schildmacher, 1950).

Food is conveyed along the foregut and hindgut by the peristaltic movements of these organs but the movements of the midgut appear not to affect the food column within the peritrophic membrane (Jones, 1960). It therefore seems likely that the food column in the midgut is pushed backwards when contraction of the cardiac sphincter distends the blood sinus in the oesophageal invagination. The rate of passage of food along the gut is said by Bruck (1930) to be governed by the rate of ingestion, but Jones (1960) found no change in defaecation rate for an hour after transfer of feeding larvae to fasting conditions.

Ingested micro-organisms have frequently been seen active and unharmed in the hindgut of mosquito larvae, while the faeces contained unchanged cells. Organisms recorded as undigested include ciliates, flagellates, rotifers, fungal spores and unicellular and filamentous algae (van Thiel, 1928; Hinman, 1930; Laird, 1956). Laird (1956) found that ciliates rapidly became unrecognizable and that degenerative changes took place in most thin-walled algae and flagellates. Digestion could be increased by delaying passage through the gut. After 15 min fasting, when food stopped moving through the gut, certain protozoa and algae were seen to be digested although the Chlorococcales and some Eugleninae were not (Howland, 1930). It seems likely that thick-walled microorganisms often pass through the gut unharmed while the more delicate species are digested.

Nutritional Requirements

The nutritional requirements of mosquito larvae reared under sterile conditions have been the subject of intensive investigation for many years. In 1948 Trager was able to specify the vitamins which would supplement casein to provide a satisfactory diet for *Aedes aegypti*, and in the same year Golberg and De Meillon established which amino acids were necessary to supplement yeast autolysate for full development in this species. By combining the results of these workers, Lea, Dimond and DeLong (1956), Singh and Brown (1957) and Lea and DeLong (1958) produced chemically-defined diets on which larvae of *Aedes aegypti* could be reared to produce healthy adults capable of reproduction. The chief problem which remained had been the high osmotic pressure produced by the amino acid solution, since high concentrations of nutrients inhibited development and low concentrations contained insufficient amino acids for growth. Lea, Dimond and DeLong solved this problem by supplying the food in a solid agar medium, whereas Singh and Brown obtained satisfactory results by adjusting the osmotic pressure to $\triangle 0 \cdot 39°C$ (see Singh, 1957). The diets devised by Singh and Brown (1957) and Lea and DeLong (1958) are given in Table 2. Akov (1962a, b) has added further details to our knowledge of the nutritional requirements of *Aedes aegypti* larvae.

Larvae kept in media lacking protein and amino acids but complete in other respects fail to reach the 2nd instar (Golberg and De Meillon, 1948). The requirement for individual amino acids was tested by omitting them one at a time from the diet, and in this way the following 10 amino acids were found by both groups of workers to be essential: arginine, histidine, isoleucine, leucine, lysine, methionine, phenylalanine, threonine, tryptophan and valine. The same amino acids are essential for growth in a number of other insects (Gilmour, 1961). Singh and Brown (1957) found that omission of hydroxyproline or serine slowed down development and that cystine was indispensable for pupation. Lea and DeLong (1958) were

TABLE 2. TWO CHEMICALLY-DEFINED DIETS ON WHICH LARVAE OF *Aedes aegypti* WILL DEVELOP, UNDER STERILE CONDITIONS, TO PRODUCE HEALTHY ADULTS CAPABLE OF REPRODUCTION.

	Diet of Singh and Brown (1957)	Diet of Lea and DeLong (1958)
L-Alanine	1·00 g/l.	—
* L-Arginine	0·39	2·40 g/l.
L-Aspartic acid	—	0·80
L-Cysteine	—	1·20
L-Cystine	0·13	—
L-Glutamic acid	—	3·00
Glycine	0·25	2·40
* L-Histidine	0·25	0·40
L-Hydroxyproline	0·18	—
* L-Isoleucine	1·12	3·20 (DL)
* L-Leucine	1·00	3·00
* L-Lysine	0·66	6·00
* L-Methionine	0·70	0·80 (DL)
* L-Phenylalanine	1·00	1·50 (DL)
L-Proline	0·75	3·60
L-Serine	1·40	—
* L-Threonine	0·75	1·50 (DL)
* L-Tryptophan	0·36	0·50
L-Tyrosine	0·50	0·40
* L-Valine	1·20	1·50 (DL)
Fructose	—	4·00
Glucose	5·00	4·00
Ribonucleic acid	1·00	5·00
* Cholesterol	39·00 mg/l.	500·00 mg/l.
Cephalin	39·00	—
Lecithin	78·00	—
* Salts	1·00 g/l.	1·00 g/l.
p-Aminobenzoic acid	25·00 mg/l.	—
* Biotin	0·50	0·10 mg/l.
* Calcium pantothenate	15·00	30·00
Carnitine	4·00	—
* Choline chloride	200·00	500·00
Cyanocobalamin	0·05	—
Glutathione	200·00	—
* Nicotinic acid	15·00	5·00
Pteroylglutamic acid	50·00	0·02
* Pyridoxin	15·00	0·20
* Riboflavin	20·00	20·00
* Thiamine	5·00	20·00

* Compounds found to be essential in both diets.

able to omit both cystine and cysteine but found that glycine was essential. In both cases omission of proline seriously retarded development and caused heavy mortality.

When alanine, cystine, glycine, proline, serine and tyrosine were omitted singly from the diet devised by Singh and Brown (1957) they were later detected as free amino acids in the 4th instar larvae, and β-alanine, aspartic acid, glutamic acid, glutamine and taurine which had never been included in the diet were also present in the larvae (Singh and Micks, 1957). Although these larvae were capable of synthesizing proline and cystine it appeared that they could not form enough to meet their requirements since they did not grow well on a proline-deficient diet and could not pupate in the absence of cystine. A quantitative study of the free amino acids of larvae reared on sterile and non-sterile, chemically-defined diets showed that the levels of the various amino acids differed fairly widely under the two conditions (Singh and Micks, 1957).

When phenylalanine and tyrosine were not present in the diet in sufficient quantities, larvae were produced in which the normally sclerotised and darkened regions—head, saddle and respiratory siphon—were unpigmented, presumably through lack of melanin. Adults emerging from unpigmented larvae were normally pigmented and there appeared to be little relation between pigmentation and growth or survival. Pigmentation of larvae could be brought about by addition of 0·4 g/l L-tyrosine or 1·4 g/l DL-phenylalanine (Golberg and De Meillon, 1948b).

In the absence of lipids larvae did not develop beyond the 3rd instar (Singh and Brown, 1957; Lea and DeLong, 1958). Golberg and De Meillon (1948a) found that saturated and unsaturated fatty acids and triglycerides were inactive when added to a lipid-free diet but that the addition of cholesterol or of the phospholipid lecithin permitted the development of healthy adults. They were unable to say what the cholesterol and lecithin molecules had in common. The highest proportion of adult mosquitoes resulted from the use of lecithin, cephalin and cholesterol in the proportion of 2 : 1 : 1. Cephalin, another phospholipid, was inactive if supplied as the only lipid.

Lea and DeLong (1958) omitted sugar without affecting larval growth but Singh and Brown (1957) obtained no development beyond the 3rd instar when sugar was omitted from the diet, and Akov (1962a) has suggested that the diet of Singh and Brown (1957), which contained only about one-third as much amino acid as that of Lea and DeLong (1958), provided insufficient calories when sugars were omitted. Lea and DeLong (1958) found that omission of ribonucleic acid slowed larval growth and caused a poor yield of adults, revealing only a limited ability of the larvae to synthesize nucleic acids, but Singh and Brown (1957) obtained no development beyond the 3rd instar in the absence of ribo-nucleic acid. Attempts by Akov (1962a) to replace ribonucleic acid in the food of *Aedes aegypti* with single purines or pyrimidines were unsuccessful. Singh and Brown (1957) found that omission of the salt mixture prevented full larval growth; Lea and DeLong (1958) could omit the salt mixture without affecting larval growth, but salts must have been present as impurities.

The following vitamins appear to be indispensable for production of healthy adults: biotin, choline, nicotinic acid, pantothenic acid, riboflavin, pyridoxin and thiamine. Singh and Brown (1957) found that in the absence of pteroylglutamic acid (folic acid) the larvae grew slowly and failed to pupate; Akov (1962a) also found that this vitamin was necessary for pupation in *Aedes aegypti* but Lea and DeLong (1958) did not find it to be essential. Omission of riboflavin from the diet of Singh and Brown (1957) prevented development beyond the 2nd instar, and Lea and DeLong (1958) also considered that riboflavin was essential for normal development although they found that a few adults emerged after a lengthy period of development when riboflavin was omitted from their diet. Although Singh and Brown (1957) obtained 35 per cent emergence when choline was omitted from their diet both Lea and DeLong (1958) and Akov (1962b) found choline to be essential, and Akov (1962a) suggested that lecithin (phosphatidyl choline) was a source of choline in Singh and Brown's diet. The choline antagonist 2-amino-2-methyl-1-propanol inhibits development of *Aedes aegypti* larvae, but its toxicity can be overcome by the addition of more choline; 2,2-dimethylamino-ethanol shows some choline-sparing activity but cannot replace choline completely (Akov, 1962b). Pteroylglutamic acid deficiency causes loss of all body pigments except in head and siphon (Golberg *et al.*, 1945).

Omission of glutathione from the diet of Singh and Brown (1957) caused early death in most larvae, none pupating; glutathione was not an essential constituent of the diet of Lea and DeLong (1958) but this may have been due to its high cysteine content, and it seems likely that either glutathione or cysteine must be included in the diet. Singh and Brown (1957) found that development was poor when carnitine was omitted, but this compound was not used by Lea and DeLong (1958) and Akov (1962b) found the that presence of the specific carnitine antagonist γ-butyrobetaine in amounts up to 1 mg/ml had no detrimental effect. Pyridoxine can be replaced in the diet of *Aedes aegypti* by pyridoxal or pyridoxamine, and nicotinic acid can be replaced by nicotinamide (Akov, 1962a). Akov (1962a) noted that the amounts of the various B vitamins required by *Aedes aegypti* larvae showed the same relative proportions as the amounts described in the whole tissues of *Aedes aegypti* adults by Micks *et al.* (1959).

Both diets permitted development of fertile adults of *Aedes aegypti*, and although certain constituents could be omitted from either diet without stopping all development the full diets provided more rapid growth and a higher yield of adults. That certain compounds were essential or important for one diet and not for the other probably reflects the different proportions of the constituents of each. Akov (1962a) has pointed out that these two chemically-defined diets are not optimal for growth and she has described a diet containing casein which she considers more suitable for quantitative nutritional studies.

Healthy adults of *Culex pipiens* var. *molestus,* of which the females are capable of autogenous egg production, can be obtained when the larvae are reared on a sterile medium consisting of 2 per cent casein hydrolysate, 0·1 per cent glucose, 0·2 per cent salts, and biotin, pantothenic acid, pteroylglutamic acid, pyridoxin, riboflavin and thiamine. Development is accelerated greatly by addition of nicotinic acid and slightly by addition of ascorbic acid. In the absence of pteroylglutamic acid larvae reach the 4th instar but do not pupate (Lichtenstein, 1948).

In nature essential growth factors are obtained from micro-organisms in the food and there are several reports of growth of mosquito larvae in laboratory cultures being stimulated by addition of bacteria or yeast (Buddington, 1941; Hinman, 1933a; Rozeboom, 1935). Addition of antibiotics to the diet has been shown to affect the rate of development. When penicillin and chloromycetin were added to larval cultures of *Aedes aegypti* fed on yeast the bacterial populations were considerably reduced. In cultures with a relatively low food supply addition of antibiotics speeded up larval development compared with controls, but under conditions of more abundant food the antibiotics slowed larval development down (Bar-Zeev, 1957a).

Food Reserves

The principal storage organ is the fat body which consists of a parietal sheet of cells applied to the epidermis throughout the thorax and abdomen, and of lobes which extend into the body cavity ensheathing some of the organs. In a well-nourished larva the cytoplasm of the fat body cells is packed with globules of fat and vacuoles of protein and glycogen, the vacuoles of glycogen occurring principally around the periphery of the cell. Other vacuoles contain uric acid (Fig. 22b) (Wigglesworth, 1942; de Boissezon, 1930a, 1932). Fat and protein first appear around the nucleus whereas glycogen is first seen at the periphery of the cell (Wigglesworth, 1942) but there is no evidence that they are synthesised in these positions.

Other tissues also contain reserves. In larvae of *Aedes aegypti* as much glycogen may be laid down in the sarcoplasm of the muscles (Fig. 22c) as in the fat body and further glycogen may be stored in the cells of the caeca and of the posterior part of the midgut and in the central nervous system. Protein is stored in muscles, in oenocytes and in cells of the caeca and of the posterior half of the stomach. Fat is principally stored in

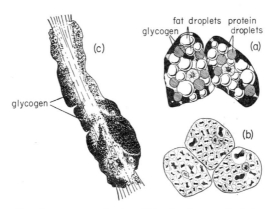

Fig. 22a–c.   Food reserves and uric acid in the tissues of *Aedes aegypti* larvae.

(a) Fat body cells of a well-nourished larva; (b) uric acid crystals in fat body cells of a starved larva; (c) abdominal muscle of a larva fed on starch, stained with iodine to show deposits of glycogen. (From Wigglesworth, 1942).

the fat body but it can also be found in cells of the caeca and of the anterior half of the midgut and in the oenocytes (Wigglesworth, 1942). In many species the abdominal muscles provide abundant protein when they are broken down during the first days of adult life (Roubaud, 1932; Rosay, 1961).

Wigglesworth (1942) studied the formation of fat body reserves when 4th instar larvae of *Aedes aegypti*, reared under sterile conditions and starved until all their reserves had been depleted, were fed on various compounds. Within 6 hr of feeding on glucose solution glycogen was deposited in the posterior half of the midgut and had started to accumulate in the sarcoplasm of the muscles and in the fat body. Solutions of fructose, sucrose or maltose did not lead to such a rapid appearance of glycogen, but within 12 hr glycogen was abundant in the fat body. Feeding on galactose, mannose, trehalose, α-methyl-D-glucoside, mannitol, sorbitol or lactose led to fairly large deposits of glycogen appearing in the posterior half of the midgut within 12 hr but none was found in the fat body within that time. No glycogen was formed from the pentoses arabinose and rhamnose, the hexose sorbose or the trisaccharide raffinose. Sugars of many sorts were converted to glycogen in the epithelium of the posterior half of the stomach before any appeared in the fat body, and deposition of glycogen in the fat body sometimes coincided with its appearance in the muscles. After feeding starch, glycogen was rapidly deposited in many tissues, and 1–2 days later fat appeared in the oenocytes and in the fat body.

Within 24 hr of feeding with olive oil or lecithin minute droplets of fat appeared in the cells of the anterior half of the midgut and in scattered cells in the caeca, in the oenocytes and throughout the fat body. Fat may appear in the oenocytes at a time when none is laid down in the fat body. Glycogen was never found to accumulate after feeding with olive oil.

When larvae fed on alanine, glycogen appeared in the cells of the posterior half of the midgut and in some cells of the caeca within 24 hr, and it was plentiful in the fat body within 48 hr. After 48 hr there were minute amounts of fat in the fat body of a few larvae. Glutamic acid gave somewhat similar results. It appears that amino acids can be deaminated and converted to glycogen in the midgut epithelium. Protein, glycogen and fat started to appear in the fat body 24 hr after feeding on casein. After a few days the fat body cells contained all the reserves of a well-nourished larva (Fig. 22a), the posterior part of the midgut became very rich in protein, deposits of glycogen appeared in the sarcoplasm and gut, and fat droplets could be seen in the oenocytes. However, after 7 days of feeding on casein alone the imaginal discs showed no sign of growth although larvae fed on casein in the presence of micro-organisms pupated within 4 days. Fat, protein and glycogen were used concurrently throughout starvation and there was no indication that glycogen was used up first (Wigglesworth, 1942).

Excretion and Detoxication

The Malpighian tubes and rectum are the organs principally concerned in ridding the haemolymph of unwanted substances. Fluid passes to the Malpighian tubes from the haemolymph and thence to the rectum where certain substances are reabsorbed, the remainder being discharged. Regulation of inorganic ions in this way is described in Chapter 3.

Scattered through the cytoplasm of the Malpighian tube cells are crystals with spoke-like radiations resembling the crystals of uric acid (Tulloch and Goldman, 1942). A considerable amount of solid uric acid accumulates in the tubule lumens when larvae of *Aedes aegypti* are kept in salty water but never when they are kept in fresh water, presumably because the tubules are then well flushed (Wigglesworth, 1933b, c). In this species the Malpighian tube cells normally remain translucent until the 4th instar when the distal parts of the tubules become opaque through granular deposits and remain so throughout life (Christophers, 1960).

The larval fat body acts as a kidney of accumulation, uric acid being deposited in special vacuoles within the fat body cells (Fig. 22b) (de Boissezon, 1930c; Wigglesworth, 1942). Very little uric acid is deposited in the fat body of *Aedes aegypti* larvae if the larvae are well nourished but starvation rapidly leads to the appearance of uric acid (Wigglesworth, 1942). More uric acid accumulates in the fat body during starvation than can have been produced from the protein originally present in the fat body cells, leading Wigglesworth (1942) to conclude that it is the product of deamination within the fat body cells of amino acids or proteins brought from elsewhere. When a starved larva is fed the amount of uric acid in the fat body falls, possibly through discharge of uric acid into the blood and its elimination by the Malpighian tubes (Wigglesworth, 1942). When mosquito larvae are fed ammonia carmine the pericardial cells become densely packed with carmine granules which are retained within the cells throughout life (Pal, 1944; Jones, 1954).

The ability to render harmless toxic organic compounds foreign to the body is called detoxication. Concentrations of benzoic acid which are lethal to larvae of *Aedes aegypti* can be made harmless by adding glycine. When larvae are reared in a dilute solution of benzoic acid and glycine-2-^{14}C they synthesize the conjugation product hippuric acid-^{14}C which is relatively harmless. Addition of certain other amino acids to the culture medium also leads to detoxication but they are less effective than glycine, efficiency decreasing with increasing chain length (Casida, 1955).

The study of resistance to insecticides has produced further examples of detoxication. Conversion of DDT to the non-toxic compound DDE has been reported in several species of *Anopheles, Aedes* and *Culex* (Brown, 1960) and activity of the enzyme concerned, DDT-dehydrochlorinase, has been obtained in homogenates of resistant *Aedes aegypti* (T. Kimura and A. W. A. Brown *in lit.*). Malathion is hydrolysed by a phosphatase and a carboxyesterase in *Aedes aegypti* and *Culex tarsalis* (Matsumura and Brown, 1961a, b) and γ-benzene hexachloride is converted to water-soluble metabolites in *Anopheles gambiae* (Bradbury and Standen, 1956). However, detoxication is not necessarily the principal mechanism of resistance to insecticides. In several species of mosquitoes both DDT-sensitive and DDT-resistant strains convert DDT to DDE, and although the resistant strains may absorb more DDT because they can withstand exposure to higher doses they do not necessarily convert a larger proportion of the DDT which is absorbed (Brown, 1960). Physiological mechanisms appear to play some part in DDT resistance. When larvae of certain resistant strains of *Aedes aegypti* are exposed to DDT they extrude considerable lengths of peritrophic membrane from the anus and these contain a large proportion of the ingested DDT (Abedi and Brown, 1961).

A Malayan resistant strain of *Aedes aegypti* which does not extrude peritrophic membrane nevertheless absorbs much less DDT from the gut than normal strains (Brown, 1961). Detoxication has been found to be of variable importance in resistance to other insecticides also. Susceptible and resistant strains of *Anopheles gambiae* showed similar rates of uptake of γ-benzene hexachloride and somewhat similar rates of detoxication (Bradbury and Standen, 1956). A malathion-resistant strain of *Aedes aegypti* did not detoxicate malathion more rapidly than normal strains but it absorbed very much less of the insecticide across the gut (Matsumura and Brown, 1961a). A malathion-resistant strain of *Culex tarsalis,* on the other hand, was several times more active in carboxyesterase activity than normal strains and this high enzyme activity was found to be genetically inseparable from the malathion resistance (Brown, 1961; Matsumura and Brown, 1961b). Resistance to insecticides clearly occurs by a number of different mechanisms and in some cases detoxication is probably important.

Respiration

The tracheal system of the larva comprises 2 large, dorsal, longitudinal trunks and 2 smaller, lateral, longitudinal trunks, connected to one another and sending tracheae to all regions of the body. The larvae are metapneustic, only the terminal pair of spiracles, on the 8th abdominal segment, being open. In *Anopheles* the spiracles are sessile but in all other mosquitoes they open at the end of a respiratory siphon. Air sacs are present in *Orthopodomyia* and *Mansonia* but their function is not known. In mosquito pupae the cuticle of the thorax is extended into 2 large trumpets, the bases of which are connected by short lengths of trachea to the anterior thoracic spiracles.

The spiracular peritreme is extended into 5 lobes which are folded inwards when the larva dives to prevent entry of water, and which, after it has risen, open into the plane of the water surface and support the larva from the surface membrane. Brocher (1910) has described the significance of capillarity, contact angle and surface tension in the opening of the spiracular valve and the suspension of larvae from the water surface. A lobed spiracular valve is absent in *Malaya genurostris* but the larva is capable of hanging from the surface membrane nevertheless and closes its spiracles by a membranous cap when submerged (Iyengar and Menon, 1948).

Perispiracular glands have been described in larvae of *Anopheles, Culex, Culiseta* and *Orthopodomyia*. Staining with Sudan III leads to coloration of the glands and of the lining of the felt chambers of the spiracles, suggesting that the perispiracular glands secrete an oily substance which produces the hydrofuge property of the spiracle openings. This secretion can be wetted by oils which are able to enter the spiracles, and it can be dissolved by ether so permitting penetration of water (Keilin, Tate and Vincent, 1935).

Larvae of most species are normally to be found at the water surface with the tracheal system open to the atmosphere, but some species make extensive use of cutaneous respiration. The older larvae of *Culiseta morsitans*, for example, rarely seek the water surface in nature (Wesenberg-Lund, 1921) and 4th instar larvae of *Aedes flavescens* spend most of the time among vegetation at the bottom of pools (Hearle, 1929). Larvae of *Aedes aegypti* kept in flowing water at about 30°C and denied access to the surface lived up to 53 days and developed to the 4th instar. Larvae of *Culex thalassius* lived at least a fortnight under such conditions but larvae of *Culex pipiens fatigans* could not survive one day (Macfie, 1917).

Wigglesworth (1933b) investigated the site of oxygen uptake in submerged larvae of *Aedes aegypti* by noting the distribution around the larvae of the flagellate *Polytoma* which shows klinokinesis, accumulating at a certain low concentration of oxygen. The flagellates first aggregated at the base of the anal papillae but later formed a band around the larva, slowly moving away from it, and at each stage being slightly further from the papillae than from the general body surface. It was concluded that oxygen was absorbed over the whole body surface and at a slightly higher rate over the anal papillae. By use of suitable chemical indicators, carbon dioxide was found to be excreted more or less uniformly over the whole body surface with no increased excretion at the anal papillae. Oxygen passes along the tracheae of *Culex* larvae by diffusion alone, there are no respiratory movements (Krogh, 1941).

The larvae of certain species are strikingly adapted to live on the bottom. In *Aedes argenteopunctatus* 2 pairs of large, thin-walled and densely-tracheated papillae extend from the ventro-lateral regions of the head where feeding currents will pass over them (Fig. 23b), and the anal papillae are long and densely tracheated (Fig. 23c). The larvae lie on the bottom in an inverted position, resting on modified hairs of the thorax and siphon, and water currents produced by the labral brushes pass over both the papillae on the head and the anal papillae (Fig. 23e). Similar structures and habits are developed in *Culex poicilipes*, *Culex sinaiticus*, *Aedeomyia africana* and other species (Lewis, 1949). Wesenberg-Lund (1921) described how larvae of *Culiseta morsitans* resting on the bottom spread out their anal papillae and maintain a water current over them with their labral brushes, so such habits may be more widespread than is generally thought. Size of anal papillae is not a guide to the extent of cutaneous respiration, however, for *Culex thalassius* which can survive prolonged submergence has very small papillae whereas *Culex pipiens fatigans* which cannot has large papillae (Macfie, 1917).

In *Mansonia* the respiratory siphon is pointed and bears a sharp cutting edge (Fig. 23a). It is placed against the root or rhizome of an aquatic

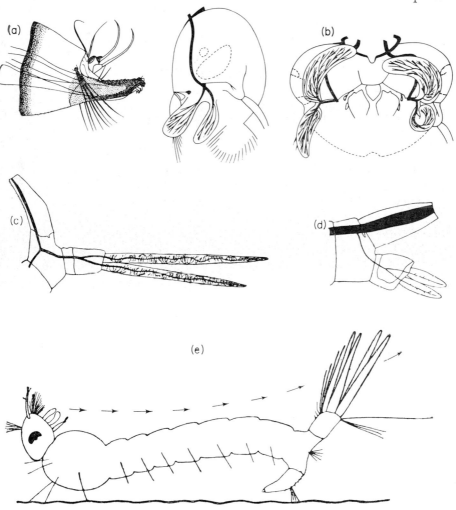

FIG. 23a–e.   Respiratory modifications in mosquito larvae.

(a) Respiratory siphon of *Mansonia richiardii* modified for piercing (from Lang, 1920); (b) head of *Aedes argenteopunctatus* in lateral and ventral view to show cephalic gills; (c) terminal segments of *Aedes argenteopunctatus* to show modified anal papillae; (d) terminal segments of *Aedes luteocephalus* for comparison; (e) *Aedes argenteopunctatus* in resting position, arrows show the path of the water current produced by the labral brushes. (From Lewis, 1949).

E

plant and by twisting movements of the abdomen is driven into the tissue until connection is made with the intercellular spaces which contain air. The pupal trumpets are pointed and used in a similar manner (Krogh, 1941). The larvae of *Ficalbia pallida, Ficalbia hybrida* and *Aedeomyia furfurea* also have modified respiratory siphons which are plunged into the air spaces of aquatic plants (Mattingly, 1957; van den Assem, 1958). These adaptations are thought to help the aquatic stages to remain immotile and concealed from predators, enabling them to colonize bodies of water not available to other species (van den Assem, 1958).

The rate of oxygen uptake by larvae of *Anopheles labranchiae atroparvus* increases in each successive instar. It rises to a maximum about the middle of each instar but falls considerably over the period of moulting (Olifan, 1947). Respiration shows the typical U-form during the pupal stage, falling to a very low level for a short time and later rising again. At the time of maximum depression almost all organs of the adult mosquito are formed and show some histological differentiation (Olifan, 1949).

Lang (1959, 1961) has shown the presence in homogenates and other preparations of the thorax and abdomen of *Aedes aegypti* larvae of DPNH-cytochrome *c* reductase, TPNH-cytochrome *c* reductase and succinate-cytochrome *c* reductase. DPNH-cytochrome *c* reductase activity was fairly high in the larva, decreased markedly in the pupal stage and then increased in the adult to more than 5 times its rate of activity in the larval stage. A lower rate of activity but similar pattern was observed for the succinate enzyme. In contrast, TPNH-cytochrome *c* reductase showed a moderate rate of activity during larval life but its activity was low in both pupal and adult stages. Augenfeld and Neess (1961) have reported the presence of the succinic oxidase and cytochrome oxidase systems in homogenates of whole *Aedes aegypti* larvae and Murthy and Micks (1961) have described TPNH-isocitric dehydrogenase in particulate and soluble fractions of *Aedes aegypti* larvae.

CHAPTER 3

OSMOTIC AND IONIC
REGULATION OF BODY FLUIDS

Uptake of Water and Salts

Most mosquito larvae live in fresh water and consequently take up water by omosis and lose ions by diffusion across permeable regions of the body wall. A few species live in salt marshes where the medium fluctuates from strongly hypo-osmotic to the haemolymph to strongly hyperosmotic, owing to changes in salinity. Both fresh-water and salt-marsh larvae are faced with the problems of maintaining the osmotic pressure of their haemolymph at the right level and of maintaining the inorganic ions of their haemolymph and tissues at suitable concentrations and in proportions different from those of the external medium. The detailed investigations of a small number of workers have thrown much light on the mechanisms of osmotic and ionic regulation in mosquito larvae.

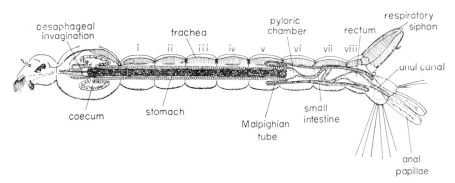

FIG. 24. Anatomy of the mosquito larva (semi-diagrammatic). The numbers i, ii, etc. indicate abdominal segmentation. (From Wigglesworth, 1933b).

Four papillae which surround the anus (Fig. 24) are of great importance in the flux of water and salts. The anal papillae are extensions of the body wall with lumens continuous with the haemocoele. Their cells rest directly on the delicate cuticle of the papillae and no cell boundaries are visible. The cytoplasm adjacent to the cuticle shows regular vertical striations (Wigglesworth, 1933a) suggestive of microvilli or of rows of mitochondria. In well-fed larvae the cells are thick but under starvation conditions they become very thin (Stobbart, 1959). The anal papillae can be destroyed for experimental purposes by placing the larvae in 0·85 M-NaCl for 2 or 3 min; on returning the larvae to fresh water the papillae fall away and within a few days heal completely leaving only 4 small scars (Wigglesworth, 1933b).

Aedes aegypti larvae shrink when placed in hypertonic glucose solution but if a ligature is first tied near the end of the abdomen only the region behind the ligature, including the anal papillae, shrinks. Larvae deprived of their papillae and kept in fresh water pass much less water from the anus than normal larvae. These experiments and the observation that mosquito larvae swallow negligible amounts of water with their food show that the anal papillae are the principal site of water uptake (Wigglesworth, 1933b). In the brackish-water mosquito *Aedes detritus* the anal papillae are never more than minute protuberances (Fig. 30) and ligature experiments have shown that water uptake in this species occurs via the gut, the papillae being impermeable to water (Beadle, 1939).

Larvae which normally live in fresh water have a striking ability to take up salts from very dilute solutions. When larvae of *Culex* sp. were washed in a stream of distilled water for several hours, their chloride content fell by one-third but when transferred to 1 mM-Ringer solution, approximately the concentration of fresh water, they restored their chloride content to normal. The ability to take up the chloride was lost when the anal papillae were destroyed (Koch, 1938). *Aedes aegypti* larvae have been found to concentrate chloride from 1 mM-NaCl (Wigglesworth, 1938a) and sodium and potassium from 1·7 mM-NaCl and 1·7 mM-KCl respectively (Ramsay, 1953a). Measurement of uptake of radioactive sodium by normal larvae of *Aedes aegypti* and by larvae lacking anal papillae or with their mouths blocked or both showed that 90 per cent of sodium uptake occurs across the anal papillae, and the remainder across the gut (Treherne, 1954; Stobbart, 1959). The rate of sodium uptake is not affected by the presence of 0·16–4·0 mM-potassium in the medium indicating that potassium does not compete with sodium for transport into the haemolymph (Treherne, 1954). Application to the outside of the larva of physostigmine, an inhibitor of cholinesterase, does not affect uptake of sodium as it does in certain other animals (Stobbart, 1960). Ligature experiments show that the minute anal papillae of the brackish-water species *Aedes detritus* are impermeable to salts and that uptake occurs across the gut. These larvae are unable to concentrate chloride from 1 mM-NaCl but they are able to do so from a 7 mM solution (Beadle, 1939).

When *Aedes aegypti* larvae are placed in a hypertonic solution containing only monovalent ions the epithelial cells of the anal papillae swell, but in a hypertonic medium containing a di- or trivalent anion or cation the cells shrink. The cells of amputated papillae, which are exposed to the medium from inside and outside, swell in all hypotonic media and shrink in all hypertonic media. It appears that monovalent ions penetrate the cells of the anal papillae in the intact larva and that when the external medium is hyperosmotic they cause an osmotic uptake of water from the haemolymph; di- and trivalent ions do not penetrate the cells at a high rate, even from concentrated solutions (Wigglesworth, 1933a). Larvae of *Aedes aegypti* can concentrate phosphorus from dilute solutions of $H_3{}^{32}PO_4$. Uptake is faster in normal larvae than in larvae deprived of their anal papillae although the same level of radioactivity is ultimately attained by both suggesting that uptake occurs partly through the anal papillae and partly across the gut (Hassett and Jenkins, 1951). Little zinc is accumulated by fasting larvae in zinc chloride solution but it is taken up by feeding larvae (Lang, 1958).

Stobbart (1959, 1960) studied sodium flux in larvae of *Aedes aegypti*. When larvae were reared in 2 mM-NaCl the sodium level of the haemolymph remained steady at about 100 to 105 mM whether the larvae were fed or starved. The steady-state exchange of sodium in 4th instar larvae in 2 mM-NaCl was measured after transferring larvae to a medium containing ^{22}Na. The time for half exchange was about 10 hr in fed larvae and about 60 hr in starved larvae, all the sodium in the haemolymph being exchangeable with that in the medium. In both cases 90 per cent of the exchange occurred across the anal papillae. Larvae which had been reared in a sodium-deficient medium had a haemolymph sodium concentration of about 30 mM. When well-nourished but sodium-deficient larvae were transferred to 2 mM-NaCl net uptake of sodium occurred in two phases: a rapid net uptake of 55–65 m-mole Na/l haemolymph/hr proceeded until the sodium level had risen to 85–95 mM and there was then a slow increase to the normal level of 105 mM. The transition between the 2 rates of net transport was rapid. When starved, sodium-deficient larvae were transferred to 2 mM-NaCl the sodium level of the haemolymph increased slowly by 7–10 m-mole/l/hr to 110 mM and then declined to about 105 mM.

When starved larvae of *Aedes aegypti* were placed in running distilled water haemolymph sodium gradually fell to about 60 per cent of the original level during the first 150 hr but thereafter the fall was more rapid and the larvae started to die. Larvae are therefore able to retain sodium to a considerable extent against a big concentration difference. To measure outflux of sodium during a period of net uptake, fed and starved sodium-deficient larvae were placed in a medium containing ^{22}Na for a short time before being transferred to 2 mM-NaCl. Sodium uptake started in the radioactive medium and continued in the unlabelled medium. Net uptake, measured by flame photometry, occurred rapidly in the fed larvae and slowly in the starved larvae as was expected. Outflux was measured by fall in radioactivity and initial outfluxes of 49–70 and 3–9 m-mole/l. haemolymph/hr were recorded in the fed and starved larvae respectively, both rates slowing down considerably after 2 hr (Fig. 25 and Table 3).

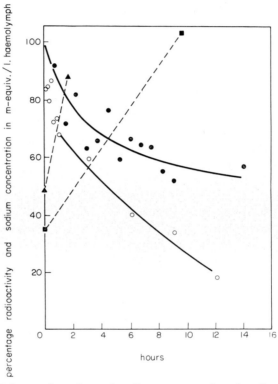

FIG. 25. Influx and outflux of sodium on transfer of sodium-deficient larvae of *Aedes aegypti* to 2 mM-NaCl (after a short period in a medium containing ^{22}Na). ▲ =Na level in haemolymph of fed larvae; ■ =Na level in haemolymph of starved larvae; O = outflux of ^{22}Na from haemolymph of fed larvae; ● = outflux of ^{22}Na from haemolymph of starved larvae. (From Stobbart, 1960).

The gut must be able to do osmotic work since papilla-less larvae in 2 mM-NaCl can keep their haemolymph sodium concentration at 80 mM indefinitely. Papilla-less, fed, sodium-deficient larvae perform no net transport of sodium during the first 20 hr after transfer to 2 mM-NaCl but they effect considerable net transport, presumably across the gut, between 30 and 50 hr (Stobbart, 1959, 1960).

The rates of sodium flux in *Aedes aegypti* submitted to different conditions are summarized in Table 3. It is seen that well-nourished larvae in a sodium-rich medium exchange sodium at a fairly high rate but that starved larvae have a much lower rate of exchange. Outflux of sodium is low in distilled water, in starved larvae at least. When sodium-deficient larvae are placed in 2 mM-NaCl a rapid net uptake of sodium occurs in fed individuals and a much slower net uptake in starved individuals, accompanied in both cases by relatively high rates of outflux. In both cases the initial rates of influx and outflux are higher than the fluxes which occur during steady-state exchange. Thus feeding increases the rate of sodium transport, whether in steady-state exchange or net uptake, by a

TABLE 3. RATES OF SODIUM FLUX IN *Aedes aegypti* LARVAE EXPOSED TO DIFFERENT CONDITIONS, FOUND BY FLAME PHOTOMETRY AND MEASUREMENT OF ^{22}NA LEVELS OF THE HAEMOLYMPH. (FROM THE DATA OF STOBBART, 1959, 1960).

Type of flux	Flux in m-mole/l. haemolymph/hr	
	Fed	Starved
1. Steady-state exchange in 2mM-NaCl	7·1–8·8	1·0–1·1
2. Outflux in distilled water	—	0·3
3. Net uptake by Na-deficient larvae on transfer to 2mM-NaCl (initial rate)	39–50	7–9
4. Outflux from Na-deficient larvae on transfer to 2mM-NaCl (initial rate)	49–70	3–9
5. Total initial influx on transfer of Na-deficient larvae to 2mM-NaCl (= 3+4)	88–120	10–18

factor of 5 or more. Stobbart (1959, 1960) has accounted for these phenomena by postulating a carrier mechanism in the anal papillae associated with a barrier impermeable to sodium. The carrier mechanism is thought to comprise something similar to an exchange diffusion mechanism which operates without active transport and which is linked to a pump. The pump is supposed to remove sufficient sodium from the exchange diffusion mechanism to balance passive losses and when necessary to raise the sodium concentration of the haemolymph to its normal level. The carrier mechanism is linked to metabolism in such a way that both influx and outflux increase when the larva is fed.

Regulation of the Haemolymph

When larvae of *Aedes aegypti* are kept under more or less natural conditions the haemolymph contains approximately 100 to 105 mM-sodium, 4 mM-potassium and 50 mM-chloride. These ions will exert a pressure of about 159 m-osmolar but vapour pressure measurements of haemolymph give a value of 288 m-osmolar (equivalent to 144 mM-NaCl) so that much of the osmotic pressure must be exerted by other substances such as amino acids (Wigglesworth, 1938a; Ramsay, 1953a; Stobbart, 1960).

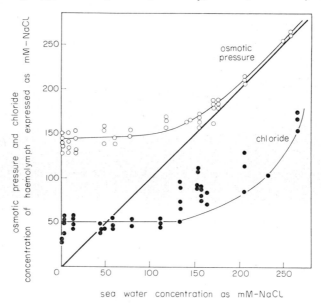

Fig. 26. Variations in osmotic pressure and chloride concentration of the haemolymph of *Aedes aegypti* larvae in different concentrations of sea water. All values are expressed as equivalent concentrations of NaCl. The diagonal straight line represents haemolymph and medium as continuously isosmotic. At higher sea-water concentrations the curve for chloride has been drawn through the lowest chloride concentrations and so represents the condition of the most successful larvae. (From Wigglesworth, 1938a).

When larvae of *Aedes aegypti* are kept in various dilutions of sea water their haemolymph osmotic pressures remain the same as long as the external medium is hypo-osmotic to the haemolymph, but when the concentration of the medium reaches 128–153 mM or more the haemolymph osmotic pressure rises so that it is always a little greater than that of the medium (Fig. 26). The haemolymph chloride concentration varies in a similar way. When larvae are kept in distilled water with very little food the chloride concentration is 27 mM, but in 1 mM-saline, the concentration of tap water, and all hypo-osmotic media the haemolymph chloride concentration varies only between about 37 and 58 mM. Chloride regulation breaks down, as does osmoregulation, in a medium of 128 to 153 mM (Wigglesworth, 1938a). Haemolymph sodium and potassium concentrations are also regulated in hypo-osmotic media, the concentrations of these elements rising only slightly when the external concentrations vary between 1·7 and 85 mM (Table 4) (Ramsay, 1953a).

Regulation of the non-chloride fraction of the haemolymph is apparent in the far greater individual variation of chloride concentration than of total osmotic pressure when larvae of *Aedes aegypti* are subjected to high concentrations of saline (Fig. 26). Regulation of the non-chloride fraction is also found when larvae are starved in distilled water. After 7 days the chloride concentration has fallen by 75 per cent while the total osmotic pressure has fallen only 21 per cent (Wigglesworth, 1938a). Chloride is lost far more rapidly than sodium from the haemolymph of larvae

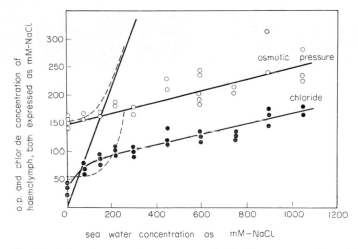

FIG. 27. Variations in osmotic pressure and chloride concentration of the haemolymph of *Aedes detritus* larvae in different concentrations of sea water. All values are expressed as equivalent concentrations of NaCl. The diagonal straight line represents haemolymph and medium as continuously isosmotic. The corresponding curves for *Aedes aegypti* (Fig. 26) are superimposed as dotted lines. (From Beadle, 1939).

starved in distilled water. Sodium fell from about 100 mM/1. to about 64 mM/1. during the first 96 hr after transfer to distilled water (Stobbart, 1959) whereas chloride fell from 51 mM/1. to 14 mM/1. over a similar period (Wigglesworth, 1938a). Chloride is lost at an even faster rate when the larvae have previously been kept in high chloride concentrations (Wigglesworth, 1938a).

Larvae of the brackish-water species *Aedes detritus* are able to maintain the chloride concentration and total osmotic pressure of their haemolymph at nearly normal levels in both dilute and very concentrated media. A rise from zero to 1M-NaCl in the external medium is reflected by an increase from 137 mM to 239 mM in the osmotic pressure of the haemolymph. The relationships between the osmotic pressure of the medium and the osmotic pressure and chloride concentration of the haemolymph are shown in Fig. 27 where they can be compared with the corresponding results for *Aedes aegypti*. In dilute solutions both species can maintain their haemolymph hyperosmotic to the external medium but only *Aedes detritus* is able to regulate the osmotic pressure of its haemolymph in hyperosmotic media. Similarly, only *Aedes detritus* can maintain approximately normal chloride levels at high external concentrations (Beadle, 1939). Although both osmotic pressure and chloride concentration are kept approximately normal in *Aedes detritus* there is nevertheless a progressive change in both which is roughly proportional to the change in the external concentration. In hyperosmotic solutions the progressive rise in total osmotic pressure is due mainly to increase in the chloride fraction, the non-chloride fraction remaining approximately constant. Much chloride is lost in a medium of distilled water but the total osmotic pressure is regulated by a corresponding increase in the non-chloride fraction.

The Mechanism of Regulation

The basis of the regulatory mechanism, in *Aedes aegypti* at least, is a circulation of water and potassium through the Malpighian tubes, gut and haemocoele. The circulation starts when fluid derived from the haemolymph passes down the Malpighian tubes and accumulates in the pyloric chamber. Peristalsis of the hindgut causes some of this to pass to the rectum, and since less fluid is discharged from the anus than enters the rectum some water must return to the haemolymph across the rectal wall. Antiperistalsis of the midgut also causes fluid to move forwards between the stomach epithelium and the peritrophic membrane. Non-diffusible dyes added to food are later found precipitated in the caecal lumens showing that water is absorbed in the caeca, which must be the principal, if not the only, site of water absorption in the midgut (Wigglesworth, 1933b; Ramsay, 1950). From ligation experiments and from a few direct measurements of Malpighian tube fluid Ramsay (1951) concluded that the fluid which passed down the small intestine was mainly derived from the Malpighian tubes and that its composition could be taken as an indication of the composition of Malpighian tube fluid. In this way it has been found that the Malpighian tubes secrete large amounts of potassium which circulate with the water and which, like the water, are normally reabsorbed in midgut and rectum:

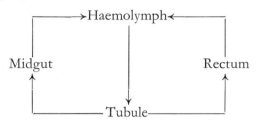

Regulation by *Aedes aegypti* larvae in distilled water will be considered first. If the abdomen is ligatured in front of the Malpighian tubes no visible abnormalities result but if the abdomen is ligatured between segments 6 and 7 the Malpighian tubes are unable to discharge and it is found that the ends of the tubules and the end of the abdomen become distended with water. Discharge of water by the Malpighian tubes is therefore an essential counter to the osmotic uptake which occurs across the anal papillae (Wigglesworth, 1933b). Considerable amounts of uric acid are sometimes seen in the Malpighian tube lumens when *Aedes aegypti* larvae are kept in dilute sea water, but the tubules are always flushed free of solid matter when larvae are kept in fresh water (Wigglesworth, 1933a). This suggests that the passage of water from haemolymph to Malpighian tubes increases when there is a water load.

The osmotic pressures of the haemolymph and of fluids from different parts of the alimentary canal of *Aedes aegypti* larvae kept in distilled water are shown in Figure 28. The fluid produced by the Malpighian tubes (intestinal fluid) is slightly hypo-osmotic to the haemolymph but it is concentrated in the stomach and caeca, presumably by reabsorption of water, and strongly diluted in the rectum by reabsorption of salts (Ramsay, 1950). The sodium and potassium concentrations of the haemolymph, intestinal fluid and rectal fluid of larvae in distilled water are given in Table 4. Compared with the haemolymph, the fluid produced by the Malpighian tubes is low in sodium and extremely high in potassium although the osmotic pressures of the two fluids have been shown to be very similar. Fluid removed from the rectum contains little sodium and a relatively high concentration of potassium, but the survival of larvae in distilled water indicates that both elements must normally be almost completely reabsorbed before the rectal fluid is discharged. The composition of midgut fluid of larvae in distilled water is not known but when larvae are kept in a saline medium (85 mM-NaCl and 4·3 mM-KCl) the stomach fluid contains 165 mM-Na and 26 mM-K thus showing a substantial return towards the sodium : potassium ratio of the haemolymph and indicating reabsorption of potassium (Ramsay, 1953a). It seems likely that sodium must return to the haemolymph via the caeca, possibly by diffusion because of the concentration difference. It can be concluded

TABLE 4. THE EFFECTS OF VARIOUS EXTERNAL MEDIA ON SODIUM AND POTASSIUM CONCENTRATIONS IN BODY FLUIDS OF *Aedes aegypti* LARVAE. SAMPLES WERE TAKEN AFTER EXPOSURE FOR 5 DAYS TO THE RELEVANT MEDIUM EXCEPT IN THE CASE OF RECTAL FLUID WHICH WAS SAMPLED AFTER 3 WEEKS. ALL MEASUREMENTS ARE MEAN VALUES EXPRESSED AS mM. (FROM RAMSAY, 1953a).

External Medium	Haemolymph		Intestinal Fluid		Rectal Fluid	
	Na	K	Na	K	Na	K
Distilled water	87	3	24	88	4	25
1·7 mM-NaCl	100	—	—	—	—	—
85 mM-NaCl	113	—	71	90	100	18
1·7 mM-KCl	—	4	—	—	—	—
85 mM-KCl	—	6	23	138	14	90

that larvae of *Aedes aegypti* in distilled water rid themselves of the excess water derived from osmotic uptake by discharging water through the Malpighian tubes and hindgut, salts being reabsorbed from this fluid by the rectum.

The effects of a hyperosmotic external medium on the haemolymph and other body fluids of *Aedes aegypti* are shown in Fig. 28. The inability of *Aedes aegypti* to regulate the osmotic pressure of its haemolymph under these conditions is confirmed and it is seen that the Malpighian tubes secrete a fluid slightly hypo-osmotic to the haemolypmh, as they do when the larvae are in distilled water, and that this fluid is hardly modified by the rectum (Ramsay, 1950). The sodium and potassium levels of body fluids of *Aedes aegypti* exposed to low or moderate concentrations of NaCl and KCl are given in Table 4. The haemolymph levels rise only slightly in the face of substantial changes in the external medium. Sodium and potassium are found in higher concentrations than normal in the intestinal fluid, reflecting the slight increase in haemolymph concentrations, and reabsorption in the rectum is reduced so that the elements escape from the body (Ramsay, 1953a).

Aedes detritus larvae can regulate their haemolymph osmotic pressure in both hypo- and hyperosmotic media. Figure 28 shows that in distilled water the mechanism of osmoregulation is the same as that of *Aedes aegypti*, the Malpighian tubes discharging a fluid which resembles the haemolymph in osmotic pressure and which is diluted in the rectum, doubtless by reabsorption of salts. When larvae are kept in sea water the Malpighian tubes produce a fluid somewhat hyperosmotic to the

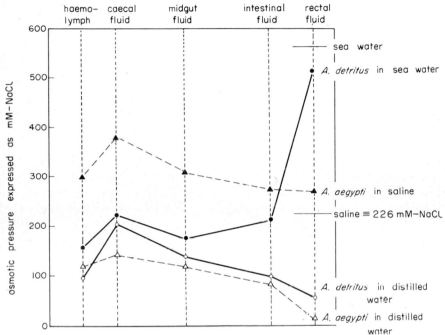

F IG. 28.   Mean values of the osmotic pressure of various body fluids from larvae of *Aedes aegypti* and *Aedes detritus* kept in different media. All values are expressed as the equivalent concentrations of NaCl. (After Ramsay, 1950).

haemolymph and this is strongly concentrated in the rectum, presumably by reabsorption of water, the rectal fluid becoming hypertonic to sea water in some individuals (Ramsay, 1950). In *Aedes detritus* the rectal epithelium consists of 2 regions, anterior and posterior, which differ in structure. Ramsay (1950) has tentatively suggested that the ability of *Aedes detritus* to produce a rectal fluid hypertonic to the haemolymph is a property of the anterior region of the rectum, since in *Aedes aegypti*, which is unable to concentrate the contents of its rectum, the whole rectal epithelium resembles the posterior region in *Aedes detritus*. In fresh water, therefore, both *Aedes aegypti* and *Aedes detritus* regulate their haemolymph osmotic pressure by excreting water from which salts have been removed by the rectum. *Aedes detritus* can concentrate the contents of its rectum and so osmoregulate in a hyperosmotic medium but *Aedes aegypti* apparently cannot do this.

The forces involved in the movements of water and salts in *Aedes aegypti* and other insects have been investigated and discussed by Ramsay (1953a, b; 1956). When *Aedes aegypti* larvae are kept in distilled water the Malpighian tubes produce a fluid containing less than one-third as much sodium as the haemolymph and nearly 30 times as much potassium. Measurements of potential difference across the wall of the Malpighian tubes show that the interior of the tubes is positive to the haemolymph by 13–21 mV whatever the external medium. When related to sodium and potassium concentrations in haemolymph and tubule fluid these results indicate that potassium is actively transported against an electrochemical gradient but that sodium may possibly pass into the tubule lumen by passive diffusion. The function of the secretion of potassium by the Malpighian tubes and its circulation is not known but Ramsay (1953a) has suggested that it is fundamental to the process of 'urine' formation by the Malpighian tubes. The low pressure of the insect circulatory system does not permit filtration of blood, such as occurs in the vertebrate glomerulus, and because the Malpighian tube fluid is hypo-osmotic to the haemolymph Ramsay (1956) concluded that the passage of water into the Malpighian tubes was most probably due to secretion although, in the absence of any evidence, electro-osmosis could not be discounted.

The mechanism of regulation may be summarized as follows. The Malpighian tubes discharge a fluid obtained from the haemolymph but differing from it in composition, some components being actively secreted and others entering the Malpighian tubes without direct expenditure of energy. This fluid passes forwards to the midgut and backwards to the hindgut. Much may be reabsorbed, the rectum being particularly important in selective reabsorption of water and solutes, and whatever is surplus, whether of water or solutes, is discharged through the anus. When the external medium is rich in sodium or potassium more of that element is discharged in the Malpighian tube fluid and less is reabsorbed in the rectum. Salt losses in hypo-osmotic media are compensated by active uptake by the anal papillae. *Aedes detritus* can live in hyperosmotic media because it is able to concentrate its rectal fluid by removal of water until it is highly hypersomotic to its haemolymph.

Larval Distribution in Nature

A number of ecologists have analysed the waters in which mosquito larvae are found and from which they are absent and have concluded that certain solutes are harmful to the larvae, preventing the breeding of mosquitoes where they occur. Harmful properties have been ascribed to ammonium salts (Beattie, 1932), nitrites (Williamson, 1928), nitrates (Bates, 1941a) and protein (Sen, 1957) but these results have generally been contradicted by other workers (Russell and Rao, 1942a; Senior-White, 1928b; Muirhead-Thomson, 1941a). Similarly, the view that *Anopheles* larvae cannot breed in polluted water has been proved wrong in the laboratory in the case of *Anopheles minimus* (Muirhead-Thomson, 1941a) and *Anopheles stephensi* (Russell and Mohan, 1939), typical clear water species. There is no doubt, however, that larvae of *Culex pipiens* var. *molestus* can survive in polluted water which rapidly kills *Culex pipiens pipiens* and that in nature the former are often found in foul water (Roubaud, 1933).

The distribution of larvae in natural waters of varying *p*H shows that many species are able to live under both alkaline and acid conditions (MacGregor, 1929). *Anopheles culicifacies*, for example, has been recorded in the *p*H range 5·4–9·8 (Senior-White, 1926, 1928b) and the tree-hole species *Anopheles plumbeus* and *Aedes geniculatus* from *p*H 4·4 to *p*H 9·3 (MacGregor, 1921; Keilin, 1932). *Aedes flavopictus* larvae develop in the laboratory in media ranging from *p*H 2 to 9 and *Armigeres subalbatus* larvae in media ranging from *p*H 2 to 10 (Kurihara, 1959). In the laboratory acid conditions are sometimes unfavorable to larvae but this may be due to the bacteria which develop under acid conditions or to the acid present, hydrochloric acid, for example, being more toxic than phosphoric acid (MacGregor, 1929).

Observations such as these and the knowledge that female mosquitoes are highly selective in nature in choice of oviposition site have prompted the suggestion that the distribution of larvae is controlled not by survival in suitable and extinction in unsuitable habitats but by the discrimination of the ovipositing female (Beattie, 1932; Beklemishev and Mitrofanova, 1926; Macan, 1961). This view is now generally accepted but unfortunately the means by which gravid females select the oviposition site are very incompletely known (see Chapter 16).

Although most mosquitoes are restricted to fresh water a number of species can develop in extremely high concentrations of salts. Larvae of *Aedes natronius* have been found in a crater lake in Uganda which had a salinity equivalent to 3·9 per cent NaCl (0·67 M), an alkalinity of 0·7 N and a *p*H exceeding 10·5 (Beadle, 1939). The larvae of brackish-water species are able to develop in the concentrated sea water which occurs in littoral pools. *Aedes australis* will develop in sea water containing 7·4 per cent salts (Woodhill, 1936) and *Aedes detritus* has been found in sea water containing 10 per cent salts (Beadle, 1939). Certain fresh-water species can tolerate a fairly high salinity. *Anopheles superpictus*, for example, will develop normally in 30 per cent sea water (Bates, 1939). Larvae of *Aedes aegypti* reared in fresh water are killed by 0·19 M-NaCl (1·1 per cent NaCl) or by sea water isosmotic with 0·22–0·24 M-NaCl, but by gradually increasing the concentration the larvae can be adapted to 0·19 M-NaCl and to 50 per cent sea water (isosmotic with 0·3 M or 1·75 per cent NaCl) (Wigglesworth, 1933c).

The anal papillae of brackish-water species are reduced to minute protuberances which are impermeable to salts and water (Woodhill, 1936; Beadle, 1939) whereas in fresh-water species the length of the anal

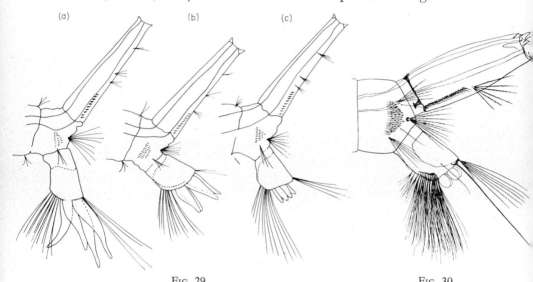

FIG. 29   FIG. 30

FIG. 29a–c.   Terminal segments of *Culex pipiens* larvae reared in different media showing the effect on the anal papillae.
(a) In distilled water; (b) in tap water; (c) in salt water equivalent to 11 mM-NaCl. (From Wigglesworth, 1949).

FIG. 30.   Terminal segments of the larva of the salt marsh species *Aedes detritus*. (From Marshall, 1938).

papillae varies with the salinity of the medium, the papillae being hyper-trophied in distilled water and rain water (Gibbins, 1932; Kettle, 1948). In *Aedes aegypti* the most striking difference in length is to be seen when larvae from distilled water are compared with larvae from tap water, but in *Culex pipiens* a further considerable decrease in size accompanies further increases in salinity (Fig. 29) (Wigglesworth, 1938a). Most species which breed in small containers, where the water is poor in salts, have large, sausage-shaped papillae, e.g. *Aedes aegypti*, but the few predatory species found in this situation have very short papillae and apparently obtain sufficient salts from their food (Hopkins, 1938). In the laboratory *Aedes aegypti* and *Aedes detritus* are able to obtain sufficient salts from their food alone (Wigglesworth, 1938a; Beadle, 1939) but *Culex pipiens* and *Aedes australis* require a low level of sodium chloride in the water for development (Wigglesworth, 1938a; Woodhill, 1941) and larvae of *Anopheles superpictus* will not develop unless the water contains a trace of calcium (Bates, 1939).

We may conclude that the composition of most bodies of still, fresh water is suitable for the survival and growth of larvae of most species although high levels of pollution or salinity may prove fatal to all except a few species. The restriction of species to particular larval habitats is probably due to discrimination by ovipositing females, an activity which will be affected in the long term by selective pressures operating during the larval stage as well as by those effective at oviposition.

F

CHAPTER 4

GROWTH AND METAMORPHOSIS

Larval Growth

Little is known of the control of growth in mosquito larvae but the visible aspects of growth have been studied in some detail. The larva passes through 4 instars. The heavily-sclerotized parts of the integument, the head capsule and respiratory siphon, increase in size immediately after ecdysis but not between ecdyses, whereas the thorax and abdomen which are covered with thin, extensible cuticle grow continuously throughout larval life showing no sudden change at ecdysis. The anal papillae, however, show a mixed pattern of growth since they grow steadily though slowly during each instar and also increase in length abruptly at each ecdysis (Kettle, 1948). In *Anopheles* the sclerotization of the head capsule extends backwards during each instar so that the anterior region of the neck becomes thickened, except in the dorsal midline, forming a band called the collar. This is not renewed at moulting but grows again during the next instar (Mitrofanova, 1929; Jones, 1953b). The function of the collar is not known.

The growth of the head follows Dyar's rule in some species, the width of the head capsule increasing by a constant factor at each moult; in *Anopheles sergentii* this factor is 1·5 (Kettle, 1948) and in *Culex pipiens fatigans* it is 1·4 (Sen and Das Gupta, 1958). However, certain other species do not follow Dyar's rule and it has been found in *Aedes trivittatus, Aedes aegypti* (Abdel-Malek and Goulding, 1948), *Anopheles quadrimaculatus* (Jones, 1953b) and *Culex tritaeniorhynchus* (Oka, 1955) that at successive moults the width of the head increases by a variable factor.

The soft parts do not grow at a perfectly uniform rate; for example in *Anopheles sergentii* the thorax grows more rapidly in length than in breadth (Kettle, 1948). The anal papillae grow slowly during each instar, at rather more than half the rate at which the thorax and abdomen grow, but a sudden increase in size at ecdysis makes their over-all growth rate similar to that of the rest of the body. The anal papillae are small in larvae reared in salty water (p. 70), and it was found on rearing *Anopheles sergentii* larvae in different concentrations of sea water that high salinity prevented the stretching which normally occurred at ecdysis but did not affect growth during each instar (Kettle, 1948).

Different larval tissues grow in different ways. This is described in detail on p. 102 but it may be mentioned here that nervous tissue and the fat body grow by cell multiplication with only slight increase in cell size, whereas tissues such as the salivary glands, Malpighian tubes, small intestine, rectum, anal papillae and larval ocelli are incapable of cell division during the larval stage and grow entirely by increase in cell size. The cells of the midgut epithelium are also incapable of division and increase greatly in size but their number is increased during larval life by the differentiation of embryonic or replacement cells. Most of the organs which grow by increase in cell size are histolysed at metamorphosis but the Malpighian tubes, foregut and small intestine survive. Certain adult organs such as the gonads and imaginal buds develop slowly with cell division throughout the early larval instars and develop at an increased rate in the 4th instar. According to Hance (1917) mitosis occurs cyclically in the central nervous system and imaginal buds of *Culex pipiens* larvae, at any moment either being entirely absent or occurring in many cells at once, all cells being in approximately the same stage of division.

The 4th instar lasts longer than the earlier instars. In *Aedes taeniorhynchus* at 30°C and in *Aedes aegypti* at 28°C the first 3 instars last 1 day each whereas the 4th instar lasts 2 to 3 days, a little less than the first 3 instars put together (Nielsen and Haeger, 1954; Christophers, 1960). In *Aedes aegypti* the weight of the larva does not increase to the same extent in the 4th instar as in earlier instars (Christophers, 1960) so the lengthening of the 4th instar may reflect an increase in differentiation. In some species, though not all, the female pupa is larger than the male (Cantrell, 1939) and this is reflected in the earlier pupation of males than females (Shannon and Putnam, 1934; Nielsen and Haeger, 1954; Haddow, Gillett and Corbet, 1959).

The rate of growth rises with increase in temperature over a wide temperature range but rapid growth is also dependent upon an adequate food supply and in conditions of starvation the larval stage may be prolonged for several months (Wigglesworth, 1929; Marcovitch, 1960). The size attained by the mature larva is also affected by temperature since rapid development at high temperatures leads to production of small individuals and slow development at low temperatures leads to production of large individuals. The effects of temperature on growth are described in detail on p. 74. Larvae of *Aedes mariae* (Trensz, 1934) and *Culiseta incidens* (Frost *et al.*, 1936) will not reach maturity in the absence of light, although *Aedes aegypti*, *Culex pipiens fatigans* (Jobling, 1937), *Anopheles quadrimaculatus* (Barber, 1927) and *Anopheles maculipennis* (Danilova and Zubareva, 1932) will develop in complete darkness.

Mosquito larvae contain the normal insect endocrine organs but practically nothing is known of the hormonal control of growth. Differentiation of imaginal buds appears to be controlled by the internal environment, presumably by hormones, since imaginal buds transplanted into 4th instar larvae develop into perfect adult organs during metamorphosis of the host whereas buds transplanted into pupae show only slight growth, and into adults, none. The larval Malpighian tubes, in contrast, show some growth in an adult environment (Bodenstein, 1945a). Williams (1960) reported that emulsions of Cecropia juvenile hormone failed to interfere with the metamorphosis of *Culex* larvae. On the basis of histological changes in the thoracic glands of hibernating larvae of *Anopheles claviger*, Mednikova (1952) considered that larval diapause resulted from the absence of thoracic-gland hormone. Jettmar, Lieb and Exner (1949) claimed that certain physiologically-active compounds, including thyroxine and chorionic gonadotrophin, stimulated hibernating 4th instar larvae of *Anopheles claviger* to pupate and emerge while control larvae showed no development.

Effects of Temperature on Growth Rates

The rate of postembryonic growth follows the familiar S-shaped curve with temperature. Below a developmental threshold no growth occurs; above the threshold the rate of growth increases with increasing temperature, reaching a maximum at the so-called 'optimum temperature' above which it declines. In *Aedes aegypti* some growth takes place at 10°C but development is not completed. Above 14°C growth becomes increasingly rapid with rising temperature, reaching the 'optimum' at 32°C. The rate of growth decreases at still higher temperatures and above 36°C development is not completed (Bar-Zeev, 1958). As would be expected subarctic species are able to develop at much lower temperatures. The lowest temperature to permit any development in *Aedes impiger* is 1·1°C and in *Aedes punctor* 3·3°C, and these species will develop fairly rapidly at 9°C (Haufe and Burgess, 1956).

Although each species develops most rapidly at the so-called 'optimum temperature' this is not the most favourable temperature biologically since mortality is higher than at lower temperatures (Nielsen and Evans, 1960) and the adults produced are small (p. 79). The temperature at which development proceeds fastest varies at different stages of development. When *Anopheles quadrimaculatus* are reared at constant temperatures throughout the life cycle, development of the egg is found to be most rapid at 33·3°C, of 1st instar larvae at 32·5°C, of 4th instar larvae at 30°C and of pupae at 30·5°C. Development of the larval and pupal stages considered as a whole is most rapid at 31°C (Huffaker, 1944). Similar variations are found in *Aedes aegypti* (Bar-Zeev, 1958). The apparent drop in 'optimum temperature' is possibly due to the cumulative injurious effects of high temperature (Huffaker, 1944).

When the immature stages are subjected to fluctuating temperatures there is a tendency for development to be faster than at the constant temperature, equal to the mean of the fluctuating temperatures. When larvae and pupae of *Anopheles quadrimaculatus* were exposed to a raised temperature for 9 hr each day the velocity of development was accelerated by 13 per cent when the lower temperature was 15°C, by 3 per cent when the lower temperature was 19°C and by 4 per cent when the lower temperature was 23°C, compared to the velocity of development at a constant temperature equal to the mean of the fluctuating temperatures. When the temperature was raised for a period of 12–18 hr each day development was accelerated by 5 per cent when the lower temperature was 15°C but was retarded by 2·7 per cent, 2·3 per cent and 1·4 per cent when the lower temperatures were 19°, 23° and 24·5°C respectively (Huffaker, 1944). Variable temperature has been shown to accelerate development in *Aedes aegypti* also, but only over the middle portion of the curve relating developmental rates and temperature. At higher temperatures a fluctuating temperature does not increase the rate of development and at lower temperatures it slows development down (Headlee, 1942).

The accelerating effect has been explained by the assumption that the maximum rate of growth at a high temperature can only be sustained for a short time after which it declines, whereas too short a period at the lower temperature does not allow recovery from the deleterious effects of the higher temperature (Huffaker, 1944). An alternative explanation is that on the rapidly rising part of the growth curve the rate of growth at the temperature above the mean has increased so much that it is not completely nullified by the lower growth rate at the temperature below the mean (Pradhan, 1945).

A number of attempts have been made to analyse mosquito development in mathematical terms and this is of some use in predicting the course of development of mosquitoes in the field (Haufe and Burgess, 1956). A shortage of food will greatly prolong the larval stage (Bar-Zeev, 1957a; Nielsen and Haeger, 1954) and will therefore affect estimates of development rates. Although in the laboratory larvae can be provided with abundant food, in nature food is often insufficient for rapid growth and for this reason the estimates must always be restricted to particular situations. The following formulae have been applied to growth of mosquitoes.

Thermal Summation Formula

The rate of development is assumed to be directly proportional to the temperature so that the time required for development in hours or days multiplied by the temperature in °C is a constant. Or

$$t(T - c) = k$$

where t = time; T = mean environmental temperature; c = threshold temperature below which development does not occur; and k = thermal constant. The curve given by this equation over the middle part of the

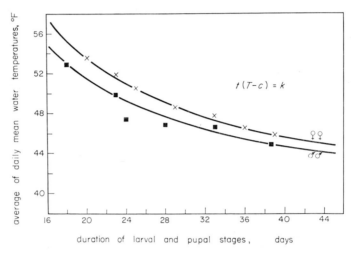

FIG. 31. Duration of the larval and pupal stages of *Aedes communis* in nature at different mean temperatures. The curves are drawn according to the thermal summation formula such that k=271 degree days for males and 318 degree days for females. (From Haufe & Burgess, 1956).

temperature range is a hyperbola. If the velocity of development $(v = 1/t)$ is plotted against temperature a straight line is obtained for the same middle range of temperatures. The duration of development of *Anopheles quadrimaculatus* reared out of doors is proportional to the mean temperature. Because the thermal constant varies little at different mean temperatures the number of degree-days required in early spring approximates the value found in midsummer (Hurlbut, 1943). In *Aedes aegypti* reared at constant temperatures, the thermal constant for development of newly-hatched larvae to the adult stage is also independent of temperature between 20° and 32°C, but the thermal constants for the individual larval instars vary at different temperatures so the curves obtained are not hyperbolic (Bar-Zeev, 1958). In a study of various species of *Aedes* in northern Canada it was found that the bigger species generally have larger thermal constants than the smaller species, and that the thermal constant of females of *Aedes communis* (318 degree days) is larger than that of the males (271 degree days) (Fig. 31) (Haufe and Burgess, 1956). The method of thermal summation can be used to give an approximate indication of developmental rates when the temperatures are in the middle of the temperature range of the species concerned but at the extremes of temperature the method becomes unreliable.

Catenary Formula

This takes into account the slowing up of development at temperatures above the 'optimum'. The curve relating time required for development with temperature is regarded as a catenary curve and is derived by the addition of two exponential curves, $t_1 = \frac{1}{2}ma^{-T}$ representing the acceleration of development through rising temperature, and $t_2 = \frac{1}{2}ma^{T}$ representing the retarding effects of higher temperatures. The complete equation is

$$t = \frac{m}{2}(a^{T} + a^{-T})$$

where $t(= t_1 + t_2) =$ time required for development; $m =$ time for development at the experimentally determined 'optimum temperature'; $a =$ constant; and $T =$ temperature in degrees above or below the

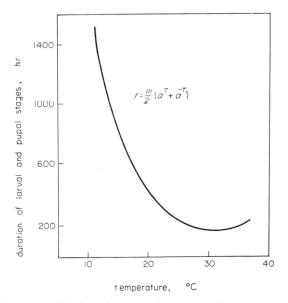

FIG. 32. Duration of the larval and pupal stages of *Anopheles quadrimaculatus* at different constant temperatures. The curve is drawn according to the catenary formula. (From Huffaker, 1944).

'optimum' (Janisch, 1932). A more orthodox expression of this equation would be

$$t = \frac{m}{2}(e^{kT} + e^{-kT})$$

where the constant e^k replaces a (above). According to this equation the factors retarding development are active at all temperatures but the accelerating effects of rising temperature are dominant below the 'optimum' whereas the retarding effects are dominant above the 'optimum'. The reciprocal of the catenary curve relates velocity of development to temperature and has the characteristic S-shape of biological curves (Janisch, 1932). The catenary formula may be criticised for its assumption that the same constant adequately describes both the accelerating and retarding effects of high temperatures but it has been satisfactorily applied to the development of *Anopheles quadrimaculatus* at various temperatures (Fig. 32) (Huffaker, 1944).

Modified Logistic Curve

This equation also takes into account the accelerating and retarding effects of high temperatures. The velocity of development is given by the equation

$$v = v_o e^{-kT^2}$$

where v = velocity of development at a given temperature; v_o = the highest velocity; e = 2·718282 (constant); k = constant; and T = the difference between the given temperature and the temperature at v_o. According to its author (Pradhan, 1945, 1946) this equation is superior to others in having a sound theoretical basis, in that the value v_o and the corresponding temperature need not be determined experimentally but can be calculated from measurements made at other temperatures, and in that an equation can be developed from it for calculating developmental periods at fluctuating temperatures. It has been used by Lal (1953) to establish the growth rates of *Anopheles subpictus* and *Anopheles stephensi*.

Krogh-Jørgensen formula

Nielsen and Evans (1960) measured the rates of development of pupae of *Aedes taeniorhynchus* at various constant temperatures and found that these rates were described best by the Krogh-Jørgensen formula which was first used to describe the relation of temperature to respiratory metabolism. Nielsen and Evans (1960) rewrote the equation as

$$v = a + bc^T$$

where v = velocity of development at temperature T; and a, b and c are constants. This equation also describes the accelerating effect of rising temperature (Fig. 33).

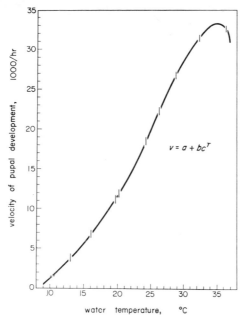

FIG. 33. Velocity of pupal development in females of *Aedes taeniorhynchus* at different constant temperatures. The curve is drawn according to the Krogh-Jørgensen formula. (From Nielsen and Evans, 1960).

All of these formulae are more conveniently used after conversion to logarithms.

Effects of the Environment on Structure

When mosquito larvae are provided with abundant food and are not overcrowded the size of the adults is determined by breeding temperature, large adults being produced at low and small adults at high temperatures. It appears that at higher temperatures metamorphosis proceeds at such a rate that the capacity of the species to form tissue is not fully reached. This is found both in the laboratory (Bates, 1947) and in nature (Detinova, 1955). A progressive decline in fecundity has been demonstrated in females of *Anopheles maculipennis* emerging through the summer, and this is possibly correlated with the progressive decrease in adult size resulting from steadily rising summer temperatures (Detinova, 1955). The temperatures experienced by larvae and pupae also affect the bodily proportions of the adult. It is well known that mosquitoes caught in the winter have longer wings than summer mosquitoes, and it has also been shown that the increase in wing length at low temperatures is proportionately greater than the increase in thorax length (Mer, 1937) or dry weight (Hosoi, 1954b). *Anopheles sacharovi* adults of any size group based on thorax length have longer wings in the winter than in the summer (Mer, 1937).

A number of other characters have been found to be affected by temperature. In *Culex pipiens* the number of ovarian follicles decreases at lower breeding temperatures (Hosoi, 1954b). In *Anopheles gambiae* the number of teeth on the adult maxillae increases at higher breeding temperatures (Gillies and Shute, 1954). In *Aedes pseudoscutellaris* the amount of white scaling on the adult increases with rise in breeding temperature and the shape of the white scales is also affected by the breeding temperature (Marks, 1954). At low breeding temperatures the patches of dark scales on the abdominal sternites of *Culex pipiens* disappear (Ghelelovitch, 1950). The chorion of *Anopheles* eggs is known to change in structure at different seasons. It has been shown in *Anopheles sacharovi* that the presence or absence of 'floats' on the eggs depends entirely upon the temperature prevailing during development of the ovarian follicles, 'floats' being formed when the females are subjected to low temperatures and absent when the same females are subjected to high temperatures (Mer, 1931). Exposure of females of the tropical species *Anopheles gambiae* to 13°C for 3 days immediately after gorging leads to changes in sculpturing of all eggs of the next batch to be laid. Delay of chilling until 15 hr after gorging leads to production of fewer abnormal eggs and delay for 48 hr eliminates all abnormalities (Deane and Causey, 1943). Exposure of individuals of *Aedes stimulans* of male genotype to 29°C throughout larval life causes them to develop into adult females (Horsfall and Anderson, 1962) (see p. 22).

In a detailed study of the effect of temperature during the larval and pupal stages on the morphology of adult *Aedes aegypti* van den Heuvel (1961), working at 11 different temperatures between 15° and 34°C, found that dry weight, wing length, leg length and thorax length increased progressively with fall in breeding temperature. The change in wing length was not proportional to the change in dry weight for it increased more rapidly than dry weight with fall in temperature (Fig. 34), although in mosquitoes bred at the same temperature the ratio of wing length to dry weight was constant. Thorax length varied in much the same way as dry weight since over the middle of the temperature range the ratio of dry weight to cube of thorax length was constant. Between 20° and 30°C the ratio of dry weight to cube of hind-leg length was constant but the hind legs showed disproportionate growth at the 2 ends of the temperature scale. The temperature at which 1st instar larvae and pupae were bred had little or no effect on adult dry weight, but when larvae were held for different periods at 20°C and then transferred to 32°C adult dry weight increased by 25 per cent for each instar between the 2nd and the 4th for which larvae had been held at the lower temperature. Wing length also increased progressively the longer the larvae were held at the lower temperature, the effect of temperature being least in the 1st instar and

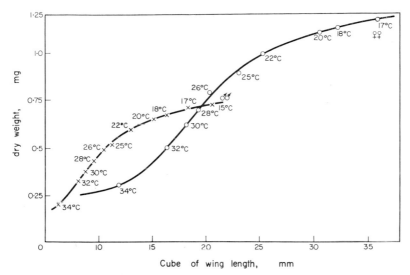

FIG. 34. Relationship of dry weight to wing length in *Aedes aegypti* reared at different temperatures. (From van den Heuvel, 1961).

greatest in the pupa. The wing assumes its final length at emergence and about 30 per cent of the effect of temperature attributed to the pupal stage was found to be due to the effect of temperature at the moment of emergence. The number of ovarioles increased from a mean of 101 at 33°C to 125 at 18°C but the rate of increase was less rapid than that of dry weight so that the number of ovarioles per unit dry weight decreased with fall in breeding temperature. Lower breeding temperatures caused a decrease in the number of white scales on the body and legs.

Phenotypic variations are also caused by environmental factors other than temperature. The size of adult *Aedes pseudoscutellaris* decreases with an increase in the salinity of the larval environment, and salinity also affects the scaling pattern of the adult (Marks, 1954). Some characteristic of the water of tree holes causes changes in the size and structure of the larval setae in *Aedes scutellaris* and *Aedes aegypti* (Colless, 1956a), and overcrowding of larvae affects adult wing length and maxillary index in *Anopheles gambiae* (Gillies and Shute, 1954).

Colour variation is found in some mosquitoes in response to the environment, as in *Anopheles maculipennis* and *Anopheles claviger* where a green background during the larval stage produces whitish-green larvae, white pupae and pale adults, whereas a black or brown background produces dark brown larvae, black pupae and dark adults. The dark coloration is due, at least in part, to an accumulation of pigment in epidermal and fat body cells (Achundow, 1928; Corradetti, 1930).

These phenotypic variations are not only of physiological interest but are of importance to the systematist since diagnostic characters are sometimes affected.

Moulting, Pupation and Emergence

Without any known exception mosquitoes pass through four larval instars. At moulting the epidermis can be seen to separate from the cuticle and to secrete new cuticle and bristles beneath it while the tracheal epithelium similarly retracts from the tracheal linings and secretes new cuticular linings around them so that a wide space filled with fluid can be seen between the two. When the larva of *Aedes aegypti* is about to shed its skin it rests at the surface and swallows water by contractions of the pharynx until the soft body wall becomes extremely taut. From time to time it flexes its head sharply until finally the head capsule splits. The ecdysial line along which the capsule splits follows the epicranial suture, starting in the dorsal midline of the collar and then diverging widely and passing forward on each side of the dorsum of the head to the bases of the antennae. A midventral ecdysial suture is also found in many species. Movements of the head free it from the old head capsule and the dorsal split extends back over the thorax so that by peristaltic movements of its body the larva is able to escape from the skin. Meanwhile, the old tracheal trunks have broken across just behind their connections to the non-functional spiracles in each segment and as the larva leaves its old skin the fractured pieces of the tracheal system are withdrawn, the fragments in each case passing out through the pair of spiracles immediately behind them. All the spiracles except the terminal pair are then sealed until the next ecdysis. The skin may be shed in less than a minute and after ecdysis the tracheae fill with air while the expanded head capsule hardens and slowly darkens. Air sometimes escapes into the new tracheal system as the cuticular linings are withdrawn, but in any case air enters through the respiratory siphon when the newly-moulted larva hangs from the surface and the fluid in the tracheal branches disappears (Mitrofanova, 1929; Wigglesworth, 1938b; Christophers, 1960). Feeding is interrupted for only a short period before and after each ecdysis, sometimes for less than an hour (Bekman, 1935).

Although metamorphosis appears to start with ecdysis to the pupa considerable changes of form occur during the larval stage. The imaginal buds practically complete their growth if not their differentiation in the larva and late in the 4th instar the epidermis separates from the cuticle and most of the imaginal buds are extruded from their peripodial cavities and extend over the surface of the body, although still concealed beneath the larval cuticle. The epidermis of the head and thorax is largely re-formed into the shape of the pupa at this time and the indirect flight muscles are already present as rudiments. Metamorphosis is thus a more gradual process than is outwardly apparent, starting during the larval stage and only concluded in the adult.

The process of pupation has been described by Hurst (1890a, b), Thompson (1905), Wigglesworth (1938b) and Christophers (1960). Shortly before the 4th-instar larva sheds its skin the respiratory trumpets and float hairs of the pupa appear as dark bodies beneath the cuticle. The larva comes to lie horizontally at the surface and shortly afterwards air appears in the short tracheae linking the respiratory trumpets to the longitudinal tracheal trunks, subsequently spreading between the larval and pupal cuticles. The source of this air is not known but it is possibly drawn from the larval tracheae through the respiratory trumpets as a result of absorption of ecdysial fluid into the body. Certainly the larval tracheae collapse at this time.

After the appearance of air the larval cuticle splits in the dorsal midline and as the pupal thorax protrudes through the split the respiratory trumpets spring up and attach the pupa to the surface film. The larval cuticle and tracheal linings are shed much as at previous ecdyses and during this period the labial and maxillary-palp buds are extruded from their peripodial cavities. After ecdysis the appendages of the head and thorax become cemented to one another, possibly by the residue of the ecdysial fluid (Christophers, 1960), and they form a shield over the front and sides of the body retaining a bubble of air which is outside the cuticle but enclosed by the appendages. This ventral air space makes the pupa lighter than water and causes it to float with its respiratory trumpets uppermost. If air is removed from the ventral air space the pupa sinks and drowns.

The respiratory trumpets are lined with a mass of hairs and presumably act as felt chambers, replacing the mesothoracic spiracles. The spiracles of the 1st abdominal segment, which have well-developed felt chambers and closing mechanisms, open into the ventral air space and are connected to the tracheal trunks by stout tracheae, but the spiracles of the metathorax and 2nd–8th abdominal segments seal up after withdrawal of the larval tracheal linings and the tracheal connections to them collapse, while the epithelial lining of the respiratory siphon is withdrawn into the body.

After pupation practically the whole cuticle hardens and darkens, in contrast to the small area of cuticle which is sclerotized in the larva. The pupa usually rests at the surface, held in position against the surface film by the tips of the trumpets and the 2 float hairs on the 1st abdominal segment, but it can swim well and when disturbed swims downwards by the beating of the abdomen with its large paddles, later floating to the surface again.

Some mosquitoes show a strong tendency to pupate at a particular time of day. In *Aedes taeniorhynchus* maximum pupation occurs around sunset and 83 per cent pupate during the 9 hr which precede midnight (Nielsen and Haeger, 1954) whereas in *Anopheles gambiae* most pupation occurs during the late morning and afternoon, and none between 11 p.m. and 7 a.m. even under conditions of constant temperature (Goma, 1959). A tendency to pupate by day has been reported in several other species of *Anopheles* (Sen, 1935; Rozeboom, 1936) and at night in yet others

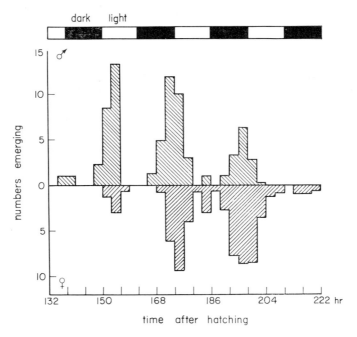

FIG. 35.   The times of emergence of males and females of *Aedes taeniorhynchus* which hatched simultaneously from the egg. (From Nielsen and Haeger, 1954).

(Lamborn, 1922). In contrast, the time of pupation of *Aedes aegypti* is quite uninfluenced by the course of light and dark (Haddow, Gillett and Corbet, 1959).

The time spent in the pupal stage is inversely proportional to the temperature and in *Aedes taeniorhynchus,* for example, the average duration is 37 hr at 29°C and 61 hr at 21°C (Nielsen and Haeger, 1954). Males spend an hour or two less in the pupa than females in *Aedes taeniorhynchus* (Nielsen and Haeger, 1954) and *Aedes aegypti* (Haddow, Gillett and Corbet, 1959), and combined with the difference in duration of the larval stage this means that males tend to emerge about a day earlier than females from the same egg batch. Since *Aedes taeniorhynchus* pupates around sunset and the duration of the pupal stage is determined by temperature alone, a rhythm of emergence is also found (Fig. 35) but the peak may occur at any time of day or night, varying with the temperature (Nielsen and Haeger, 1954). *Aedes aegypti* shows no diurnal rhythm or response to light or dark in emergence (Haddow, Gillett and Corbet, 1959).

The first sign of emergence is the appearance of a small amount of air beneath the pupal cuticle, at the bases of the respiratory siphons and elsewhere. The abdomen is slowly raised to a horizontal position and shortly after this the pupal cuticle splits along the middorsal line of the thorax. A minute later the thorax of the adult, which is quite dry, protrudes through the split and slowly the whole body of the adult rises into view.

It is most probable that the air which appears between the pupal and adult cuticles before the pupal cuticle splits penetrates through the respiratory trumpets when the tracheae from these organs fracture, for pressure on the pupal cuticle causes the bubble to escape through the trumpets (Brumpt, 1941). Since air can also be found in the alimentary canal just before the cuticle splits it is thought that some of the air which penetrates the trumpets is swallowed, presumably directly through the mouth as the mouthparts are still sheathed, and soon sufficient air is swallowed to burst the pupal skin (Marshall and Staley, 1932). In some species at least, a tuft of erect hairs on the thorax is the first part to emerge through the cuticle and possibly plays a part in splitting it (Brumpt, 1941). Once the cuticle has split the adult can be seen swallowing air by regular contractions of the pharyngeal pump and this air slowly distends the stomach, forcing the adult up and out of the pupal skin (Fig. 36a) (Marshall and Staley, 1932).

The longitudinal split extends further back and transverse splits appear while alternate movements of the abdomen and legs disengage the body from the surrounding cuticle. The pupal tracheae are withdrawn through the spiracles and the linings of the fore- and hindgut are also shed. The various appendages are freed from their sheaths, in the case of the mouthparts and legs partly by muscular action, and the insect steps on to the water. The blood pressure is high at this time due to the air-filled stomach; it causes the legs and wings to extend to their full size and no doubt also maintains the rigidity of the legs until they harden. The process of emergence takes about 15 min, and 10 min after the mosquito is free it can make short flights although it usually remains for a time on the water. It can fly more or less normally after about an hour when it flies off to

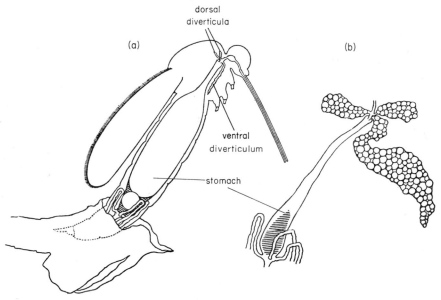

FIG. 36a–b. The distribution of air in the alimentary canal of a mosquito. (a) During emergence, the stomach is distended with air but the diverticula are empty; (b) 15 hr after emergence, the diverticula are full of air and the stomach is empty. (From Marshall and Staley, 1932).

another resting place. Fluid is passed from the anus about this time. Within an hour of emergence air starts to disappear from the stomach which becomes quite empty within a day, and since air simultaneously fills the diverticula (Fig. 36b) it seems most probable that it has been transferred from the stomach (Marshall and Staley, 1932).

The Imaginal Buds

The rudiments of certain adult organs start to appear in the 2nd instar as thickenings of the epidermis and they develop slowly during the rest of the larval stage. These are the imaginal buds and they have been described in most detail in *Culex* (Thompson, 1905) and *Anopheles* (Imms, 1908; Prashad, 1918) in which they are very similar. In the head of the larva are found the paired buds of the antennae, labium and maxillary palps and an unpaired labral bud. In the thorax each segment contains a dorsal and a ventral pair of buds, the dorsal buds being those of the pupal respiratory trumpets, the wings and halteres, and the ventral buds those of the legs (Fig. 38a). Towards the posterior end of the abdomen are a dorsal and a ventral pair of buds which will form the pupal paddles and the male genitalia respectively. In the thorax at least, each bud gives rise to a part of the adult wall as well as to an appendage (Bodenstein, 1945a).

The epidermal thickenings which appear during the 2nd instar consist of plates of columnar cells which grow slowly with cell division, each becoming invaginated in the form of a shallow cup (Fig. 37a). Subsequently the base of the cup becomes evaginated into the lumen and mesenchyme cells enter this outgrowth. An appendage develops from the outgrowth and lies in a peripodial cavity surrounded by the peripodial membrane, part of the invaginated epidermis, and the surfaces of the appendage and of the peripodial membrane develop a thin cuticular covering (Figs. 37b, c). In every case the peripodial cavity remains open

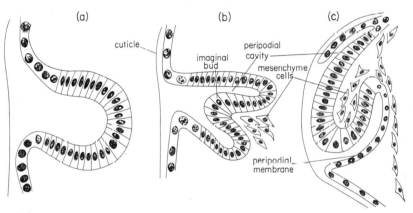

FIG. 37a–c.   The early development of an imaginal bud as seen in transverse sections.
(a) Invagination of bud; (b) the evagination which forms an appendage; (c) formation of the peripodial cavity and penetration of the bud by mesenchyme cells. (From Prashad, 1918).

to the surface. The buds of the labrum and of the pupal paddles are formed directly by outgrowths of the epidermis and are not enclosed by peripodial membranes. The main increase in size takes place in the 4th instar and this is accompanied by numerous mitoses (Risler, 1959), but in most cases the bud is shaped only very approximately like the adult appendage at this time. Thoracic buds removed from 4th instar larvae and kept in a tissue

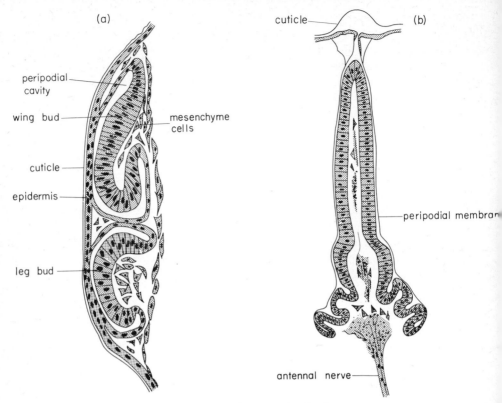

FIG. 38a–b.   Imaginal buds.

(a) T.S. of the mesothorax of a larva of *Anopheles maculipennis* showing the wing and leg buds; (b) sagittal section through an antennal bud in the larva of *Anopheles maculipennis*. (From Imms, 1908).

culture medium sometimes showed rhythmic contractions (Chabaud, Ghelelovitch and de Lalun, 1960).

The antennal buds lie deep within the head below the larval antennae and as each enlarges its peripodial membrane becomes stretched and reduced to a thin layer of tissue (Fig. 38b). In a fully-grown larva the 2nd segment of the antennal bud is much enlarged, especially in the male, and its wall is greatly thickened through the formation of Johnston's organ.

In development of the pupal trumpets the walls of each evagination meet and fuse to form a plate consisting of a single layer of cells. This then folds and takes the form of the respiratory trumpet, and cuticle is secreted on both the inner and outer surfaces of the cells. The imaginal bud also forms the short trachea which connects the trumpet to the tracheal trunk, secreting it around the collapsed connective from the larval mesothoracic spiracle. The trumpets become fully developed during the 4th instar so that they are functional immediately after pupation (Prashad, 1918; Christophers, 1960).

The antennal and the various thoracic buds and those of the male genitalia are extruded from their peripodial cavities towards the end of the 4th instar and extend along the sides of the body between the epidermis and the cuticle, but the labial and maxillary-palp buds are not extruded until the 4th instar cuticle is partly shed at pupation. The mandibles and maxillae undergo almost no metamorphosis during the larval stage; during the last larval moult their epidermis develops some of the staining reactions of an imaginal bud and at the ecdysis the epidermis lining these appendages is withdrawn in the form of hollow tubes (Figs. 39–40).

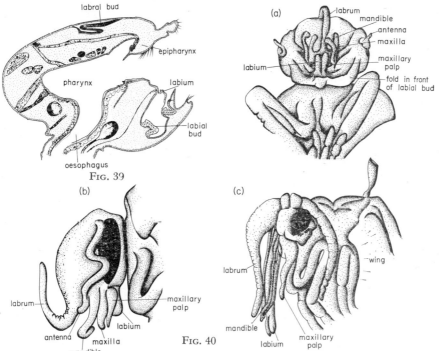

Fig. 39

Fig. 40

FIG. 39. Sagittal section through the head of a fully-grown larva of *Culex* to show the labral and labial buds. (From Thompson, 1905).

FIG. 40a–c. Extension of the head appendages of *Culex* during pupation as seen in individuals dissected from the 4th instar cuticle at different stages of ecdysis.

(a) Ventral aspect of pupal head at the moment when the larval head capsule is ruptured; (b) side view at the moment when the respiratory trumpets free themselves by rupture of the thoracic cuticle; (c) side view just before final release of mouthparts and legs from the larval cuticle. (From Thompson, 1905).

A few hours after pupation the epidermis of the mouthparts retracts from the pupal cuticle and the various mouthparts become capable of re-modelling. The ventral surface of the labrum folds inwards to form the food canal. The dorsal surface of the labium rises to form a crest and cells migrating from this region enclose the salivary canal while in the female the ridge containing the salivary canal separates as the hypopharynx.

Before pupation the wing membranes are folded owing to lack of space but at pupation the wings are able to stretch. During the pupal stage the lumen between the 2 layers of columnar cells disappears except in particular regions which correspond to certain of the veins of the adult wing, and tracheae and blood cells appear within these remaining spaces. The wing cuticle with its setae and scales is secreted in the pupa when the cell boundaries disappear.

The imaginal buds of mosquitoes show a relatively primitive condition compared with those of higher Diptera—most of the buds remain just below the epidermis, the peripodial cavities are never closed, the compound eyes do not develop from invaginated buds, and the large larval head capsule provides space for development of the adult head. The buds which give rise to the respiratory trumpets and paddles of the pupa are adaptations to acquatic life.

Development of the Central Nervous System and Compound Eyes

The postembryonic development of the supraoesophageal ganglion or brain in *Culex pipiens* has been described by Rogoff (1954) and Hinke (1961). Hinke analysed the differential growth of the brain and its parts using the formula

$$y = bx^k$$

devised by Huxley (1932) for analysis of allometric (heterogonic) growth, where x and y are 2 dimensions, b the initial growth index and k the ratio of the 2 growth rates. During the first 3 larval instars the brain grows less rapidly than the rest of the body ($k = 0.7$), but it shows positive allometric growth in the 4th instar ($k = 1.8$) and pupa ($k = >1.0$).

Hinke (1961) has shown that the periods of most active growth of the various regions of the brain occur at different stages of the life history. Thus the mushroom bodies grow less strongly than the brain as a whole during the larval stage ($k = 0.5$–0.9) but much more strongly in the pupal stage ($k = 1.8$), whereas the central body grows most actively in the 4th instar ($k = 2.0$). The antennal centres grow slowly compared to the brain as a whole in the larva ($k = 0.8$), very rapidly at the time of pupation ($k = 4.0$) and slowly again in the late pupa and early adult ($k = >1.0$). The optic lobes show strong growth in the 1st instar ($k = 1.9$), isometric growth during the rest of the larval stage and further positive allometric growth in the pupa ($k = 1\cdot3$). The optic lobes comprise 9 per cent of the brain in the 4-day-old larva and 45 per cent in the adult. Rogoff (1954) has pointed out that the nerve tracts directly associated with vision are organized in their final form during the larval stage, corresponding to the early development of the compound eyes, whereas the nerve trunks associated with the adult antennae undergo extensive elaboration at metamorphosis. The main regions of the brain are all present in the young larva and by differential growth they form the adult brain with its very different proportions. The brain is smaller, relative to total body volume, in the adult female than in the male. The optic lobes are smaller relative to the whole brain in the female than in the male but the female has relatively larger mushroom bodies, central body and antennal centres. The central body forms $1\cdot2$ per cent of the female brain, the mushroom bodies only $0\cdot4$–$0\cdot5$ per cent (Hinke, 1961). The suboesophageal ganglion of *Culex pipiens* is considerably more complex after metamorphosis when there is also a change in the nerves arising from it and a great increase in the size of the circumoesophageal commissures (Rogoff, 1954).

In *Aedes dorsalis* and *Aedes aegypti* metamorphosis of the central nervous system involves a small amount of histolysis but the principal changes result from growth by cell multiplication and from fusion of ganglia. The suboesophageal ganglion moves forward to become more closely and broadly connected to the brain, the thoracic ganglia fuse with one another and with the 1st abdominal ganglion to form a single mass which still shows signs of its original segmentation, and the 8th abdominal ganglion moves forward to fuse with the 7th (Woolley, 1943; Christophers, 1960).

The development of the compound eyes in *Culex pipiens* has been described by Constantineaunu (1930), Satô (1951a) and Haas (1956). According to Satô (1951a) the rudiments of the compound eyes are present in newly-hatched larvae as thickenings of the epidermis just in front of the lateral ocelli, but Haas (1956) found no modifications of the epidermis at that time although he saw development of the eye rudiments 12–24 hr after hatching. The formation of ommatidia starts at the posterior edge of the thickened epidermis and proceeds anteriorly, dorsally and ventrally.

Each ommatidium develops in the following manner. Mitotic figures appear in the thickened epidermis and a group of 7 or 8 nuclei forms without evidence of cell boundaries. The cell mass moves inwards away from the cuticle and forms a spindle-shaped body surrounded by small cells, the future retinula and iris cells. Long processes grow inwards from the retinula cells and eventually meet the ocellar nerve along which they pass to the optic lobe. A mitotic figure present distally at this time later forms the four cone cells which look like a pointed cap over the retinula

(Fig. 41a). Pigment granules appear successively in the retinula cells and primary and secondary iris cells, and the rhabdom starts to differentiate. The retinula cell nuclei migrate below the basement membrane. A heavily-staining structure now appears between the rhabdomeres. Satô (1951a) calls this 'distal rhabdom' but Haas (1956) states that it is secreted by the cone cells and it will here be called the crystalline-cone body. Shortly afterwards the cone cells fill with a non-staining liquid to form a large, sac-like structure which will be called the crystalline-cone vesicle (Fig. 41b). If the ommatidia are functional in the larva, as seems likely, the crystalline-cone vesicle must function in light transmission. The rhabdom is capable of movement, even in the 2nd instar larva, migrating inwards in the light and outwards in the dark. Ommatidia reach this stage in the 2nd instar in *Culex pipiens* but no further differentiation occurs in the larva although the number of ommatidia continues to increase until early in the pupal stage.

In the larva and early pupa the ommatidium is covered by an un-modified part of the head capsule but during the pupal stage the ommatidium retracts from the cuticle, a secretion fills the space and the outer part of the corneal lens forms in the middle of the secretion, its outer surface convex and its inner surface concave. The secretion over-lying the corneal lens hardens to form the 'cornea' which is shaped like a watch glass but the secretion under the lens remains unhardened through-out the pupal stage. Further changes in the pupa are a thickening of the primary iris cells, return of the retinula cell nuclei above the basement membrane, greater differentiation of rhabdomeres, absorption of the crystalline-cone body by the cone cells and disappearance of the crystalline-cone vesicle as the cone cells assume their final form (Fig. 41c). Shortly after emergence most of the secretion remaining under the lens hardens making the lens biconvex but a certain amount of unhardened secretion remains below this, for a time at least (Fig. 41d).

The time and manner of compound-eye formation varies among different species. It appears to be usual for the initial thickening of the epidermis to occur during the 1st instar but variation is found in the rate of further development, pigmented ommatidia forming by the 2nd instar in *Culex pipiens* (Satô, 1951a) but not before the late 3rd instar in *Aedes aegypti* (Haas, 1956; White, 1961) or before the 4th instar in *Armigeres subalbatus* (Satô, 1960). The ommatidia of *Aedes aegypti* develop without

FIG. 41a–d. Development of an ommatidium.
(a) Early differentiation of cells of the imaginal bud in a 3rd instar larva of *Aedes aegypti;* (b) L.S. through an ommatidium in a larva of *Culex pipiens;* (c) L.S. through an ommatidium in a pupa of *Culex pipiens;* (d) L.S. through an ommatidium in an adult of *Aedes aegypti*. (From Haas, 1956.)

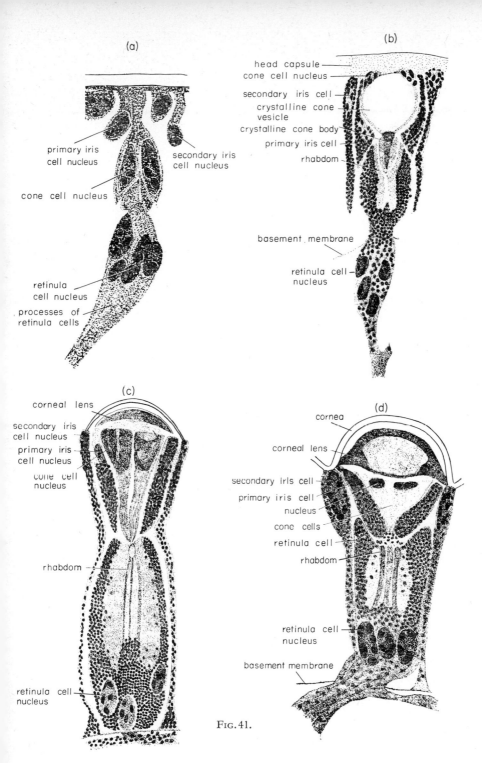

(a)

primary iris
cell nucleus

secondary iris
cell nucleus

cone cell nucleus

retinula
cell nucleus

processes of
retinula cells

(b)

head capsule
cone cell nucleus

secondary iris cell

crystalline cone
vesicle

crystalline cone body

primary iris cell

rhabdom

basement membrane

retinula cell
nucleus

(c)

corneal lens

secondary iris
cell nucleus

primary iris
cell nucleus

cone cell
nucleus

rhabdom

retinula cell
nucleus

(d)

cornea

corneal lens

secondary iris cell

primary iris cell

nucleus

cone cells

retinula cell

rhabdom

retinula cell
nucleus

basement membrane

FIG. 41.

crystalline-cone vesicle or body (Haas, 1956) and the vesicle at least is absent in *Anopheles sinensis* (Satô, 1953b).

White (1961) has analysed the development of the compound eye in *Aedes aegypti*. In the 1st instar the epidermal thickening, called the optic placode, appears at the posterior margin of the prospective compound-eye area. Throughout the rest of the larval stage the optic placode expands anteriorly across the prospective eye area, a wave of mitoses converting the thin prospective eye epidermis into thick placodal plate. Mitoses occur in other parts of the head epidermis also but at a much slower rate. In the last 2 larval instars a wave of ommatidial differentiation passes across the optic placode following behind the wave of cell proliferation. By extirpation of the optic placode and by transplantation of epidermis into the prospective eye area White showed that the expansion of the optic placode reflects the passage of a determining factor arising in the optic placode and passing through the prospective eye area, this factor stimulating the cell divisions by which the prospective eye epidermis is converted into placodal plate. When pieces of epidermis were transplanted from various regions of the head into the path of the determining factor only those from a limited area, the prospective eye area, were competent to respond. Epidermis from other areas not only failed to respond but, if it extended across the full width of the prospective eye area, prevented the further passage of the determining factor, in which case the isolated portion of the prospective eye area failed to develop into eye. If a narrow bridge of competent tissue remained the factor could pass, suggesting that it is a diffusible substance. When competent tissue was transplanted into the prospective eye area correct orientation of the graft was not essential for normal eye formation, showing that the normal temporal and spatial pattern of eye development is not predetermined within the cells of the prospective eye epidermis but is superimposed on them during later development. If part of the optic placode was removed the remainder rapidly expanded to regain its normal size and a normal eye subsequently formed. The development of a compound eye therefore involves a number of separate processes: first, the prospective eye area is made competent to respond to the determining factor; later, the determining factor passes forward from the anterior edge of the optic placode, causing a rapid increase in the rate of cell proliferation in the competent epidermis and converting it to placodal plate; and, finally, a wave of ommatidial differentiation passes across the optic placode.

Metamorphosis of the Alimentary Canal

The metamorphosis of the alimentary canal of *Culex pipiens* has been described in considerable detail (Thompson, 1905; Berger, 1938) and brief accounts of the process in other species suggest that it is similar in these (Samtleben, 1929; Richins, 1938; Christophers, 1960; Risler, 1961).

Metamorphosis of the foregut starts late in the 4th instar with the withdrawal of the invaginated portion of the oesophagus from the midgut, and at pupation the lining of the foregut is shed with the rest of the larval cuticle. The muscle coat of the oesophagus degenerates early in pupal life and is replaced later with imaginal muscles. The foregut epithelium is not histolysed but the nuclei which have become polyploid during the larval stage undergo somatic reduction. As the foregut becomes re-modelled the two sucking pumps of the adult are formed. The anterior pump develops from the epithelium of both the buccal cavity and pharynx of the larva (Thompson, 1905), so the name 'cibarial pump' can reason-ably be given to this organ. The posterior pump develops from the former eosophageal epithelium but as it corresponds in function to the pharynx of other insects it may be called the 'pharyngeal pump'. At about the 10th hour of pupal life the oesophageal diverticula evaginate from the oesophageal epithelium, but they grow slowly until about the 30th hour after which they quickly reach their adult size.

In *Aedes aegypti* active mitosis occurs in the foregut a few hours after pupation, starting in the pharynx and extending backwards into the oesophagus. These mitoses involve somatic-reduction divisions by which the big foregut cells containing polyploid nuclei give rise to many small cells containing diploid nuclei which form the pupal foregut. At the junction of foregut and midgut in the mosquito larva there is a narrow band of embryonic cells, the anterior imaginal ring (Fig. 42). A similar structure is present in many other insects and it is interpreted by Henson (1946) as the reactivated oral half of the blastopore which at meta-morphosis produces endoderm posteriorly and ectoderm anteriorly. In *Culex pipiens* its activities are said to be restricted to the formation of the posterior part of the adult oesophagus which grows into the lumen of the midgut to form the oesophageal invagination (Fig. 42b) (Thompson, 1905) but according to Risler (1961) in *Aedes aegypti* it forms the adult foregut diverticula also.

Degenerative and regenerative processes are well established in the midgut before the pupal ecdysis at which time many disintegrating epi-thelial cells are lying in the lumen and embryonic replacement cells are very numerous. As soon as pupation occurs rapid changes take place: the epithelium of the cardia, caeca and stomach separates from the base-ment membrane and lies free in the lumen of the gut, later to be absorbed or discharged, while the replacement cells divide rapidly and form a new epithelium of small cells. The caeca are not replaced and the adult midgut consists of 2 main regions—cardia and stomach.

The pyloric chamber of the adult hindgut is formed during the 6th–10th hr of pupal life by the posterior imaginal ring, a zone of embryonic cells situated at the junction of midgut and hindgut, which in other insects is considered to be the reactivated anal half of the blastopore (Henson, 1946).

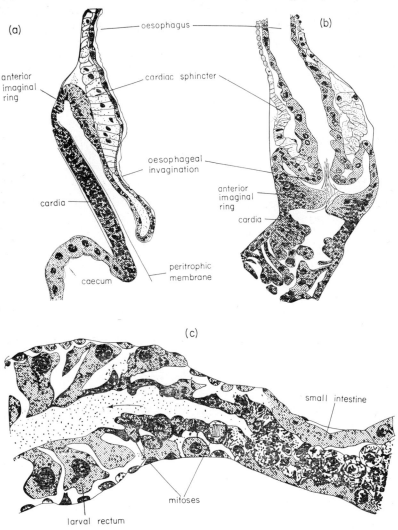

FIG. 42a–c.   Metamorphosis of the alimentary canal.
(a) L.S. through one side of the oesophageal invagination, anterior imaginal ring and cardia of a fully-grown larva of *Culex;* (b) L.S. through the junction of foregut and midgut of a *Culex* pupa 4 hr old; (c) L.S. through part of the hindgut of a *Culex* pupa 17 hr old, showing the invasion of the larval rectum by cells of the small intestine. (From Thompson, 1905).

In mosquitoes it is found just behind the openings of the Malpighian tubes and early in the pupal stage its cells multiply by mitosis and cell division and migrate backwards forming the epithelium of the adult pyloric chamber (Berger, 1938b). The fate of the larval pyloric chamber has not been described.

The metamorphosis of the small intestine begins between the 4th and 8th hr of pupal life in *Culex pipiens* (Berger, 1938b; Schuh, 1951) when by a series of somatic-reduction divisions the big polyploid cells of the larval epithelium produce a large number of much smaller cells (see p. 105). Few cells, if any, degenerate. When this process is nearly finished, about the 18th hr, the new cells begin to invade the lumen of the rectum at its anterior end (Fig. 42c) while cells of the anal canal multiply and penetrate from the posterior end. These latter cells have been described as arising from the 'anal ring', a band of embryonic cells (Thompson, 1905) which possibly arises as an ingrowth of epidermis in the anal region (Richins, 1938), but Berger (1938b) has described polyploid cells in the anal canal, similar to those in the small intestine, and considers that these cells divide at metamorphosis and invade the rectum. The 2 cell migrations meet and form a new cylindrical epithelium while the old rectal cells are pushed out into the body cavity and destroyed. The new epithelium is later transformed into the adult small intestine anteriorly and anal canal at the posterior end while the intermediate region expands to form the adult rectum, rectal papillae developing by rearrangement of some of the cells. The muscles of the larval hindgut. histolyse and are replaced by adult muscles which develop from myoblasts. The cuticular linings of the foregut and hindgut are secreted just before emergence under the pupal linings.

The Malpighian tubes pass from the larva to the adult without visible reorganization. Experiments with phosphorus-32 show that phosphorus starts to accumulate in the Malpighian tubes late in the 4th instar and increases in concentration there throughout most of the pupal stage. This phosphorus is contained almost entirely in acid-soluble compounds and it is localized in cytoplasmic granules 1–3 μ in diameter. Such granules are absent in the early 4th instar larva. The phosphorus is thought to originate from histolysed organs, particularly the gut, and to reach the Malpighian tubes via the haemolymph. The Malpighian tubes thus regulate the phosphorus balance of the mosquito by removing excess phosphorus from the blood and storing it (Stich and Grell, 1955).

Growth of the alimentary canal during the larval stage proceeds almost entirely by increase in cell size with formation of polytene and polyploid nuclei. The only gut regions whose cells do not increase in size are the pyloric chamber, the posterior section of the oesophagus and the regions composed of embryonic cells, i.e. the anterior and posterior imaginal rings and the anal ring. Midgut cells may be replaced during larval life by development of embryonic replacement cells lying between them. At metamorphosis the cells with polyploid nuclei undergo somatic reduction and cell division to yield a large number of small cells which have apparently undergone de-differentiation and which are capable of forming adult tissues. All cells with polytene but not polyploid nuclei, except those of the Malpighian tubes, degenerate at metamorphosis and are replaced by embryonic cells or by some of the cells formed in somatic reduction. Embryonic cells also give rise to the posterior part of the oesophagus and the pyloric chamber. The Malpighian tubes are carried into adult life without visible change.

Metamorphosis of Other Organs

The epidermis is carried over to the adult without histolysis. In *Aedes aegypti* the number of epidermal cells increases approximately 8-fold during the 4th instar (Risler, 1959) and the imaginal buds also contribute to the formation of the adult epidermis (Bodenstein, 1945a).

The only functional spiracles of the larva are the terminal pair, the other 9 pairs being reduced and merely serving for the withdrawal of tracheae at ecdysis. At pupation the sections of the main tracheal trunks between the terminal spiracles and the 7th abdominal segment are withdrawn and not replaced and the cellular layers surrounding them shrink to form solid cords attached posteriorly to the 9th tergite. The collapsed larval tracheae which connect the non-functional spiracles of the mesothorax to the tracheal system are replaced by stout tracheae connected to the respiratory trumpets, while the non-functional 1st abdominal spiracles of the larva and the collapsed tracheae running from them are replaced by functional structures, the spiracles opening into the ventral air space. The remaining pupal spiracles are non-functional. When the adult mosquito is formed within the pupal cuticle functional spiracles develop on the meso- and metathorax and on the 2nd–7th abdominal segments. The pupal moult involves some replacement of tracheae, but when the pupal tracheal linings are withdrawn at emergence they are seen to be very thin and devoid of taenidia (Hurst, 1890a, b; Christophers, 1960).

The larval muscles characteristically consist of a single fibre composed of numerous fibrils, surrounded by a mass of sarcoplasm containing nuclei and bounded by sarcolemma. Certain imaginal muscles, such as those of the legs and the direct flight muscles, are of the tubular type and consist of bundles of fibres 10–20 μ in diameter, each fibre consisting of myofibrils surrounding a core of sarcoplasm and nuclei; they are said to have no sarcolemma. Other muscles of somewhat similar type have peripherally-placed nuclei. The indirect flight muscles consist of a number of large fibres, each comprising hundreds of fibrils 2 μ in diameter embedded in sarcoplasm; between the fibrils are said to be rows of nuclei but these bodies may well be mitochondria. The muscles in the head of the adult are mostly of the tubular type but some approach the indirect flight muscles in character. The abdominal muscles remain of the larval type although a few tubular muscles are developed in the pupal stage (Christophers, 1960).

Great changes take place in the muscular system during metamorphosis. Most of the larval head muscles are histolysed but some are carried over to the adult, developing the structure of adult muscle and acquiring a new relationship to the other parts of the head. In addition, new muscles arise about the 8th hr and by the 17th hr the sides and floor of the head are traversed by belts of small myoblasts whose origin is uncertain. The muscles of the thorax and abdomen are carried over to the adult but the main part of the adult thoracic musculature is new and consists of the muscles of the appendages, largely formed within the imaginal buds, and of the indirect flight muscles which develop principally in the pupal stage although they are present as rudiments below the epidermis in the 4th instar larva. (Thompson, 1905; Hinton, 1959; Christophers, 1960).

The larval abdominal muscles degenerate early in adult life, having been used in swimming by the pupa, and movements of the adult abdomen are due to small adult muscles which develop from myoblasts in the pupa (Roubaud, 1932a; Berger, 1938b). The histolysis of the musculature, as of other organs, takes place entirely by autolysis and without the intervention of phagocytes (Thompson, 1905; Hulst, 1906; Jones, 1954).

The imaginal buds of the male genitalia arise in *Anopheles* and *Aedes* during the 3rd instar behind a fold of the body wall which later becomes the 9th abdominal sternite of the adult, and they are extruded during the 4th instar as two large pouches (Fig. 43a), named primary phallic lobes by Snodgrass (1957), which become more clearly visible in the pupa. Late in the 3rd instar 2 thickenings appear in the primary phallic lobes and these later form hollow pear-shaped buds from which 2 extensions grow forwards. A tiny invagination which arises between the bases of the primary phallic lobes late in the 4th instar is the first sign of the adult ejaculatory duct (Fig. 43b). Secondary lobes or mesosomes bud from the primary phallic lobes and elongate and unite to form the tubular aedeagus whose cavity becomes continuous with that of the ejaculatory duct, and the remainder of the main lobes forms the parameres which by elongation and development form the two-segmented claspers of the adult (Fig. 43b). The claspette lobes of the genitalia also form by separation from the parameres. During the larval stage the membrane which invests the testes grows back as two mesodermal genital strands, the future vasa efferentia.

The 2 buds which arose within the primary phallic lobes differentiate in the pupa and form the seminal vesicles, accessory glands and vasa deferentia. The male external genitalia therefore develop from the primary phallic lobes, and the male efferent ducts from a number of different structures—the vasa efferentia from mesodermal strands, the vasa deferentia and seminal vesicles from paired buds forming within the primary phallic lobes, the ejaculatory duct from an invagination at the base of the primary phallic lobes and the aedeagal lumen through the apposition of the mesomeres (Hurst, 1890a; Imms, 1908; Christophers, 1922, 1960). The male reproductive system develops in a similar manner in other Diptera including *Chironomus, Anisopus* and *Mycetophila* (Abul-Nasr, 1950).

Development of the female terminalia proceeds without formation of invaginated imaginal buds although it starts as in the male with the appearance of epidermal thickenings in the 4th instar larva. These thickenings are found at the posterior end of the 8th sternite, behind the 9th sternite, the position of which is indicated by muscle insertions, and flanking the anus (Fig. 43c). At pupation the thickening behind the 9th sternite forms a shield-shaped plate which occupies the same position as the primary phallic lobes in the male (Fig. 43d), and this plate develops into the postgenital plate and cowl of the adult. The 2 thickenings flanking the anus become separated by fissures from the rest of the epidermis, forming lobes in the pupa which develop into the cerci of the adult. (Similar thickenings in the male larva develop into small sclerites flanking the anus in the adult.) The thickening on the 8th sternite does not form any structure visible externally in the pupa but develops into the region anterior to the gonotreme, the entrance to the genital chamber, a region which is largely membranous but which contains the sigma and insula (Fig. 43e) (Christophers, 1923).

In the fully-grown larva the rudiment of the common oviduct is present as a thickened epidermal invagination behind the 8th sternite and immediately behind it there is another invagination which eventually forms the spermathecae and their ducts. A third invagination arises in the larva in front of the thickening which gives rise to the postgenital plate; this forms

---

Fig. 43a–f. Development of male and female terminalia.
(a) Primary phallic lobes in a male pupa of *Culex fuscanus;* (b) development of mesomeres and parameres within the primary phallic lobes of a male pupa of *Culex fuscanus,* also showing the terminal ampullae of the efferent system (after Christophers, 1922); (c) ventral aspect of the terminal segments of a female larva of *Aedes pulchriventer* showing the epidermal thickenings; (d) terminalia of a female pupa of *Aedes pulchriventer;* (e) terminalia of an adult female of *Aedes pulchriventer;* (f) formation of the female genital chamber by the approximation of originally separate invaginations. (From Christophers, 1923).

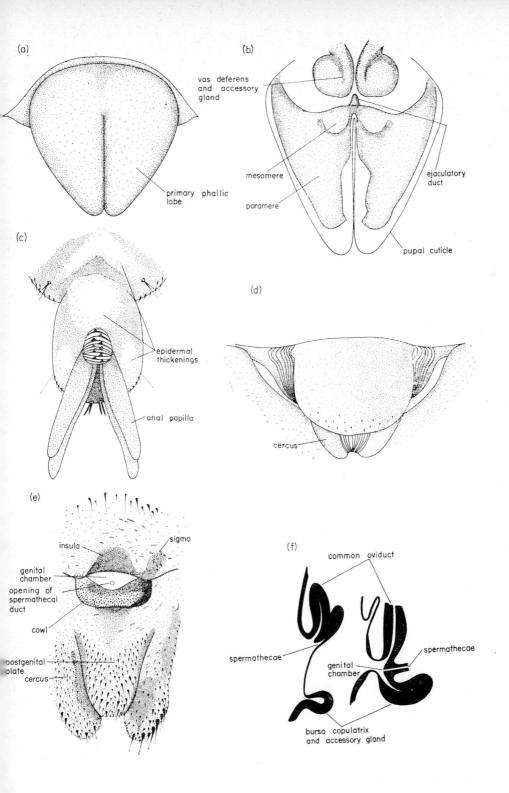

(a)

primary phallic lobe

(b)

vas deferens and accessory gland

mesomere

paramere

ejaculatory duct

pupal cuticle

(c)

epidermal thickenings

anal papilla

(d)

cercus

(e)

insula

sigma

genital chamber

opening of spermathecal duct

cowl

postgenital plate

cercus

(f)

common oviduct

spermathecae

spermathecae

genital chamber

bursa copulatrix and accessory gland

the bursa copulatrix and it arises in the same position as the ejaculatory duct in the male, behind the 9th sternite (Fig. 43f). A portion of the bursa copulatrix rudiment subsequently separates to form the accessory gland. As development proceeds the rudiment of the postgenital plate is drawn under the 8th sternite and in this way the bursa copulatrix and accessory gland are carried forward to open with the common oviduct and sperma-thecae into a new invagination of the body wall, the genital chamber or atrium (Fig. 43f). There is thus in the adult a single genital opening behind the 8th sternite. The ovaries develop slowly during the larval stage and follicles start to appear in the 4th instar. The lateral oviducts develop from mesodermal genital strands which grow back from the ovaries and fuse with the common oviduct (Christophers, 1923).

A ring of minute imaginal cells becomes visible at the anterior end of each salivary gland during the 1st instar. In *Anopheles albimanus* they number 12–15 and the number of cells in each ring doubles in each subsequent instar so that over 100 cells are present in the mature larva. Degeneration of the larval glands may start before pupation and it continues during the first day of pupal life, the posterior parts degenera-ting first. Differentiation of the adult glands from the imaginal cells is completed in the first few hours after pupation and the glands then become greatly elongated as the cells increase in size, although development is not completed until after emergence (Thompson, 1905; Jensen and Jones, 1957).

Development of the oenocytes has been described in *Culiseta annulata* (Hosselet, 1925) and *Aedes aegypti* (Trager, 1937; Christophers, 1960). A group of 5 large oenocytes is present at hatching in the ventro-lateral portion of each abdominal segment. These are the larval oenocytes which grow in size during the larval stage, developing polytene chromosomes, and which degenerate after a peak of secretory activity in the pupa. Many small imaginal oenocytes appear in the abdomen during the 4th instar; they do not grow very large but persist throughout adult life, although reduced in numbers.

The dorsal vessel and the pericardial cells pass intact to the adult (Jones, 1954) although the altered structure of the head probably necessitates changes in the outlet of the aorta. The fat body passes from the mature larva to the newly-emerged adult unchanged and little, if at all, diminished in size.

Cytogenetic Aspects of Growth and Metamorphosis

During embryonic development the egg divides into a large number of diploid cells, most of which become differentiated into the various organs of the larva by the time of hatching. In holometabolous insects subsequent development involves not only an increase in size of the individual but also metamorphosis with a change of cell type, and these two processes may be accomplished in a variety of ways by different organs.

The central nervous system grows in the larva by cell multiplication with only a very slight increase in cell size (Table 5). The nuclei show a normal 'resting' structure and are almost certainly always diploid. Only slight histolysis of nervous tissue occurs in the pupa and the adult nervous system develops by further cell multiplication (Trager, 1937; Woolley, 1943). The fat body appears to grow in the same way, persisting in the adult without change (Trager, 1937).

In striking contrast are organs which grow in the larva entirely by increase in cell size; they include the salivary glands, Malpighian tubes, rectum, abdominal muscles, trichogen cells, larval oenocytes and anal papillae. In each of these tissues the cells are incapable of division and except for the Malpighian tubes they are incapable of transforming into adult organs. During larval development the cells grow extremely large (Table 5) and chromosome reduplication occurs without separation of the sister chromatids, producing polytene (many stranded) chromosomes in a cell which retains its diploid character (Trager, 1937; Berger, 1938b; Sutton, 1942). At metamorphosis the Malpighian tubes alone among these tissues are retained unchanged in the adult, and they apparently have dual potentialities; all the other organs are destroyed. The salivary glands are replaced by developing imaginal cells, the rectum by migration of cells from the small intestine and anal canal, the abdominal muscles by myoblasts, and so on.

The larval midgut epithelium shows a similar method of growth for the cells increase greatly in size (Table 5), develop polytene chromosomes and are incapable of division. However, from the 2nd instar onwards some of these cells are shed into the midgut lumen and when an epithelial cell is lost 2 or more embryonic replacement cells divide, some of the daughter cells remaining as replacement cells and others differentiating as epithelial cells. This leads to an increase in the number of epithelial and replacement cells without involving division of the former. At metamorphosis all the epithelial cells are destroyed and the replacement cells differentiate into the adult midgut epithelium (Samtleben, 1929; Berger, 1938b; Richins, 1945).

A further type of development called endopolyploidy is found in which larval cells grow in size and develop polytene chromosomes but do not become completely differentiated. At metamorphosis the separation of the polytene chromosomes into their constituent strands combined with a rapid series of cell divisions yields a large number of small cells with normal chromosomes, a process called somatic reduction. The larval

H

TABLE 5. THE GROWTH CHARACTERISTICS OF CELLS AND NUCLEI OF VARIOUS TISSUES OF THE LARVA OF *Aedes aegypti*. ALL MEASUREMENTS WERE MADE ON FIXED MATERIAL. DATA COMPILED FROM TRAGER (1937) AND RISLER (1959).

Structure	Size at hatching	Relative size at end of instar when size at hatching is 1				Absolute size at end of 4th instar	Chromosomes	Fate	Method of growth in larva
		1st instar	2nd instar	3rd instar	4th instar				
Body (length)	1	1·6	2·7	4·6	7·0	7·0± 0·2mm	—	—	—
Abdominal epidermis nucleus (length)	1	1·4	1·6	1·4	1·0	5·6± 0·5μ	resting nucleus diploid & tetraploid	survives in adult	cell multiplication
Thoracic ganglion cell (diameter)	1	1·0	1·4	1·5	1·8	6·2± 0·6μ	resting nucleus probably diploid	survives in adult	cell multiplication
Fat body nucleus (diameter)	1	1·2	1·4	1·3	1·1	5·4± 0·3μ	resting nucleus probably diploid	survives in adult	cell multiplication
Midgut cell (length)	1	1·8	3·3	4·2	5·5	51·7±10·4μ	—	histolysed larva pupa	increase in size
Midgut nucleus (diameter)	1	1·5	2·3	3·2	3·3	15·4± 1·9μ	polytene	histolysed larva pupa	increase in size
Malpighian tube cell (length)	1	1·5	3·3	4·9	8·0	81·3±10·7μ	—	survives in adult	increase in size
Malpighian tube nucleus (diameter)	1	1·5	2·2	3·3	5·0	22·7± 2·6μ	polytene	survives in adult	increase in size
Rectal cell (length)	1	1·5	2·9	4·6	7·3	59·7± 6·9μ	—	histolysed in pupa	increase in size
Rectal nucleus (diameter)	1	1·4	2·2	3·0	4·6	21·3± 1·8μ	polytene	histolysed in pupa	increase in size
Salivary gland nucleus (diameter)	1	1·2	1·8	2·4	3·6	20·6± 4·3μ	polytene	histolysed in pupa	increase in size
Abdominal muscle nucleus (length)	1	1·2	2·4	3·3	4·1	18·6± 2·6μ	polytene	histolysed in adult	increase in size

chromosomes are therefore effectively polyploid. Endopolyploidy and somatic reduction occur in the small intestine (ileum), pharynx, oesophagus and anal canal (Berger, 1938b; Risler, 1961) and to a reduced extent in the epidermis, tracheae and neurilemma (Risler, 1959, 1961).

The details of endopolyploidy and somatic reduction are known best in the small intestine. During the larval stage the cells grow entirely by increase in size and the number of cells at pupation is the same as in the 1st instar. However, the chromosomes split repeatedly without dissolution of the nuclear membrane or formation of a spindle in what appear to be resting nuclei, and by pupation the nuclei of the small intestine are all large though not of regular size. Early in pupal life the cells undergo a series of mitoses separated by interphases in which no reduplication of chromosomes occurs. In the prophase of the first division the chromosomes leave the 'resting' stage and become visible as polytene chromosomes, either in a haploid number as in *Aedes aegypti* or in a diploid number with homologous chromosomes loosely associated in homologous pairs through somatic pairing as in *Culex pipiens*. The polytene elements subsequently fall apart into many pairs of homologous chromosomes and in the metaphase of the first division it is seen that the small-intestine nuclei contain in *Culex pipiens* 48, 96 or rarely, 192 chromosomes, and in *Aedes aegypti* 6, 12, 24 or 48 chromosomes, the chromosomes being the same size as those of diploid nuclei ($2n = 6$). There is a direct correlation between chromosome number and nuclear size. In early anaphase the chromosomes of each pair pass to opposite poles, thereby acting in the manner normal to daughter chromatids, and homologous chromosomes subsequently combine at each pole to form half the number of pairs. A series of such somatic reductions combined with cell divisions rapidly leads to the production of many small diploid cells which reconstitute the small intestine and rectum (Berger, 1938b; Grell, 1946a, b; Schuh, 1951; Risler, 1961). This process has been described in species of *Culex, Anopheles, Aedes* and *Orthopodomyia* (Berger, 1938a, b).

The epidermal cells appear to have more than 1 potentiality for the same cells can secrete the cuticles of larva, pupa and adult. Periods of mitosis occur in each instar in the epidermis of *Aedes aegypti* and in the 1st and 2nd instars the nuclei remain diploid but approximately double their volume, although this increase in size is not found in the nuclei of the imaginal bud cells. During the 3rd instar a further increase in size takes place in some nuclei and these are found to be tetraploid. The number of tetraploid nuclei increases greatly at the beginning of the 4th instar and in the tergal regions of the abdomen the nuclei are almost all tetraploid, although none occurs in the intersegmental regions. During the long period of mitosis which precedes pupation somatic reduction leads to the forma-

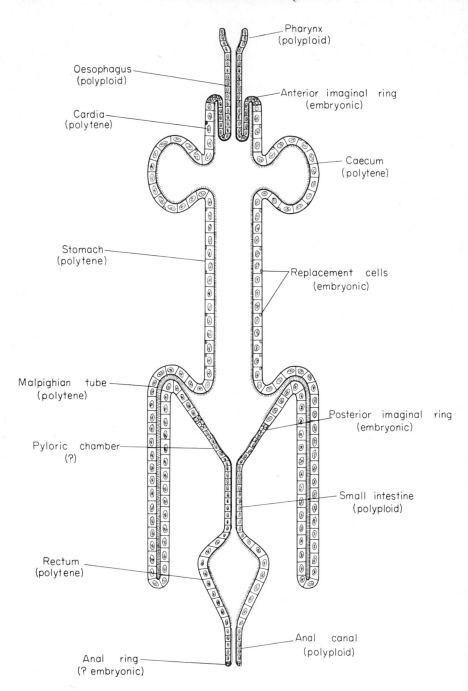

tion of a large number of small diploid cells. Only occasional mitoses occur in the pupa and these are thought to be associated with the formation of hairs and scales (Risler, 1959).

The variety of methods of growth and metamorphosis suggests that each organ has evolved its manner of development independently. It is not unlikely that the larval organs which grow by increase in cell size do so because complete differentiation early in the life history prevents cell division, while the polyteny of the chromosomes provides a means for the nucleus to keep pace with cell growth. The polyploidy of the small intestine cells appears to permit extremely rapid metamorphosis of the hindgut, for the necessity of synthesizing new chromatin material between cell divisions is avoided, and the epithelia of the adult small intestine and rectum may be largely re-formed 14 hr after pupation at 24°–30°C (Schuh, 1951). The function of polyploidy in the epidermis is not clear, however, since in most parts of the body the adult epidermis is smaller in area than that of the larva (Risler, 1959). Possibly some more fundamental reason for polyploidy is to be looked for in this organ.

Maturation

Although the adult mosquito can fly within a few minutes of emergence development is still proceeding and maturity is not reached until a day or two later. One type of change which occurs at this time is the destruction of organs which function in the larva and pupa but not in the adult. The massive abdominal muscles of the larva are used by the pupa in swimming and the thoracic glands may be presumed to control the larval and pupal moults but neither is required by the adult and both histolyse shortly after emergence.

The cuticle hardens after emergence. The antennal fibrillae cling to the shaft of the antenna in the immature male but they are subsequently erected and in *Aedes aegypti* they are sufficiently erect 15–24 hr after emergence for the antennae to function as hearing organs in detection of the female (Roth, 1948). Final development of the compound eyes in *Culex pipiens* var. *pallens* does not take place until after emergence (Satô, 1951a). In *Anopheles albimanus* (Jensen and Jones, 1957) and *Culex pipiens* (Thompson, 1905) the salivary glands attain their full size shortly after emergence and in *Anopheles quadrimaculatus* the salivary gland agglutinins and anticoagulins are first secreted 8–12 hr after emergence (Metcalf, 1945).

The males are incapable of copulating successfully until their terminal

---

Fig. 44. Chromosome constitution of the epithelia of the alimentary canal of a 4th instar larva.

segments have rotated through approximately 180°, a process which takes place during the first day or two of adult life (p. 166). Rotation proceeds more rapidly at higher temperatures (Provost *et al.*, 1961). The male antennal fibrillae become erect during this period and the mating response of the male depends upon this development of the antennae, not upon the state of the terminalia, for the males will show a clasping response on aural stimulation before they are capable of copulation (Roth, 1948). The first males to appear are normally ready to mate by the time the females start to emerge. The spermatozoa are mature when the male emerges but the ovaries of the female need to develop to the resting stage before they can be stimulated to develop further by a blood meal (p. 169). In well-nourished individuals this initial ovary development takes place at the expense of the reserves but in undernourished individuals sugar feeding is necessary. Females of *Aedes geniculatus* can bite within 2 or 3 min of emergence if placed on the skin (Shute, 1933a) but most species cannot or will not bite for several hours.

The fat body shrinks almost to nothing when the reserves are utilized during the first days of adult life (Clements, 1956a), but later it may become massive from nectar feeding. This apparently does not involve histolysis of the larval fat body and development of a distinct adult fat body as in the higher Diptera, but the fat body in the adult shows some specialization since protein is never deposited in it, even after a blood meal. Other maturation changes which have been described include a fall in the concentration of acid phosphatase (Lambremont, 1960) and a rise in the concentrations of DPNH-cytochrome *c* reductase and succinate-cytochrome *c* reductase (Lang, 1959) in males and females of *Aedes aegypti* over the first 2 or 3 weeks of adult life. An increase in wing-beat frequency also occurs, in *Aedes aegypti* reaching a maximum 3 days after emergence some 200 c/s higher than in adults a few hours older (Tischner and Schief, 1955).

Metamorphosis starts early in larval life with the slow development of the imaginal buds, compound eyes and gonads, processes which are in most cases greatly accelerated in the 4th instar and which are largely completed in the pupa. It is clear, however, that important changes continue to take place in the first days of adult life and that only in the older adult is metamorphosis completed.

CHAPTER 5

THE CIRCULATORY SYSTEM

Structure of the Dorsal Vessel and other Organs

The structure of the dorsal vessel differs little between larva, pupa and adult. It extends from the 8th abdominal segment to the head and comprises the heart, lying in the abdomen, and the aorta, in the thorax and head. The wall of the dorsal vessel consists of a protoplasmic intima containing densely-anastomosing, elastic, connective tissue fibres, with striped muscle fibres wound spirally around it (Fig. 45b) (Jones, 1954; Yaguzhinskaya, 1954).

The heart expands into 8 segmental chambers, each associated with a pair of alary muscles and containing a pair of ostia. The chambers are not

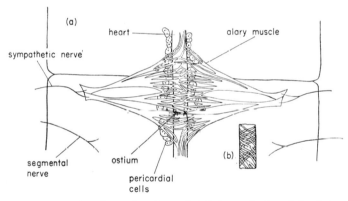

FIG. 45a–b.   The dorsal vessel and associated tissues in the adult of *Anopheles maculipennis.*
(a) Ventral aspect of a region of the heart; (b) a short length of the heart showing its spiral musculature. (After Yaguzhinskaya, 1954).

well defined and they disappear when the alary muscles are cut, indicating that they are formed by the tension of these muscles (Jones, 1954). The ostia are slit-like openings with their margins extended inwards to form valves. The 8 pairs of alary muscles extend from the lateral body wall to the heart, and each is composed of 4–5 bands of striped muscle, which divide into a number of fibres which anastomose with one another above and below the heart (Fig. 45a). The alary muscles thus delimit a pericardial sinus and form a somewhat discontinuous dorsal diaphragm. The heart is also connected to the body wall and to other organs by connective tissue filaments (Imms, 1908; Jones, 1954; Yaguzhinskaya, 1954).

In the larva only the terminal chamber is provided with tracheae and this receives an extremely rich supply in the tracheal plexus, a dense mat of tracheoles arising from crypts or short outgrowths of the main tracheal trunks. The tracheoles are attached to the surface of the heart but do not penetrate it. The tracheal plexus clearly oxygenates the terminal chamber and the haemolymph passing through it but why this is necessary is quite unknown. The tracheal plexus is lost at pupation (Imms, 1907; Jones, 1954; Christophers, 1960).

The aorta has the same histological composition as the heart but it is narrower, lacks ostia and has no alary muscles or pericardial cells associated with it. In the prothorax the aorta expands to form a large pulsatile chamber, and thickenings of the aorta wall at each end of the chamber have been interpreted as valves (Jones, 1952, 1954; Christophers, 1960). The aorta ends in front of the brain where it expands into an open-ended blood sinus (Christophers, 1960).

In *Anopheles maculipennis* the bases of the alary muscles are innervated by fibres of the ventral sympathetic nervous system which arises by median nerves from the ventral ganglia (Yaguzhinskaya, 1954). Jones (1954) reported that fine nerves supplied the bases of the alary muscles in *Anopheles quadrimaculatus*, and Christophers (1960) described the ventral sympathetic nervous system in *Aedes aegypti* but did not note any connection with the circulatory system. It therefore appears that the alary muscles may be innervated in mosquitoes but that the heart itself has no nerve supply.

A pair of pulsating organs is present in the head of the pupa and adult. Essentially, each consists of a vesicle, lying under the cuticle below the compound eyes, which is connected to the aorta by a number of striped muscle fibres and which sends a vessel to the antennal flagellum of its side. A syncytial body is found between the vesicle and the muscle fibres (Fig. 46). A valve in the wall of the vesicle is thought to permit inspiration of blood on contraction of the muscle, and it is considered that when the muscle relaxes an elastic contraction of the vesicle causes blood to flow through the antennal vessel. No nerve supply to the organ has been found and and its contractions are presumed to be myogenic (Clements, 1956b).

A thin, horizontal sheet of muscle arches across the scutellum in the adult, and both in the intact animal and in the isolated scutellum this membrane flutters extremely rapidly, though at irregular intervals, and possibly assists the circulation of haemolymph (Jones, 1954; Christophers,

1960). A ventral diaphragm is not present in the larva but in the pupa
and adult a membrane containing muscle fibres overlies the nerve cord in
the thorax and abdomen. Emargination of its edges provides con-
tinuity between the ventral and perivisceral sinuses and its slow movements possibly lead to some circulation of haemolymph (Jones, 1954).

Pericardial cells, sometimes called dorsal nephrocytes, occur in the

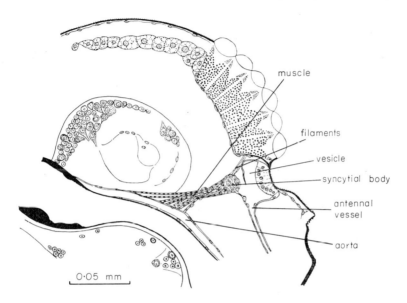

FIG. 46. Sagittal section through the head of an adult *Culex pipiens* showing
the antennal pulsating organ. (From Clements, 1956b).

abdomen along both sides of the heart, lying between the fibres of the
alary muscles where these separate to run over and under the heart. Most
are binucleate but they may contain as many as 6 nuclei (Pal, 1944; Jones,
1954; Christophers, 1960). There is dispute about the number of pericardial cells. Pal (1944) and Christophers (1960) described 2 pairs of cells
in most abdominal segments, totalling 27 or 28 pairs in all. Jones (1954)
and Yaguzhinskaya (1954) described much larger numbers of pericardial
cells. Jones (1954) counted 300 or more pericardial cells in larvae of several
species, including *Anopheles stephensi* which Pal (1944) considered to contain relatively few cells. According to Christophers (1960) the pericardial
cells in a fully-grown larva of *Aedes aegypti* measure approximately 20 ×
40 μ but Jones (1954) found that in *Anopheles quadrimaculatus* the cells
ranged from 6 × 12 μ to 22 × 48 μ. Therein may lie the cause of the disagreement. Similar cells, the ventral nephrocytes, occur in the thorax.

In *Culex pipiens fatigans* (Pal, 1944) and *Anopheles albimanus* (Jensen and Jones, 1957) they form a syncytial chain suspended between the salivary glands but in *Aedes aegypti* they overlie the ventral nerve cord (Christophers, 1960).

There is some evidence that the pericardial cells have an excretory function. If mosquito larvae are fed ammonia carmine the pericardial cells are later found densely packed with carmine granules, and the granules are retained within the cells throughout life (Pal, 1944; Jones, 1954). In *Culex pipiens* the bile pigment which accumulates in the larval fat body is found concentrated in the pericardial cells after the larval fat body has released its contents during the first day of adult life (Clements, 1956a). The breakdown products of haemoglobin are not taken up by the pericardial cells of adult *Anopheles maculipennis* and *Aedes aegypti* after feeding, as happens in some other insects, but they are discharged with the faeces (Wigglesworth, 1943). Whether the pericardial cells have other functions is not known.

Haemocytes can be seen attached to the epidermis and other organs but they are rarely found circulating in the haemolymph. Examination of living larvae showed no free haemocytes in *Aedes aegypti*, extremely few in *Anopheles quadrimaculatus*, and a small number in *Culex pipiens*. If pressure is applied to the larvae some haemocytes are set free (Jones, 1953a). The free haemocytes are round or oval cells with single nuclei and granular or non-granular cytoplasm (Jones, 1954). It has been claimed that haemocytes act as phagocytes during metamorphosis, assisting in histolysis (de Boissezon, 1934; Christophers, 1960), but this view is not supported by Thompson (1905) or Jones (1954), although Jones (1954) states that haemocytes will engulf carmine granules from the haemolymph.

Analysis of the haemolymph of larvae, pupae and adults of *Culex-pipiens* var. *molestus* has revealed the presence of the following free amino acids and amines: α-alanine, β-alanine, arginine, aspartic acid, cystine, glutamic acid, glutamine, glycine, histidine, leucine and/or isoleucine, lysine, methionine sulphoxide, proline, serine, threonine, tyrosine and valine (Laven and Chen, 1956; Chen, 1958a, b; Geiger, 1961). Taurine has been reported from whole bodies of *Culex pipiens* var. *molestus* adults (Chen, 1958b) and α-aminobutyric acid and methionine from whole adults of *Culex tarsalis* and other species (Clark and Ball, 1952). Phenylalanine and tryptophan have been reported from whole adults of *Aedes aegypti* (Thayer and Terzian, 1962). The haemolymph of larvae of *Culex pipiens* var. *molestus* has been shown to contain 3 peptides (Chen, 1958a) and 4 proteins (Chen, 1959). The relative amount of free ninhydrin-positive material in the whole body of *Culex pipiens* var. *molestus* remains constant throughout larval life but falls considerably in the pupa. Adults kept for 4–6 days on sucrose become poor in free amino acids, particularly in certain essential amino acids. β-alanine decreases in adult females but increases in adult males; methionine sulphoxide increases in females and remains constant in males (Chen, 1958a, b). The increase in methionine sulphoxide is associated with ovary development although the amino acid does not increase in the ovaries themselves (Geiger, 1961). In contrast, when females of *Aedes aegypti* are maintained on sucrose for 5 weeks after emergence without developing their ovaries, the amount of free amino acid in their tissues remains constant although their dry weight rises and falls (Thayer and Terzian, 1962). The inorganic composition of larval haemolymph is described on p. 62.

Nature and Control of the Heart Beat

Each heart beat consists of a peristaltic wave which passes rapidly along the length of the dorsal vessel. The systolic component is due to contraction of the spiral muscles and the diastolic component to relaxation of these muscles. An isolated heart becomes twisted but continues to beat, so the alary muscles normally just support the heart. In larvae the waves of contraction always run forwards but in pupae and adults they may run forwards or backwards, the forward-moving waves predominating (Jones, 1954; Christophers, 1960).

In *Anopheles quadrimaculatus* the rate of beating declines during the larval stage and the pupal heart may stop beating for prolonged periods. The heart beats more rapidly in the adult than in any other stage, giving approximately 150 beats/min compared to 85/min in 4th instar larvae at the same temperature. The rate of beat varies with temperature, increasing in 4th instar *Anopheles quadrimaculatus* from 54 beats/min at 15°C to 139 beats/min at 35°C. Activity such as swimming leads to elevation of the heart rate whereas fasting leads to an immediate fall of about 20 beats/min (Jones, 1954, 1956a).

The threshold of oxygen concentration which permits the heart to beat normally in larvae of *Anopheles quadrimaculatus* lies between 0·3 and 1 per cent. In pure nitrogen the rate of beat declines very greatly but the heart still beats after an hour, long after the activity of other organs has ceased. At low oxygen concentrations addition of 5 per cent carbon dioxide reduces the decline in rate of beating and at high oxygen concentrations it increases the rate of beat. Pure carbon dioxide stops the heart beat within 3 min (Jones, 1956b).

No ganglia or nerve cells have been found associated with the dorsal vessel and it will continue to beat after it has been isolated from the central nervous system. Cutting the dorsal vessel of a larva of *Anopheles quadrimaculatus* between the thorax and abdomen stops the aorta from beating but allows the heart to beat at a slow rate. If the cut is made further back, between abdominal segments 4 and 7, the anterior section beats more slowly than usual while the posterior section increases its rate. A cut between segments 7 and 8 stops the posterior section from beating. It appears that automatism is present throughout the heart, being strongest at the posterior end, but does not extend to the aorta (Jones, 1954). When a cut was made in the adult heart between the 3rd and 4th abdominal segments the anterior section beat almost exclusively in a backward direction while the posterior section beat largely but not exclusively in a forward direction. Both sections therefore beat in the direction of least resistance. When ventilation movements of the adult abdomen begin at the posterior end of the abdomen the heart beats forwards and when they begin at the anterior end the heart beats backwards. If ventilation movements are prevented by gluing the abdomen the hearts soon stops beating. Strong movements of the hindgut, to which the heart is tied by connective tissue fibres, can also cause the heart to stop beating (Jones, 1954).

Placing larvae of *Anopheles quadrimaculatus* in 1M-NaCl causes a very slight increase in rate of heart beat whereas placing them in 1M-KCl causes an almost immediate and very considerable increase in rate which may reach as much as 145 beats/min, but the amplitude of beat is very shallow and is apparently due to movements of the alary muscles. This effect of potassium can be prevented by ligaturing in front of the anal papillae. Immersion in $0.5M-CaCl_2$ causes a slight increase in heart rate whereas immersion in $0.1M-MgCl_2$ causes a marked depression (Jones, 1956c).

The effects of drugs on rate of heart beat have been investigated in *Anopheles quadrimaculatus* by Jones (1954, 1956d, 1957). When larvae were placed in 10^{-2} acetylcholine or 10^{-2} adrenaline the heart rate was unchanged but there was no evidence that the drugs had penetrated. However, the convulsions which ensued when larvae were placed in 10^{-3} nicotine and the hyperactivity which followed immersion in 10^{-4} pilocarpine showed that these drugs had been absorbed. Pilocarpine had no effect on the rate of heart beat and nicotine stimulated it only very slightly. A considerable increase in heart rate followed submersion of larvae in $5 \times 10^{-3}M$ 2 : 4-dinitrophenol, presumably due to an increase in metabolism since this compound has no direct pharmacological action. Exposure to ether vapour caused slowing of the larval heart beat and complete immobility of all other organs. Application of 10^{-3} acetylcholine to the exposed adult heart caused slight depression of rate on the first application; 10^{-2} methacholine chloride and 10^{-4} pilocarpine had no effect; 10^{-4} adrenaline slightly increased the rate.

The facts that no ganglion cells have been found associated with the dorsal vessel, that the dorsal vessel continues to beat when separated from the central nervous system and after transection, and that drugs such as ether and acetylcholine have little effect strongly suggest that the mosquito heart is of the non-innervated myogenic type, the pacemaker probably residing in the spiral muscle which surrounds it.

CHAPTER 6

SURVIVAL AND LONGEVITY

Survival at Low Temperatures

The results of experiments to determine thermal limits are affected by a number of factors apart from the temperature to which the mosquitoes are exposed and the criterion chosen for the thermal death point. Such factors include stage of development, conditions under which the insects have been cultured, temperature before exposure, the rate at which the temperature is changed, length of exposure and the temperature to which the mosquitoes are returned after exposure.

Not a great deal is known about the sensitivity of mosquitoes to low temperature. Some species are killed by prolonged exposure to only moderately-low temperatures. Larvae of *Anopheles quadrimaculatus* are killed by exposure to 10°C (Huffaker, 1944); eggs, larvae and pupae of *Anopheles subpictus* and *Anopheles stephensi* are killed by prolonged exposure to 10°C (Lal, 1953) and all stages of *Aedes aegypti* are killed by prolonged exposure to 8°C (Bar-Zeev, 1957b) although the larvae will recover after their container has been frozen solid for 10 hr at −2°C (Bliss and Gill, 1933). The eggs of *Anopheles culicifacies* are killed by temperatures below 10°C and the larvae by temperatures below 5°C (Pal, 1945). Subarctic and temperate region species appear to be rather more resistant to cold than tropical species. Larvae of *Anopheles claviger* recover after being embedded in ice for many days but larvae of *Culiseta morsitans* and *Aedes flavescens* survive only if they remain in water under the ice (Shute, 1929; Hearle, 1929). Larvae of *Aedes geniculatus* cannot withstand freezing of the medium (MacGregor, 1932) but larvae of *Wyeomyia smithii* and *Culex pipiens fatigans* survive the repeated freezing and thawing of the water in which they live, and swim actively long before all the ice has melted (Smith, 1901, 1902; Haufe, 1952). Eggs of *Anopheles lesteri* survive the freezing of the water on which they are laid (Otsuru and Ohmori, 1960) and the winter eggs of *Anopheles walkeri* survive exposure for a few days to −21°C (Peters, 1943). In Finnish Lapland, larvae of *Aedes punctor* are active at 0°C, the pupae are active at 1°C and the adults will crawl at 3°C and fly at about 10°C (Mellanby, 1940), while in northern USSR adults of *Aedes punctor* and *Aedes communis* have been recorded biting at 2·5°C (Gracheva and Shevkunova, 1959). Hibernating females of *Anopheles maculipennis* can survive for some months at an average temperature of −18°C (Maslow, 1930). It is interesting that the distribution of *Culex pipiens fatigans* and *Anopheles lesteri,* which show cold hardiness, extends into the tropics.

Most insects which withstand sub-zero temperatures do so by super-cooling, thus preventing their body water from freezing which would be fatal. A number of species are not injured by freezing and normally freeze during the winter (Salt, 1961). It is not known for certain to which category belong those mosquito larvae and adults which can withstand sub-zero temperatures but indirect evidence suggests that they survive by super-cooling. Freezing depends upon the formation of an ice-crystal nucleus and the probability of nucleus formation is both temperature dependent, increasing with lower temperature at least down to −50°C, and time dependent, since it depends upon favourable molecular orientations (Salt, 1958). It is found that adult mosquitoes which can survive for a time at certain very low temperatures are killed by further lowering of the temperature, and that larvae which survive short exposures to certain low temperatures are killed by prolonged exposure. Although females of *Anopheles maculipennis* survived for some months at a temperature averaging −18°C with an average minimum of −23°C, only 8 per cent recovered after 3 days at an average temperature of −37·5°C with an average minimum of −40·5°C. Fifty per cent of *Culex pipiens pipiens* females survived for 2 weeks at an average temperature of −8°C with an average minimum of −12°C but only 12·5 per cent survived that length of time at an average of −15°C and an average minimum of −16·6°C (Maslow, 1930). Eggs of *Aedes aegypti* survive exposure to −17°C for 1 hr (Bliss and Gill, 1933) but are killed by 48 hr exposure to −5·5°C (Davis, 1932). Larvae of *Aedes aegypti* recover after 10 hr in solid ice at −2°C but longer exposure is fatal (Bliss and Gill, 1933). Larvae of *Wyeomyia smithii* which survive when the water of their pitcher-plant habitat freezes solid are killed by exposure to −14°C for 3 hr and are probably protected from very low temperatures in nature by a blanket of snow (Owen, 1937).

The sensitivity to low temperature changes slightly during development. Recently-laid eggs of *Culex pipiens* are killed by exposure to 2°C for 18 hr but eggs 24 hr old survive exposure to this temperature for 5 days (Farid, 1949). Young pupae of *Aedes aegypti* are less susceptible to low temperature than larvae or old pupae whereas the eggs are the least sensitive stage (Bar-Zeev, 1957b).

Survival of Aquatic Stages at High Temperatures

The aquatic stages of mosquitoes show an increasing sensitivity to high temperature during development. When the early stages of *Anopheles minimus* were subjected to slowly rising temperature, being held for 5 min at the highest temperature, the thermal death point, at which all were killed, was 43°–44°C for the eggs, 42°C for the 1st instar larvae and 41°C for 4th instar larvae and pupae. 1st instar larvae were apparently unaffected by a temperature which killed all 4th instar larvae and eggs hatched after an exposure that would kill all larvae and pupae (Muirhead-Thomson, 1940c). *Anopheles subpictus* subjected to similar experimental conditions could withstand higher temperatures but showed the same increasing sensitivity with development. Thermal death points on 5 min exposure were 53·5°C in the egg stage, 47·5° in the 1st instar, 45·5° in the 2nd instar, 46° in the 3rd and 4th instars and 44° in the pupal stage (Lal, 1953). Similar trends were shown by *Anopheles culicifacies* (Pal, 1945), *A. quadrimaculatus*, *A. freeborni* and *A. aztecus* (Barr, 1952), with the larvae becoming progressively more suceptible to high temperatures in the later instars, but in the last 2 species the pupae showed a slight decrease in sensitivity over the 4th instar larvae. The early stages of *Aedes aegypti* also show variations in sensitivity to high temperature but in a less regular manner than in the species of *Anopheles* just described (Bar-Zeev, 1957b).

Changes in sensitivity to high temperature also occur within the egg stage, within individual larval instars and within the pupal stage. Eggs of *Aedes aegypti* less than a day old suffered heavy mortality when exposed to 40°C for 25 hr, whereas there was only slight mortality among mature eggs after exposure for 48 hr (Davis, 1932). Specimens of *Aedes aegypti* which had pupated within the previous half hour were much more resistant to high temperature than those which had been pupae for over 36 hr. The time required for 50 per cent mortality at 43°C was 65 min in young pupae and 40 min in older pupae, and the young pupae were found to be more resistant than any of the larval instars (Bar-Zeev, 1957b). Larvae of *Anopheles quadrimaculatus* which had been in the 3rd instar less than 4 hr showed a somewhat greater resistance to high temperature than larvae which were within 24 hr of moulting to the 4th instar (Barr, 1952).

There is no absolute upper thermal death point for any species because the length of exposure to high temperature is of great importance in survival. At 41°C 5 min exposure was sufficient to kill all 4th instar larvae of *Anopheles minimus,* but at 40°C one hour's exposure was required and at 39°C two hours' exposure (Muirhead-Thomson, 1940c). The time required for 50 per cent mortality of 4th instar larvae of *Aedes aegypti* was 9 min at 54°, 60 min at 43° and 208 min at 41°C (Bar-Zeev, 1957b). In pools of still water the maximum temperature may be maintained for only a short period each day so the ability to survive periods of exposure to 'sublethal' temperatures is important (Muirhead-Thomson, 1940c). The rate at which temperature rises is also important. When the temperature was raised suddenly to 40·5° C 50 per cent of 4th instar larvae of *Anopheles quadrimaculatus* were killed within a few minutes, but when the temperature was raised slowly significant mortality did not occur until the temperature reached 43°C (Love and Whelchel, 1957). Mosquito larvae are often able to avoid high temperatures by horizontal and vertical migrations (Haufe and Burgess, 1956). In shallow pools 1–3 in. deep there is little difference in temperature between top and bottom but in deep pools, such as those where larvae of *Aedes taeniorhynchus* occur, the temperature may be 33°C at the top and 28° to 29°C at the bottom where the bottom-feeding larvae spend most of their time (Nielsen and Haeger, 1954).

Although data are not available for a very wide range of species it appears that species of the temperate region tend to be more sensitive to high temperature than tropical species. Larvae of *Anopheles claviger* and *Culiseta annulata* all perished when exposed to 37°C for 5 min (Wright, 1927) whereas the thermal death points of a number of Indian species, established under similar conditions, ranged from 40°C for *Anopheles insulaeflorum* to 44·5°–45°C for *A. vagus* (Muirhead-Thomson, 1940c). *Anopheles maculatus* larvae have been reported from hot springs in Formosa at 43°C (Takahashi, 1924). Species found in the same neighbourhood but in different habitats may differ in thermal sensitivity. Larvae of *Anopheles minimus* which are restricted to flowing water have a thermal death point of 41°C whereas the larvae of *A. barbirostris* which occur in rice fields and tanks and so are subjected to higher temperatures have a thermal death point of 43·5°C (Muirhead-Thomson, 1940c). The larvae of *Anopheles gambiae* which live in exposed pools and puddles have a thermal death point, on one hour's exposure, of 42°C whereas the larvae of *A. funestus* which live in water shaded by standing herbage have a thermal death point of 39°C (Haddow, 1943). The herbage of the larval habitats of *Anopheles funestus* has a pronounced insulating effect and standing grass 1 ft high has been shown to reduce the maximum temperature of a pool by over 10°C (Haddow, 1943). High water temperatures are said to restrict summer breeding of a number of species. Larval populations of *Anopheles quadrimaculatus* decline when surface temperatures reach 38°C (Love and Welchel, 1957) and temperatures of 40°–43°C in the normal breeding sites of *Anopheles culicifacies* restrict this species in summer to wells and large tanks where the maximum temperature is 37°C (Pal, 1945). Muirhead-Thomson (1951b) has discussed in detail the effect of high water temperatures on the ecology of the early stages of mosquitoes.

Effects of Temperature and Humidity upon Survival of Adults

The survival of adult mosquitoes at moderate and high temperatures depends in most cases upon both temperature and humidity. At optimum humidity the survival of *Aedes polynesiensis* is inversely proportional to the temperature (Ingram, 1954) and at moderate temperatures the mortality of *Aedes aegypti* is roughly inversely proportional to the relative humidity, but there does not appear to be a direct relationship between longevity and either relative humidity or saturation deficit (Lewis, 1933; Bar-Zeev, 1957b). Humidity may or may not affect the thermal death point. In *Culex pipiens fatigans* the thermal death point varies with humidity, adults surviving otherwise fatal exposures of 1 hr to high temperature when the relative humidity is raised (Karamchandani, 1935), and in *Anopheles quadrimaculatus* all females exposed to 41°C die within 4 min at low relative humidity but some survive for 13 min at high R.H. (Platt *et al.*, 1957). When females of *Anopheles minimus* are subjected to temperatures rising 5°C per hour most females die after 10 min exposure to 38°C and the thermal death point is not affected by relative humidity within the range 25–90 per cent R.H. (Muirhead-Thomson, 1941b). In *Anopheles culicifacies* also relative humidity was found to have no effect on the thermal death point (Pal, 1943a). Humidity certainly affects survival at moderate temperatures. When young, unfed females of *Anopheles maculipennis* and *Anopheles labranchiae atroparvus* were kept at 19° and 30°C their longevity increased directly with relative humidity and inversely with temperature (Hundertmark, 1938). Longevity of *Anopheles stephensi* at 25°–35°C increased with rising relative humidity up to 70 per cent R.H. but at 90 per cent R.H. longevity was reduced (Mehta, 1934). At moderate temperatures (4°–35°C) the survival of *Aedes aegypti* females was increased by high relative humidities, but at extreme temperatures (0·5° and 40°C) survival was independent of relative humidity (Bar-Zeev, 1957b). The longevity of *Anopheles culicifacies* kept in very large cages out of doors and fed blood and plant juices varied almost directly with the relative humidity, males living up to 8 days and females up to 34 days (Russell and Rao, 1942c); the length of life of this species in the wild, as judged by recapture of marked specimens, became reduced as the temperature rose above 15°C (Afridi *et al.*, 1940).

When exposed to high temperature an insect may be killed by the high temperature itself or by desiccation consequent on evaporation (Mellanby, 1932). Lewis (1933) considers that mosquitoes do not possess an efficient mechanism for preventing water loss and depend for survival upon meals of blood and nectar. This is probably true at high temperatures at least, for when adults of *Culex pipiens fatigans* were exposed to different relative humidities for 1 hr at 34°C water loss increased with decreasing R.H., the males losing proportionately more than the females (Karamchandani, 1935). Evaporation probably occurs mainly through the spiracles since water loss is greatly increased when adults of *Anopheles maculipennis messeae* in dry air are made to keep their spiracles open by carbon dioxide

(Vinogradskaya, 1953). The spiracles of *Aedes aegypti* show cycles of opening and closing, being closed most of the time in inactive mosquitoes (Galun, 1960). Vinogradskaya (1950) has claimed that the thoracic spiracles of *Anopheles* do not close efficiently but the detailed study of Hassan (1944) on *Anopheles maculipennis* showed that both thoracic and abdominal spiracles have efficient closing mechanisms. Vinogradskaya (1941, 1945, 1948, 1953) has claimed that the spiracles are smaller relative to body size in xerophilous species such as *Anopheles superpictus* and *Anopheles pulcherrimus* than in hygrophilous species such as *Anopheles algeriensis* and *Anopheles claviger*, and also that the spiracles are relatively bigger in the spring than in the summer generation of *Aedes caspius* and *Aedes vexans*. The longevity of *Anopheles subpictus* at low humidities was greater in individuals fed blood or sugar solution (Vinogradskaya, 1945) and it is clear that females of many species can survive for several weeks under adverse conditions when blood meals or sugar water are continuously available. Hibernating females survive for several months, much of the time being spent at low temperatures and fairly high humidities.

Mosquitoes show a distinct heat production and at 5°–25°C the temperature of resting females of *Anopheles maculipennis messeae*, measured by inserting a thermocouple into the body, exceeded that of the air by 0·2°C when the saturation deficit was 8–10 mm Hg and by 0·8°C when the saturation deficit was 0–2 mm Hg. At air temperatures over 25°C the body temperature of the mosquitoes was lower than that of the air and under conditions of high evaporation the difference was 2°–3°C (Vinogradskaya, 1942). Since mosquitoes cannot tolerate a high rate of water loss it is unlikely that cooling by evaporation affects survival at high temperatures.

The survival of mosquitoes under laboratory conditions is no guide to their longevity in nature but it has shown that temperature and humidity can be extremely important. Females live longer than males but males of *Aedes polynesiensis* (Ingram, 1954) and *Aedes aegypti* (Liles and DeLong, 1960) can be kept for 2 months or more so there is no reason to suppose that the life of males in nature is necessarily short. Life is naturally prolonged by feeding but females which are allowed to reproduce live less long than females fed only sugar solution (Putman and Shannon, 1934). Females of *Aedes aegypti* which fed on blood frequently but which laid few eggs because they had not mated survived rather less well than mated females which oviposited normally (Lavoipierre, 1958a), but survival was not affected by forced egg retention in *Culex pusillus* which had fed on blood only once (Shalaby, 1959). Because the mortality rate rose with increased frequency of blood feeding in mated females of *Aedes aegypti*, which laid their eggs and so passed through repeated gonotrophic cycles, but not in virgin females which retained their eggs and so developed few or no eggs after the first batch, Lavoipierre (1961) considered that mortality was related to ovary development. From analysis of their own data and those of other workers, Kershaw, Chalmers and Lavoipierre (1954) concluded that the rate of mortality of male and female mosquitoes in laboratory colonies increases with age in such a manner that its logarithm is proportional to age.

Longevity of Adults in Nature

In recent years a number of attempts have been made to establish the rate of mortality of mosquitoes in nature and the age composition of wild populations. Data of this sort are important for understanding the epidemiology of mosquito-borne diseases and they also demonstrate the effectiveness of large-scale applications of insecticide. After studying published accounts of mosquito survival in the laboratory and in the field Macdonald (1952a) concluded that the full life span of a female is measurable in months and that in nature few survive to die of old age, most dying of one or other hazards of wild life. Macdonald (1952a) considered that these hazards would fall more or less equally on all age groups so that theoretically the death rate should not change much with age. From this it follows that if the probability of survival through one day is p (always a number below $1 \cdot 0$), the probability of surviving through n days is p^n, and the daily mortality rate is $100(1 - p)$.

There is no practical, direct method of measuring p in nature but it is possible to estimate it indirectly if 2 characters can be found such that all individuals showing one are above a certain age and all showing the second above another age. Where mosquitoes are numerous and many are infected with *Plasmodium* the proportion containing sporozoites at the time of capture and the proportion containing sporozoites only after an interval equal to the extrinsic incubation period of the parasite provide suitable characters. The chance of survival of the mosquitoes from the time they first receive an infective feed to the time when sporozoites appear in the salivary glands is directly related to the ratio of these 2 factors, i.e.

$$\log p = \frac{\log \text{ratio}}{n}$$

where n is the period for which the second batch was held (Macdonald, 1957).

A more widely applicable method is to determine the proportion of individuals in a population showing a condition which indicates that they are of or are over a definite age; this proportion is equal to p^n where n is the age used (Macdonald, 1952b). The proportion of a population which is parous, i.e. which has laid at least one batch of eggs, can be found by inspecting the ampullae or the ovarian tracheae (p. 188), and the survival rate per day (p) calculated from the expression

$$p^n = M$$

where M is the proportion parous and n the number of days between emergence of the adult and first oviposition (Davidson, 1954).

It has been found easiest in practice to restrict dissections to those females whose ovaries are in the commonest stage found in nature; in the hotter parts of Africa this is stage III in the case of *Anopheles gambiae*. In these individuals the survival rate equals the square root of the proportion parous if the gonotrophic cycle occupies 2 days (the cube root if it occupies 3 days), i.e.

$$p = \sqrt{M}$$

(Davidson, 1954). The same formula would apply if females in another stage were selected. All of these techniques are based on the hypothesis that mortality rates are not related to age and they are only valid when emergence is regular, a condition which is largely restricted to the tropics and subtropics.

Mortality rates have been investigated in a few populations by these methods. Table 6 gives the results of applying all 3 methods to 2 populations of *Anopheles gambiae* in East Africa and it will be seen that they produce roughly similar values. van den Assem (1959) measured the

TABLE 6. THE DAILY MORTALITY RATE IN TWO POPULATIONS OF *Anopheles gambiae* CALCULATED BY DIFFERENT METHODS. (FROM DAVIDSON, 1955).

Population	$p^n = M$	$p = \sqrt{M}$	$\log p = \dfrac{\log \text{ratio}}{n}$
Tanganyika	6% ($p = 0.94$)	9% ($p = 0.91$)	7% ($p = 0.93$)
Uganda	5% ($p = 0.95$)	7% ($p = 0.93$)	3% ($p = 0.97$)

daily mortality rates of various species in Netherlands New Guinea over a period of 3 months, using the formula $p^n = M$, and found that the daily mortality of *Anopheles bancrofti* was 31 per cent, of *Anopheles farauti* 32 per cent, and of *Anopheles amictus hilli* 5 per cent. Investigations in the same country which lasted over a year showed that the daily mortality rate of *Anopheles koliensis* fluctuated between 9 per cent and 31 per cent. Short-term fluctuations were ascribed to the irregular appearance of newly-emerged females, but there were bigger fluctuations possibly associated with seasonal changes. For example, the average daily mortality in

November and December 1957 was 25 per cent, from August to November 1958, 11 per cent.

Knowledge of the age composition of natural populations of mosquitoes is of great importance for epidemiologists in studying the transmission of disease, for it is the presence of older females in any population which makes it dangerous since these will have fed several times and will be more likely to have become infected. Fortunately, the technique of ovariole examination developed by Polovodova (1949), which indicates the number of gonotrophic cycles which any female has passed through, gives a more or less direct measure of the age structure of a population (see p. 188). Natural populations of *Anopheles maculipennis* have been studied to this end in Russia since 1947 (Detinova, 1962), and it is found that they contain a relatively high proportion of females which have passed through 5 or more gonotrophic cycles (Fig. 47). The age com-

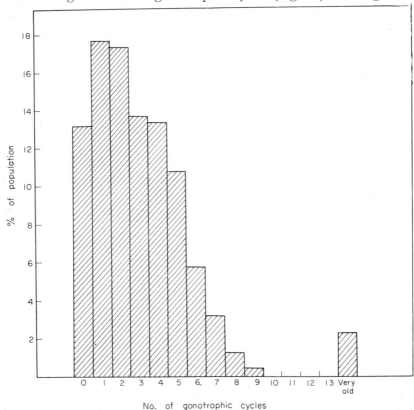

Fig. 47. The age composition of a population of *Anopheles maculipennis* near Moscow in 1952 as shown by the proportion of females which had passed through different numbers of gonotrophic cycles. (From Detinova, 1962).

position of populations was found to vary considerably at different seasons through females entering or leaving diapause, through the appearance and disappearance of different generations, and through the effects of bad weather; thus females which had passed through 4 or 5 gonotrophic cycles comprised 0·9–17·5 per cent of the females dissected in June, 2·4–32·5 per cent in July and 26–40 per cent in August. In almost all populations a few females survived to lay 9–12 batches of eggs. A disproportionately small number of nulliparous females appeared in the samples because they rested in natural shelters, whereas most of the older, parous females, which were of greater epidemiological importance, tended to rest in stables and houses. Species of *Aedes* inhabiting forests in Russia were shorter lived. Only a very small proportion of *Aedes communis* and *Aedes cinereus* passed through 4 gonotrophic cycles and their maximum length of life was 2 months. *Aedes rusticus* lived rather longer and occasionally females were found to have passed through 7 gonotrophic cycles (Shlenova, 1959).

From the age composition of several natural populations of *Anopheles maculipennis* in Russia Detinova (1962) concluded that the rate of mortality of females was independent of age up to the 4th gonotrophic cycle, but that it increased considerably thereafter. The mortality rates of *Anopheles minimus* and *Anopheles vagus* in North Vietnam remain constant through at least the 2nd to the 6th gonotrophic cycles (Zalutskaya, 1959), and in Tanganyika the recovery of marked females of *Anopheles gambiae* showed that their mortality rate remained constant through the first 23 days of adult life (Gillies, 1961). These results support Macdonald's (1952a) hypothesis that mortality rates are independent of age, at least for the first weeks of adult life, and so validate the indirect methods of determining mortality rates.

Acclimatization

Acclimatization may concern aspects of behaviour such as activity and response to stimuli, and it may also concern survival and mortality. Both aspects have been studied in mosquitoes.

When larvae of *Aedes aegypti* have been kept at a moderately low temperature for 24 hr a substantial lowering is found in chill-coma temperature (at which cold anaesthesia is produced) and a lowering is also found in the lowest temperature at which the alarm response is given (Table 7) (Mellanby, 1958). In summer in Finnish Lapland larvae of *Aedes punctor* may experience water temperatures between 5° and 34°C. These larvae always remain active when cooled to 0°C whatever their previous conditions have been. Pupae of *Aedes punctor* kept at 24°–30°C for 24 hr become immobile on transfer to 2°C but pupae kept at

10°C for 24 hr will remain active below 1°C. Adults kept for 24 hr at 10° can crawl actively at 3°C but others kept for the same period at 24°–28°C have a chill-coma temperature of 5·5°C. Similar results have been obtained with pupae and adults of *Culiseta alaskaensis* (Mellanby, 1940).

TABLE 7. EFFECT OF ACCLIMATIZATION ON THE CHILL-COMA TEMPERATURE AND ON THE LOWEST TEMPERATURE AT WHICH THE ALARM RESPONSE IS GIVEN IN LARVAE OF *Aedes aegypti*. (FROM MELLANBY, 1958).

	Acclimatization Temperature		
	10°C	17°C	34°C
Chill coma	3·4°C	5·7°C	10·8°C
Alarm response	<10·0°C	11·0°C	14·3°C

Almost all *Aedes aegypti* larvae acclimatized to 20° or 18°C survived exposure to 0·5°C for 17 hr but such treatment was always fatal to larvae acclimatized to 30°C. Little or no acclimatization took place when larvae were placed at 10°C; the larvae entered a chill coma at that temperature and few survived transfer to 0·5°C (Table 8) (Mellanby, 1960). Apparently

TABLE 8. EFFECT OF ACCLIMATIZATION ON SURVIVAL OF *Aedes aegypti* LARVAE LATER EXPOSED TO 0·5°C FOR 17 HOURS. (FROM MELLANBY, 1960).

	Acclimatization Temperature			
	30°C	20°C	18°C	10°C
Number of larvae exposed	63	122	72	108
Percent surviving	0%	93%	92%	2%

individuals which are anaesthetized by cold fail to become acclimatized.

Acclimatization to high temperature also has been shown in *Aedes aegypti*. Larvae acclimatized to 30°C had a thermal death point, for a one-hour exposure, of 42°C but when the acclimatization temperature was raised to 37°C the thermal death point rose to 44°C (Mellanby, 1954).

No acclimatization to high temperature could be found in *Anopheles minimus* in which larvae exposed to 35°C for 20 hr had the same thermal death point as larvae which had been kept at 30°C (Muirhead-Thomson, 1940c). No difference was found in the response of *Culex pipiens fatigans* which had been reared and maintained at 16°–24°C and at 30°C to various temperatures in a choice chamber (Muirhead-Thomson, 1938).

CHAPTER 7

ADULT FEEDING

Food

Nectar and to a lesser extent honeydew are important sources of energy for both males and females. Over two-thirds of the reports of flower visiting record observations on species of *Aedes*, but *Anopheles, Culex, Mansonia, Psorophora* and *Toxorhynchites* have also been found feeding on nectar (Hocking, 1953a; Haeger, 1955). Most records are from temperate climates but it seems unlikely that tropical mosquitoes would ignore sources of nectar when they were available. In certain genera, such as *Toxorhynchites,* the female mouth-parts are incapable of piercing skin and the female is restricted to a diet of nectar. Adults of *Malaya jacobsoni* hover up and down in front of bamboos and solicit food from Crematogaster ants which have been feeding at the tips of the bamboos. The mosquito alights in front of a downward-travelling ant, inserts its proboscis into the mouth of the ant, and obtains a drop of fluid (Macdonald and Traub, 1960).

The capacity of the crop or ventral diverticulum, in which most nectar is stored, has been estimated in certain Canadian species of *Aedes* from the mean volume of the contents in fed individuals and found to vary from 0·91 mm^3 in *Aedes communis* to 3·39 mm^3 in *Aedes punctor,* representing 45 per cent and 95 per cent of the basic weights respectively (Hocking, 1953a). The concentration of nectar varies greatly but in plants protected from visiting insects concentrations between 25 per cent and 50 per cent are common. Observations over several seasons showed that the peaks of flight activity of tundra and forest mosquitoes were synchronous with the peaks of nectar production in tundra and forest (Hocking, 1953a).

The most important food for the female is blood. Except in autogenous species which can develop a single batch of eggs from their reserves, the protein content of blood is essential for development of eggs; it can also serve as an energy source (Chapter 8). Blood is nearly always taken from mammals and birds but a few species feed regularly on amphibia or reptiles (Fisk, 1941; Callot, 1943; Remington, 1945; Menon and Tampi, 1959; Henderson and Senior, 1961). Some species feed exclusively on birds and others on mammals but it is probably true to say that no mosquito is absolutely specific in its host.

Weighing mosquitoes before and after blood meals has shown that they commonly ingest more than their own weight in blood. *Anopheles quadrimaculatus* has been recorded as ingesting on average 3·46 mg of blood, $1\frac{1}{2}$ times the mean unfed weight, and *Anopheles albimanus* 2·58 mg of blood, twice the mean unfed weight (Jeffery, 1956). However, a clear fluid is discharged from the anus during the course of a blood meal and shortly afterwards, leading to underestimation of blood-meal volume when measured by weight increase. *Aedes aegypti* continues to discharge droplets for 5–15 min after withdrawing the proboscis, passing a volume of approximately 1·5 mm³. The first few drops contain uric acid and the remainder contain an unknown concentration of ninhydrin-positive material; the fluid sometimes contains a few erythrocytes. When trypan blue or [144]Ce are present in ingested blood they do not appear in the clear fluid, but ^{35}S in ingested blood appears in low titre in the fluid. The fluid is thought to be derived mainly from the Malpighian tubes (Boorman, 1960). When *Aedes aegypti* females were fed blood containing radioactive cerium the cerium was not discharged with the clear fluid and so gave a true measurement of the blood ingested. This indicated a mean value of 4·2 mm³ blood ingested, which correlated well with the gravimetric determinations of 2·5 to 2·7 mm³ from weight increase and 1·5 mm³ fluid discharged (Boorman, 1960). Using ^{59}Fe de Freitas and da Silveira Guedes (1961) found that *Culex pipiens fatigans*, a much bigger mosquito, ingested on average 10·2 mm³ of blood when feeding from a chicken.

Structure of the Mouthparts and Alimentary Canal

The mouthparts of female mosquitoes are highly modified for piercing, most of the parts being extended into extremely long and slender stylets (Fig. 48). The anatomy of these organs has been described in detail by Vogel (1921) and Robinson (1939).

The labium, which is the least modified of the mouthparts, is a relatively stout organ containing a dorsal channel, the labial gutter, in which the stylets lie closely apposed to one another forming a bundle or fascicle (Fig. 48d). It also contains a large internal cavity, continuous with the haemocoele, in which run muscle fibres, tracheae and nerves. The labium ends in a pair of lobes, the labella, which are thought to represent the labial palps of other insects and which bear tactile and chemosensory hairs (p. 213).

The labrum is a broad, pointed stylet which lies dorsal to the other stylets in the labial gutter. It is curved so that its edges meet and enclose a channel, the food canal, up which all food is conveyed to the mouth at the top of the labrum. Muscles inserted on the base of the labrum (Fig. 49c) serve to raise and lower that appendage and possibly control

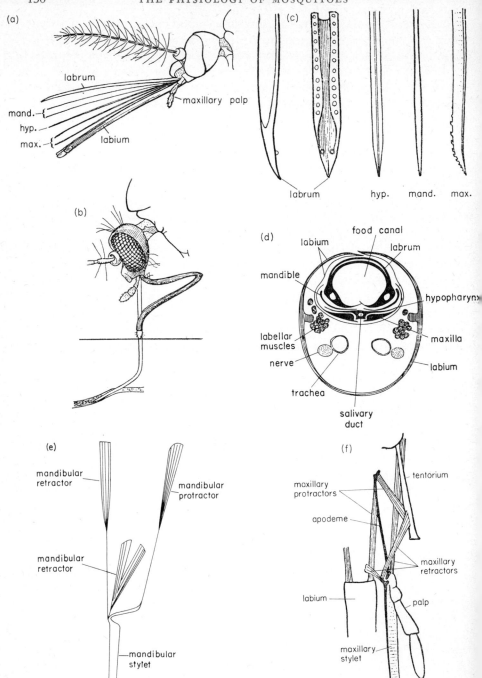

(a)

labrum

mand. {
hyp.
max. {

maxillary palp

labium

(c)

labrum   hyp.   mand.   max.

(b)

(d)

labium   food canal
                labrum
mandible

                hypopharynx

labellar   maxilla
muscles
nerve   labium

trachea

salivary
duct

(e)

mandibular
retractor
                mandibular
                protractor

mandibular
retractor

                mandibular
                stylet

(f)

maxillary   tentorium
protractors

apodeme

                maxillary
                retractors

labium   palp

maxillary
stylet

the entrance to the mouth, but the labrum cannot be protracted or re-tracted. Near the tip of the labrum are 2 or more small sensory pegs, the only sense organs on the stylets, to which nerves run through cavities in the labral wall.

The hypopharynx is a very slender stylet with a median rib containing a salivary duct which opens at or near the tip. Towards the base of the proboscis the edges of the labrum fail to meet and here the hypopharynx forms the floor of the food canal. Further back the edges of the labrum and hypopharynx fuse forming the mouth which is the entrance to the pharynx. The only muscles associated with the hypopharynx are the dilators of the salivary pump at its base (Fig. 49c).

The mandibles are extremely slender. In *Anopheles maculipennis* the distal ends are flattened and slightly expanded and bear 30–50 very fine teeth; in *Aedes aegypti* the tips come to a simple point without teeth. Most authors have described only 1 muscle, a retractor, associated with each mandible, assuming that the mandibles are protracted by the elasticity of the cuticular structures at their base, but Wenk (1961) has described 2 additional muscles. The base of the mandibular stylet tapers and bends through a right angle to form a small rod which runs vertically, articulating near its tip with an extension of the cranial wall. A protractor muscle which arises on the postgena is inserted on the end of this rod (Fig. 48e). In *Anopheles maculipennis* 2 retractor muscles are inserted on the base of the mandibular stylet, 1 arising as 2 bundles of fibres on the tentorium, the other arising on the postgena. Only the former is present in *Culiseta annulata, Culex pipiens* and *Aedes aegypti*. The mandibles cannot be seen to function actively while the stylets penetrate the skin (Gordon and Lumsden, 1939) but it has been suggested that their tips act as a cap to the entrance to the labral food canal, protecting it during penetration of the skin and being withdrawn by the retractor muscles before sucking starts (Robinson, 1939). Now that the mandibles are known to have protractor muscles a reinvestigation of their function would be of great interest.

The maxillae are the principal piercing organs. Each consists of a long, flattened stylet, thought to be the lacinia, the tip of which is curved

FIG. 48a–f. Head and mouthparts of the female mosquito.
(a) Head and mouthparts of *Aedes aegypti* with the stylets removed from the labial sheath; (b) disposition of the head and mouthparts of *Aedes aegypti* during feeding, with the fascicle inserted in a capillary; (c) distal parts of the stylets of *Aedes aegypti;* (d) T.S. of the proboscis of *Anopheles maculipennis;* (e) lateral aspect of a mandible of *Anopheles maculipennis* with musculature; (f) basal parts of the left maxilla of *Aedes aegypti* with musculature. (a–d and f from Snodgrass (1944) who modified b from Gordon and Lumsden (1939) and d from Vogel (1921); e from Wenk (1961)).

and bears backward-pointing teeth, a palp, and an apodeme-like rod within the head which is thought to comprise the cardo and stipes (Fig. 48f) (Schiemenz, 1957). Two protractor muscles are inserted on the cardo, and the base of the stylets bears the insertions of retractor, abductor and adductor muscles. The maxillary palps, which are long in female Anophelinae but short in all other female mosquitoes, bear sensilla of uncertain function.

The mouthparts of the male are not used for piercing and differ from those of the female in the development of the maxillary palps, the reduction of the mandibles and maxillae, the mandibles being absent in some species (Marshall and Staley, 1935), and in the fusion of the hypopharynx with the labium. The labrum bears sensilla resembling those in the female.

The anterior region of the alimentary canal contains the two powerful pumps which constitute the sucking apparatus of the mosquito (Fig. 49c). The cibarial pump lies under the clypeus, its thick, trough-shaped lower wall continuous with the upper surface of the hypopharynx and its thinner upper wall continuous with the inner surface of the labrum. The labral food canal thus expands into the lumen of the pump. At rest the upper wall is pressed into the pump through its own elasticity and dilatation of the pump is produced by the large dilator muscles which have their origins on the clypeus and their insertions on the upper wall. Sense organs project into the lumen at the anterior end (p. 215) while the posterior edge bears further sensilla and in females of some species a spiny armature. For a short distance behind the cibarial pump the cuticle is thin and probably forms a valve, which may be called the anterior pharyngeal valve, closed through the elasticity of the cuticle and opened by the valvular muscle (Fig. 50) (Thompson, 1905).

The pharyngeal pump is narrow anteriorly but expands considerably behind the brain. It is formed by a dorsal and 2 ventro-lateral plates hinged to each other along their margins (Fig. 49d). Dilator muscles can expand the lumen of the pump until it has a nearly circular section, and the plates can spring inwards through their elasticity until they almost obliterate the lumen of the canal. A sphincter has been described at the beginning of the oesophagus (Nuttall and Shipley, 1903; Thompson, 1905; Christophers, 1960) but according to Schiemenz (1957) this is only the normal circular muscle of the oesophagus and the pharyngeal pump is closed posteriorly by the apposition of the ends of the three plates which are drawn together when the dilators contract, forming what may be called the posterior pharyngeal valve (Fig. 50). The efficiency of the valve system of the foregut is shown by the distension of the stomach at emergence with swallowed air.

The oesophagus which forms the remainder of the foregut is a narrow tube ending in a simple oesophageal invagination containing the cardiac sphincter. The oesophageal epithelium is composed of cubical cells lined with cuticle and surrounded by a muscle coat. Just in front of the oesophageal invagination arise 2 small dorsal diverticula, which lie

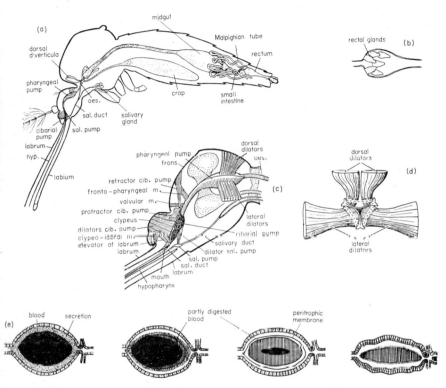

FIG. 49a–e. The alimentary canal of the mosquito.

(a) Outline of the body of a female *Aedes aegypti* showing the alimentary canal and salivary glands, the left salivary gland displaced ventrally; (b) outline of the rectum of a female *Aedes aegypti* showing rectal papillae; (c) L.S. through the head of a female mosquito, to left of median plane (from Snodgrass, 1944); (d) T.S. through pharyngeal pump of *Culiseta annulata,* the dotted lines show the open position (from Schiemenz, 1957); (e) formation of peritrophic membrane and digestion of blood in *Aedes aegypti* (diagrammatic) (from Stohler, 1957).

between the flight muscles, and a large ventral diverticulum or crop which lies in the abdomen, being joined to the oesophagus by a long duct (Fig. 49a). In *Aedes aegypti* the neck of this duct contains a group of spines (Day, 1954). The walls of the diverticula are highly elastic and consist of a thin epithelium lined with cuticle. Circular muscle fibres circumscribe the diverticula and cause peristalsis of these organs, and in the neck regions they act as sphincters although they are not concentrated into bands. The walls of the diverticula are extremely impervious to water for when a crop containing water was isolated and allowed to dry it still contained water after 2 months (Nuttall and Shipley, 1903). The oesophagus is capable of vigorous, rhythmical contractions which presumably assist the transfer of food from the diverticula to the midgut.

The anterior region of the midgut is a narrow tube but the posterior region, or stomach, is wider and capable of great distension. According to de Boissezon (1930a) the different regions of the midgut are composed of distinct types of cell but no other workers have described this. The epithelial cells vary in shape from columnar to flattened, depending upon the degree of distension of the midgut, and their luminal surface is in the form of a striated border. According to Stohler (1957) small regeneration cells lie between the bases of the epithelial cells throughout the midgut in females of *Aedes aegypti*. A fine basement membrane surrounds the midgut epithelium and over this lies a delicate network of circular and longitudinal muscle fibres. The stomach is richly supplied with tracheae and connective tissue fibres extend over its outer surface. Shortly after a female has taken a blood meal a layer of secretory material appears in the stomach separating the blood from the epithelium; no such secretion follows feeding on nectar. In the first hours after blood feeding the secretion develops as a thick viscous layer but it later becomes thinner and solidifies as a hard, inelastic skin, detached from both epithelium and blood meal (Fig. 49e). Eventually, when digestion of the blood is advanced, a resoftening of the material takes place. The secretion has been shown to contain chitin and it has been interpreted as a peritrophic membrane (Yaguzhinskaya, 1940; Pal, 1943b; Waterhouse, 1953; Stohler, 1957). If a second blood meal is taken before the first is digested, the second meal surrounds the first and distinct membranes can be seen around both (Waterhouse, 1953).

The posterior end of the stomach is strongly constricted and is surrounded by a sphincter. The Malpighian tubes open just behind this so that they empty into the pyloric chamber of the hindgut. The pyloric chamber is a short, funnel-shaped region, its epithelium lined with cuticle bearing numerous backward-pointing spines and bounded posteriorly by fibres of circular muscles. The remainder of the hindgut consists of the muscular small intestine (or ileum), the rectum (or colon) and the anal canal. The rectum is characterized by its thin epithelium and by the rectal papillae which project from its dorsal wall, 4 in males and 6 in females (Fig. 49b). The histology of the adult alimentary canal is described in detail by Nuttall and Shipley (1903), Thompson (1905) and Christophers (1960).

The fine structure of the stomach cells has been described by Bertram and Bird (1961) from females of *Aedes aegypti* and *Aedes togoi*, blood fed, sugar fed, or denied food and water (Plates I–VI). Each cell is bounded on all surfaces by a cell membrane which appears in section as 2 electron-dense layers separated by a translucent layer. Where 2 cells abut the membranes are separated by an intracellular matrix, and at the inner and outer limits of adjoining cells the pair of membranes bifurcates to form, respectively, the luminal and basal cell membranes (Plate II, Figs. 2, 3). The striated border is composed of microvilli, subcylindrical extensions of cytoplasm bounded by cell membrane, about 10 μ long and 0·1 μ in diameter. The basal cell membrane appears to invaginate into the cell to form an elaborate system of double-walled septa which tend to confine the basal mitochondria in incomplete compartments. Separated from the basal cell membrane by a space is the basement membrane, a dense layer about 300 Å thick which extends over the midgut epithelium (Plate II, Fig. 3). It has a laminar or fascicular structure which is also found in the tunica propria of the ovarian follicles and which is thought to be connected with the elasticity characteristic of both structures.

The visible groundwork of the cytoplasm is a fine granular matter taken to be ribonucleoprotein dispersed in a less dense matrix. The nucleus is bounded by a nuclear envelope composed of two closely-apposed membranes. Short dark zones on the nuclear envelope are thought to be nuclear pores (Plate VI, Fig. 18). The nucleoplasm is a diffuse granular material irregularly clumped into patches of varying density. The nucleolus is a large, electron-dense body lying centrally and forming about one-third of the nucleus; similar dense aggregations lie against the inner surface of the nuclear envelope. Mitochondria are more concentrated towards the luminal and basal surfaces of the cell but they occur throughout the cell. Cristae are visible in the mitochondria at higher magnifications. Golgi apparatus is frequently found around the nucleus and consists of dark-walled tubes associated with vesicles and dense cytoplasm. The wall of the vesicles appears to be membrane without ribonucleoprotein particles on the cytoplasmic surface. Each Golgi apparatus has approximately the diameter of a mitochondrion. Vesicles are found in the cytoplasm which range from 0·25 to 4·0 μ in diameter and which are bounded by membrane without ribonucleoprotein granules on its outer surface. The vesicles may be empty or may contain granules or other material (Plate III, Fig. 6).

In the vicinity of the nucleus are spherical or ovoid whorls of granular endoplasmic reticulum, many small particles of ribonucleoprotein occur-

K

ring on the cytoplasmic surface of their fine membranous walls. Granular endoplasmic reticulum is also found as isolated or grouped lengths scattered sparsely in the cytoplasm. The whorls are not isolated from the cytoplasmic matrix by membranes. Each whorl is a compact, coiled formation of leaflets, each leaflet consisting of particle-coated membrane bounding a space or cisterna (Plates III, VI, Figs. 6, 9, 18). There is obvious communication between whorls where they are contiguous. Bertram and Bird (1961) consider that the whorls are probably the conspicuous assemblies of a continuous canalicular system which between the whorls takes the form of vesicles or subcylindrical tubes; it is possibly continuous with the Golgi apparatus and with the large vesicles.

In females which have not recently taken a blood meal the midgut cells are up to 60 μ deep and no more than 10 μ wide. All are of the same structure. A blood meal flattens the cells so that the intercellular boundaries buckle and the luminal and basal surfaces are stretched while the mitochondria become more evenly dispersed between the luminal and basal surfaces. During the 24 hr following a blood meal the compact whorls of endoplasmic reticulum unfold and ramify widely throughout the cytoplasm of the cell (Plate IV, Figs. 10–12). This involves both a separation and an unrolling of the leaflets. This is a reversible process and the whorls are reformed 48 hr after feeding when digestion is finished and no visible blood remains in the gut. Whorl dispersion is not stimulated by sugar feeding. Bertram and Bird (1961) concluded that the unfolding of the whorls was probably related to the segregation of proteolytic enzymes from the cell contents and their conduction to the luminal surface, and that it was possibly also related to absorption of the products of digestion. Vacuoles bounded by membrane are present in the basal region 24 hr after a blood meal.

Within half an hour of gorging, copious fine particulate material which is to form the peritrophic membrane appears between the microvilli, extending from their bases to beyond their tips. This is at a time when unfolding of the whorls of endoplasmic reticulum has only just begun. After 2 hr particulate material is still visible between the microvilli and it also forms a layer between the microvilli and the blood with the nature of an amorphous matrix. The material is apparently secreted by the microvilli because striking protuberances appear on their surfaces at this time, particularly distally (Plate V, Fig. 17). Secretion appears to cease about the 15th hr and by this time, when digestion of the blood is well advanced, the secretion forms a more discrete layer around the blood meal, the layer consisting of condensed granular material loosely layered (Plate V, Fig. 15). No pores are seen in the peritrophic membrane. Stohler (1957) examined the fine structure of peritrophic membranes from *Aedes aegypti* which he had washed, exposed to protease and finally shadowed with gold. He observed a distinct fibrillar structure with an irregular arrangement of micelles.

Feeding Mechanism

From knowledge of the structure of the female mouthparts and their musculature and from observations on the activity of the fascicle of *Aedes aegypti* during feeding it is possible to give a fairly detailed description of the mechanism of piercing and sucking, although one that is still to some extent hypothetical. On landing on the skin of the host the mosquito searches for a suitable spot for piercing, apparently testing the skin with the sense organs of the labella. The initial puncture is thought to be made by a thrust of the body from the legs, the thrust being transmitted via the cervical sclerites and head to the fascicle which lies in the labial gutter (Robinson, 1939).

Further penetration of the fascicle is produced by the action of the maxillae; the cutting movements of the laciniae are visible within the skin although they are too rapid for the sequence of movements to be followed. However, from the structure of the mouthparts and from the alternate vibrations of the maxillary palps Robinson (1939) has deduced that penetration is effected in the following manner:

(1) The left maxillary protractors contract thrusting the left lacinia deeper into the skin, beyond the other stylets.

(2) The left maxillary protractors relax.

(3) The left maxillary retractor contracts simultaneously with the right maxillary protractors. Since the left lacinia is secured in the skin by its teeth its retractor draws the cranium towards the host's skin, causing all the other stylets to penetrate deeper into the wound. At the same time the right lacinia penetrates more deeply still by protraction.

(4) The left maxillary retractor and the right maxillary protractors relax.

(5) The cycle of movements starts again with the simultaneous contraction of the left maxillary protractors and the right maxillary retractor.

As the fascicle penetrates the skin the labium kinks and steadily bends backwards allowing the head to be drawn towards the skin with a minimum of resistance (Fig. 48b). The labrum is robust enough to pass through the skin without buckling but Robinson (1939) considers that the finer stylets, which by themselves could probably not be forced into the skin, are held to the labrum and to each other by the surface tension of the fluid which bathes them.

Detailed descriptions of the movements of the fascicle within the skin have been given by Gordon and Lumsden (1939), who used a microscope to follow the course of the stylets when *Aedes aegypti* fed on the web of a frog's foot, and by Griffiths and Gordon (1952) who observed *Aedes aegypti* feeding on the ear of a mouse. After entering the skin the fascicle bends at almost a right angle (Fig. 48b) and then probes the tissue with great activity over the whole area that can be reached. The shaft of the fascicle shows no lateral movement, only a passive flexibility which allows it to pass through the existing tunnel, but the tip of the fascicle bends in many directions almost as though it were moving in a liquid rather than a solid medium. The changes of direction taken by the tip of the fascicle are said to be controlled by the muscles at the base of the stylets (Gordon and Lumsden, 1939) but no mechanism has been suggested to account for the bending of the tip of the fascicle while the shaft retains its position, although it is known that the labrum can be thrown into a sigmoid shape by its musculature when separated from the other mouthparts (Robinson, 1939). Rapid protractions of the laciniae can be seen within the skin but the mandibles are not visible at any time, possibly because they are concealed between the maxillae and the labrum.

As the fascicle penetrates and probes the tissue saliva is frequently discharged from its tip, appearing as a series of puffs of clear fluid which rapidly disperse. The random probing of the fascicle sooner or later causes it to penetrate a capillary and when this happens it normally bends and passes up the lumen of the capillary, sometimes for as much as a quarter of its length. As feeding starts the rate of blood flow in the capillary becomes greatly accelerated. Occasionally the fascicle penetrates a capillary and is withdrawn producing a small haemorrhage. The insect usually detects the pool of blood and immediately starts sucking, drawing up the blood as fast as it flows into the tissue. These 2 methods of feeding have been called capillary feeding and pool feeding. Whereas capillary feeding by *Aedes aegypti* is normally completed in 3 min, pool feeding may take as long as 10 min (Gordon and Lumsden, 1939; Griffiths and Gordon, 1952). O'Rourke (1956) obtained a bimodal distribution when recording times required for *Aedes aegypti* to gorge on man and concluded that the shorter time, occurring in 40 per cent of cases, represented capillary feeding and the longer time pool feeding.

It seems reasonable to suppose that sucking starts on penetration of the skin or when the labral sensilla are stimulated by blood. Schiemenz (1957) has deduced the following sequence of actions during sucking from anatomical studies on *Culiseta annulata* and from observations on feeding mosquitoes:

ADULT FEEDING 139

(1) The mandibular retractor muscles contract exposing the entrance to the labral food canal, and the elevators of the labrum contract opening the mouth. Simultaneously, the dilators of the cibarial pump contract and blood is drawn up into its lumen; because the anterior pharyngeal valve is closed no fluid can be drawn forward from the pharynx (Fig. 50a).

(2) The elevators of the labrum and the dilators of the cibarial pump relax, closing the mouth and contracting the lumen of the cibarial pump. At the same time the anterior pharyngeal valve opens and the dilators of the pharyngeal pump contract. Blood passes into the pharyngeal pump through suction and through pressure applied by the cibarial pump. The posterior pharyngeal valve is closed at this time (Fig. 50b).

(3) The anterior pharyngeal valve closes, the posterior pharyngeal valve opens and the dilators of the pharyngeal pump relax so that the blood is forced back through the oesophagus into the midgut (Fig. 50c). The cycle of movements then starts again.

Withdrawal of the fascicle from the skin of the host is believed to proceed as follows. Pressure exerted by the legs produces a continuous pulling force on the head and proboscis. The laciniae are retracted in turn by the maxillary retractors so that their tips lie behind those of the other stylets. The maxillary retractors relax and the other stylets are pulled up level with the laciniae through the pulling force exerted by the legs. By a succession of such movements the fascicle is rapidly drawn out of the wound, the teeth of the laciniae being kept close to the fascicle and as far as possible from the surrounding tissue (Robinson, 1939).

A mosquito which feeds on a drop of sugar solution simply dips the tip of the labella into the liquid and feeds without unsheathing the fascicle. Experimental unsheathing of the fascicle has shown that the sucking response is initiated only when the fascicle is in contact with the liquid, whether or not the labella are immersed (Hosoi, 1954). Like certain other blood-sucking Diptera, mosquitoes store nectar and blood in different parts of the alimentary canal. Nectar and other sugary fluids are dispatched to the oesophageal diverticula, mainly to the ventral diverticulum, and seldom is more than a trace found in the stomach, whereas blood is passed predominantly to the stomach although in some species it may be found in the diverticula also, usually only in small amounts (Bishop and Gilchrist, 1946; Trembley, 1952; Day, 1954; Hosoi, 1954c). This separation of nectar and blood permits females to store a meal of nectar in the diverticula, passing it slowly to the midgut for absorption, while leaving the stomach empty to receive a blood meal at any time.

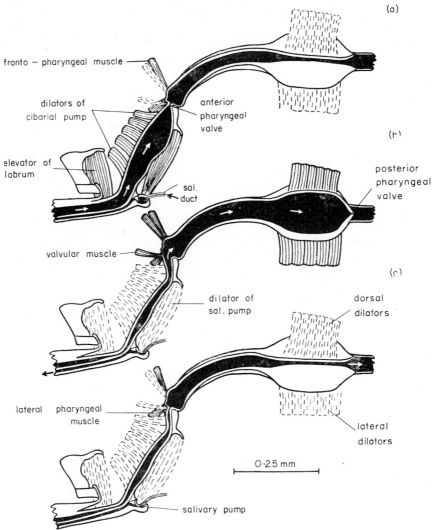

FIG. 50. The probable movements of the cibarial and pharyngeal pumps during feeding in *Culiseta annulata*. Movements of the salivary pump are also shown but there is no suggestion that they occur in phase with those of the sucking pumps. (From Schiemenz, 1957).

Sensory Aspects of Feeding

The sense organs involved in feeding include the sensory pegs at the tip of the labrum, the chemosensory hairs on the labella and the hairs, pegs and placoid sensilla within the cibarial pump. Their structure is described in Chapter 10.

Hosoi (1954c) investigated the sensitivity of the sensilla on the labrum and labella in females of *Culex pipiens* var. *pallens* by unsheathing the fascicle and measuring the amount of fluid ingested when various combinations of stimulants—distilled water, 5 per cent glucose, and erythrocytes suspended in saline—were simultaneously presented to the labella and fascicle. In females which ingested any fluid at all the cibarial sensilla must also have been stimulated by that fluid. Application of glucose to the fascicle and of distilled water to the labella led to no greater ingestion of fluid than did application of distilled water to both (Table 9). Moderate

TABLE 9. THE INGESTION OF FLUID BY FEMALES OF *Culex pipiens* VAR. *pallens* ON SIMULTANEOUS STIMULA-TION OF THE UNSHEATHED FASCICLE AND THE LABELLA BY COMBINATIONS OF DISTILLED WATER, 5% GLUCOSE, AND RABBIT ERYTHROCYTES IN SALINE. (FROM HOSOI, 1954c).

Fluid applied to labella	Fluid applied to fascicle	Relative amount ingested
Distilled water	Distilled water	0 to ±
Distilled water	Glucose	0 to ±
Glucose	Distilled water	+ to ++
Glucose	Glucose	+++
None	Erythrocytes	+++
Erythrocytes	Glucose	0 to ±
Erythrocytes	Erythrocytes	| | |

ingestion occurred when the labellar receptors were immersed in glucose and the fascicle in distilled water and full ingestion was obtained when both were immersed in glucose. These results suggest that the labellar receptors are sensitive to glucose and the labral receptors insensitive. The greater ingestion of fluid when glucose was presented to both labella and labrum suggests that the pharyngeal sensilla were being stimulated and that this was necessary for the full feeding response. These results must be interpreted with caution since application of distilled water to the labellar chemoreceptors of the blowfly leads to loss of electrical activity in the receptors (Hodgson and Roeder, 1956). The lowest concentration of glucose on which females of *Culex pipiens* would gorge when able to feed normally was 0·12M, and the threshold for sucrose and maltose was approximately 0·06M (Hosoi, 1959).

Stimulation of the labrum alone with erythrocytes led to gorging whereas presentation of erythrocytes to the labella and glucose to the labrum produced a negligible response (Table 9). The properties of the labral sensilla cannot at present be separated from those of the cibarial sensilla but it is clear that one group or both are sensitive to blood, whereas the labellar sensilla do not mediate a drinking response when stimulated with blood. The importance of the cibarial sensilla was shown by individuals which would ingest blood and other fluids after being deprived of all but the proximal quarter of the proboscis (Hosoi, 1954c).

Blood and suspensions of erythrocytes are dispatched to the stomach when they are presented to the unsheathed fascicle of *Culex pipiens* var. *pallens* but they are sent to the diverticula if the labella are simultaneously strongly stimulated with sugar (Hosoi, 1959). When *Aedes aegypti* and *Culex pipiens* var. *pallens* were fed mixtures of blood and sugar the mixture was sent to the stomach or to the diverticula or to both in the same individual, the result depending on the relative concentrations of blood and sugar (Day, 1954; Hosoi, 1959). In *Culex pipiens* var. *pallens*, at least, the mixture was only rarely shared equally between crop and stomach and it appeared that the mosquito could detect relatively slight changes of concentration and tended to disregard the minor stimulus, indicating an integration of sensory input in the central nervous system (Hosoi, 1959).

Females of *Aedes aegypti* will readily feed through a membrane on a suspension of erythrocytes in saline but they will seldom ingest plasma offered in this or any other manner, indicating that the factor in blood which stimulates gorging is contained in the erythrocytes (Bishop and Gilchrist, 1946; Hosoi, 1959). Females will also feed on a solution of lysed erythrocytes from which the stroma has been removed (Bishop and Gilchrist, 1946) and on a suspension of red cell ghosts (Day, 1954). *Culex pipiens* var. *pallens* also feeds on whole or fractionated erythrocytes, particularly when the osmotic pressure is equal to that of 0·15M-NaCl (Hosoi, 1959). Hosoi (1959) fractionated ox erythrocytes and obtained a compound which was extremely active in stimulating gorging in *Culex pipiens* var. *pallens* when added to 0·15 M-NaCl and forcibly presented to the mouthparts. This was identified as adenosine-5′-phosphate. Adenosine-5′-diphosphate and adenosine-5′-triphosphate were also active and a number of other nucleotides showed some potency (Table 10). Consideration of the structure of the active nucleotides showed that the adenine moiety was of great importance; replacing the ribose moiety with deoxyribose or the sulphate with phosphate affected the stimulating property slightly, and migration of the phosphate from the 5′ to the 2′ or 3′ position almost eliminated it.

Hosoi (1959) has calculated that if a 50-fold dilution of ox erythrocytes

TABLE 10. THE PERCENTAGE OF FEMALES OF *Culex pipiens* VAR. *pallens* WHICH FED WHEN VARIOUS NUCLEOTIDES IN 0·15 M-NaCl AT pH 7 WERE PRESENTED TO THE PROBOSCIS. (FROM HOSOI, 1959).

Compound	10^{-3}M			10^{-4}M		
	Number exposed	% gorged	% partially fed	Number exposed	% gorged	% partially fed
Adenosine-5'-phosphate	50	52	10	475	49	15
Adenosine-5'-diphosphate	–	–	–	50	50	12
Adenosine-5'-triphosphate	–	–	–	50	36	12
Adenosine-2' (or 3')-phosphate	45	7	11	45	2	7
Adenine deoxyribose-5'-phosphate	20	60	15	40	10	22
Adenosine-5'-sulphate	25	24	4	25	12	4
Guanosine-5'-phosphate	20	0	15	20	0	5
Adenosine	39	5	13	39	5	2

represents the threshold for gorging, and if ox erythrocytes contain the same amount of adenine nucleotides as human erythrocytes, i.e. $1 \cdot 5 \times 10^{-3}$ mole/l., then the mosquitoes must be sensitive to $0 \cdot 3 \times 10^{-4}$ M. When the mouthparts of females were forcibly placed in 10^{-4}M-adenosine-5'-phosphate, 49 per cent gorged. This fell to 16 per cent at 10^{-5}M and to 6 per cent at 10^{-6}M. It was concluded that the concentration of adenine nucleotides in blood could account for gorging provided that all the adenine nucleotides present in the erythrocytes were available for stimulation as effectively as adenosine-5'-phosphate in solution. These results were obtained with forcible feeding; it is not certain that nucleotides are the stimulating agent in normal feeding.

It may be concluded that chemoreceptors on the labella, on the tip of the labrum and within the cibarial pump mediate the responses of mosquitoes to blood and sugar solutions, influencing acceptance or rejection of the fluid and its destination in the alimentary canal.

The Salivary Glands and their Secretions

A pair of salivary glands lies in the front of the thorax. In both males and females each gland is composed of 3 lobes or acini, 2 lateral and 1 median, each consisting of a single layer of cells disposed around a central duct. In the female all 3 lobes are clearly demarcated into anterior and posterior regions which differ in cell structure, but the anterior region of the median lobe is relatively small and composed of small cells not found in the lateral lobes (Fig. 51). Orr, Hudson and West (1961) called the

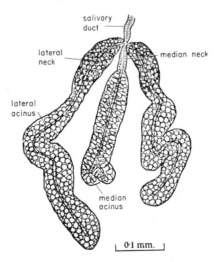

FIG. 51.   Salivary gland of an adult female *Aedes aegypti*. (From Christophers, 1960).

anterior regions 'necks' and the posterior regions 'acini', terms which are useful labels rather than accurate descriptions but which will be used here. A duct runs the length of each lobe. These ducts fuse with one another as they emerge from the lobes and a salivary duct runs forward on each side of the insect to fuse with its fellow in the neck or head, the common duct entering the salivary pump at the base of the hypopharynx (Fig. 49b). The salivary glands are smaller in males than in females and in males the lobes are not clearly divided into anterior and posterior regions although there is a difference in cell structure in the 2 regions (Shishliaeva-Matova, 1942; Bhatia *et al.,* 1957; Christophers, 1960; Orr *et al.,* 1961).

Three distinct secretory regions are present in each gland, the median acinus, the lateral acini and the lateral necks. In these regions each cell is largely filled with secretion while its nucleus is displaced to one corner and its cytoplasm distributed as a scarcely-perceptible rim at the margin (Shishliaeva-Matova, 1942). From histochemical tests on the salivary glands of *Aedes aegypti* females Orr, Hudson and West (1961) concluded that the central acinus secretes a conjugated mucopolysaccharide, the lateral acini a carbohydrate-protein complex as well as a protein, and the lateral necks a neutral mucin and a protein. No change in appearance of salivary gland cells is visible immediately after a female of *Aedes aegypti* has taken a blood meal but 24 hr later the nucleoli of the central and lateral acini become greatly enlarged and there is an increase in RNA around the nuclei, probably related to resynthesis of secretory products (Orr, Hudson and West, 1961).

The salivary secretions of mosquitoes may cause agglutination of erythrocytes, may inhibit coagulation of blood, and may cause the typical reaction of the skin to a mosquito bite. Digestive enzymes are not found in the salivary glands (Metcalf, 1945). Marked agglutination or clumping of erythrocytes occurs 10–15 sec after blood is added to a crushed salivary gland from a female *Anopheles quadrimaculatus.* Division of the salivary gland shows that agglutinin is produced only by the median lobe. Agglutination has been obtained with blood of 10 species of mammals but not with blood of chick or turtle. The agglutinin gives a strong though delayed reaction after dilution to 10^{-5} and is destroyed on heating the mosquito at 50–55°C for 5–10 min (Metcalf, 1945). Agglutinins effective with the blood of certain mammals and the canary have been demonstrated in the salivary glands of several species of *Anopheles* including species of the *Anopheles maculipennis* complex but they are absent from *Anopheles claviger* and *Anopheles plumbeus* (Shute, 1935). Negative results were obtained in tests for agglutinins on 11 culicine species in the genera *Aedes, Culex, Culiseta, Mansonia* and *Psorophora* (Yorke and Macfie, 1924; Shute, 1935; Metcalf, 1945) but de Buck (1937) claimed to have found a very weak agglutinin in both median and lateral lobes of the salivary glands of *Culiseta annulata.*

Extracts of both median and lateral lobes of the salivary glands of *Anopheles quadrimaculatus* females inhibit coagulation of human blood but those of the median lobe are the more active. The anticoagulin can function at a dilution of 10^{-4} and is not affected by heating the mosquito to 55°C for 15 min (Metcalf, 1945). Anticoagulins have also been demonstrated in *Anopheles maculipennis, Anopheles crucians, Anopheles punctipennis* and *Anopheles subpictus* but they could not be demonstrated in *Anopheles claviger* or in 6 species of the genera *Aedes, Culex* and *Psorophora* (Cornwall and Patton, 1914; Yorke and Macfie, 1924; de Buck, 1937; Metcalf, 1945). de Buck (1937) differed from other workers in finding a very weak anticoagulin in salivary glands of *Culex pipiens* and *Culiseta annulata.* The salivary glands of male mosquitoes contain neither agglutinins nor anticoagulins (Metcalf, 1945).

The functions of the agglutinins and anticoagulins are not clear and many species feed successfully without either. The occasional presence of sporozoites in the stomach of *Anopheles* (Yorke and Macfie, 1924) indicates that saliva may be sucked in with blood, and the subsequent condition of the blood suggests that it is affected by the saliva. In *Anopheles quadrimaculatus,* which has a salivary agglutinin and anticoagulin, blood becomes agglutinated in the stomach but not coagulated; in *Aedes aegypti,* which lacks both, blood coagulates in the stomach 15 min after gorging but does not agglutinate (Metcalf, 1945). A powerful coagulin is present in the wall of the posterior part of the stomach in females of *Culiseta annulata* and this will over-ride treatment of blood with the salivary glands of *Anopheles. Culex pipiens* contains a weak coagulin in the stomach wall, *Anopheles maculipennis* contains none (de Buck, 1937). In most species ingested blood forms a semi-solid body in the stomach through coagulation or through separation of red cells after agglutination. Most species with a salivary anti-coagulin contain an agglutinin. A peritrophic membrane forms around ingested blood a few hours after feeding but it is not known whether the blood must be in a non-fluid condition for this to occur successfully.

Skin Reactions of the Host

The act of feeding by a mosquito on human skin is sometimes accompanied by pain. A few minutes later a soft whitish wheal appears around the puncture, and this is usually surrounded by a reddened area and accompanied by itching. This is the immediate reaction which disappears within an hour. Several hours or a day later the skin around the puncture may swell, become reddened and itch. This is the delayed reaction which may wax and wane in intensity for several days (Gordon and Crewe, 1948; McKiel and West, 1961a). In rabbits, rats and guinea pigs a wheal may start to appear 15 min after a mosquito bite and may last several hours or 2–3 days, but distinct immediate and delayed reactions have not been seen (McKiel, 1959). The skin reactions are caused by injection of saliva, for neither immediate nor delayed reactions occur in human skin bitten by females of *Aedes stimulans* whose salivary ducts have been cut (Hudson, Bowman and Orr, 1960). Intracutaneous injection of the lateral lobes of the salivary glands of female *Anopheles maculipennis* has been reported to cause immediate and delayed reactions whereas injection of median lobes caused only a slight immediate reaction (de Buck, 1937).

One view of the skin reaction is that it is caused by injection of toxins. For example, Eckert, Paasonen and Vartiainen (1950, 1951) considered that it was due to histamine in the saliva. They applied Code's method of histamine extraction to whole bodies of *Culex pipiens* and extracted a sub-stance which caused contraction of guinea pig intestine. Histaminase inhibited this response exactly as it inhibited the response to histamine. However, the fact that both the immediate and delayed reactions are allergic in nature, requiring previous sensitization, suggests that the skin reactions cannot be due to histamine in the saliva; moreover, injection of histamine does not sensitize rabbits to the bites of *Aedes aegypti* (McKiel, 1959).

There is abundant evidence that animals must be sensitized before they will react to mosquito bites. McKiel (1959) found no skin reaction to the bites of *Aedes aegypti* in 'normal' rabbits, rats and guinea pigs, i.e. which had not previously been exposed to mosquitoes. These animals could be sensitized, however, by mosquito bites or by injection of extract of whole mosquitoes so that they subsequently gave a reaction when bitten. Young children not previously exposed to mosquitoes show neither immediate nor delayed reactions to the first bites they receive (Heilesen, 1949). Children later show a delayed reaction alone to mosquito bites and subsequently both immediate and delayed reactions (Heilesen, 1949; McKiel and West, 1961a). Repeated exposure of human beings to mosquitoes leads to disappearance of the delayed reaction and very pro-longed exposure can lead to loss of the immediate reaction also (Mellanby,

1946). The course of the skin reaction in man can therefore be illustrated as proposed by Mellanby (1946) and extended by Hudson *et al.* (1958):

	Immediate Reaction	Delayed Reaction
Stage I	—	---
Stage II	—	+
Stage III	+	|
Stage IV	+	—
Stage V	—	—

Sensitization and desensitization are characteristic of allergic reactions and it is now generally agreed that the immediate and delayed reactions to bites of mosquitoes and other insects are allergic in nature (Benjamini *et al.*, 1960; McKiel and West, 1961a).

General studies of hypersensitivities (or allergies) in man and animals show that they fall into 2 categories—immediate and delayed. Immediate hypersensitivities have the following characteristics: (a) the reaction occurs soon after application of the allergen; (b) it is associated with circulating antibodies; (c) sensitivity may be transferred passively by injection of serum from a hypersensitive into a normal individual; (d) release of histamine follows union of antigen with antibody leading to dilatation of blood vessels and other effects. Delayed hypersensitivities have the following characteristics: (a) the reactions become apparent only after several hours and affected sites show progressive changes for 2–3 days or more; (b) circulating antibodies are not involved; (c) passive transfer of sensitivity by injection of serum is impossible but may occur after transfer of living cells (Carpenter, 1956). Human skin reactions to mosquito bites clearly fall into these 2 categories but further work is necessary before it can be known whether they have all the characteristics of immediate and delayed hypersensitivities.

A number of attempts have been made to characterize mosquito allergens. Extracts of abdomens of female *Aedes aegypti* contain a substance which causes a skin reaction in sensitized rabbits and guinea pigs but injection of such extracts into normal rabbits and guinea pigs does not lead to sensitization. Substances such as this which react with antibodies but which cannot induce antibody formation are called haptens. Sensitizing antigen is present, as would be expected, in extracts of the head and thorax which contain the salivary glands, and a sensitizing substance is also present in extracts of whole male *Aedes aegypti* (McKiel, 1959). McKiel and Clunie (1960) found 4 water-soluble, non-dialysable components in extracts of whole male and female *Aedes aegypti* which caused skin reactions in man. However, West and Hudson (1959) have reported the presence of circulating antibodies in normal (unbitten) rabbits which react to extracts of whole mosquitoes, and they point out that if similar antibodies are present in man the use of whole extracts for skin tests is precluded. At present it can be said that the salivary glands secrete carbohydrate-protein complexes and free protein (p. 145), that salivary gland extract possibly contains carbohydrate (McKinley and Douglass, 1930), and that non-dialyzable components of the head and thorax, which may or may not originate in the salivary glands, can cause sensitization and skin reactions when injected. Allen and West (1962) have devised a method for collecting from mosquitoes oral secretion which is capable of sensitizing guinea pigs and rabbits to mosquito bites and of causing skin reactions in sensitized individuals. The use of oral secretion, which is very probably identical with saliva, should make more exact studies of mosquito allergens possible. Skin reactions to mosquito saliva are not completely species specific, and skin reactions may result from the first bites of one species on an individual sensitized to other species (Heilesen, 1949; McKiel, 1959). This is not always the case, however, and individuals sensitized to 2 species of mosquitoes give different skin reactions to each, suggesting a certain specificity in the nature of the salivary allergens (Mellanby, 1946; McKiel, 1959).

Prolonged exposure to mosquito bites may lead to loss of the delayed reaction but desensitization leading to loss of the immediate reaction is known only in individuals exposed to mosquito bites for many years (Mellanby, 1946). A single intravenous injection of *Aedes aegypti* extract into hypersensitive rabbits caused desensitization to the bites of that species although only for a few hours (McKiel and West, 1961b). Injection of mosquito extract into man has been reported to cause desensitization for up to 4 years, but only of the delayed reaction (Benson, 1936). Short-term desensitization of the delayed reaction by injection of mosquito extract has been described by Heilesen (1949) and Rockwell and Johnson (1952). Since the delayed reaction is the more prolonged and painful one such desensitization could often be advantageous. Intradermal injection of serum from a person showing only the immediate reaction to *Aedes aegypti* bites, into a person showing an extremely strong skin reaction with necrosis led to a reduction in skin reaction to bites in the treated area but not elsewhere (Brown *et al.,* 1938). Injection of serum from a hypersensitive into a normal individual has led to passive transfer of immediate hypersensitivity in man in a small proportion of cases but not of delayed hypersensitivity (Hecht, 1929; Rockwell and Johnson, 1952).

The function of mosquito saliva has not been established. Agglutinins and anticoagulants are present in the saliva of some species but their absence from most species shows that they are not particularly important for feeding. Hudson, Bowman and Orr (1960) observed that females of *Aedes stimulans* whose salivary ducts had been cut were able to pierce human skin and ingest blood in a normal manner but that the act of biting caused more pain than usual, and they suggested that mosquito saliva contains an anaesthetic. An alternative explanation is that more probing was necessary in the absence of saliva leading to greater stimulation of pain receptors. There is no direct evidence of an anaesthetic action of saliva. Eckert, Paasonen and Vartiainen (1951) considered that mosquito saliva contains histamine which causes vasodilatation. Although histamine is probably absent from saliva, the antigen–antibody reaction which occurs in sensitized individuals is likely to cause release of histamine from a bound form in the skin leading to vasodilatation, and the increased blood flow might well be advantageous to the mosquito provided it occurred sufficiently rapidly. The only evidence for histamine release is the similarity of the immediate reaction following a mosquito bite to Lewis's triple response which follows injection of histamine into human skin, and the observation that application of antihistamine cream immediately after biting leads to some reduction in size and duration of the immediate reaction (O'Rourke and Murnaghan, 1953). Responses to histamine vary greatly between species—dog, goat and man respond to intracutaneous injection of histamine by whealing but guinea pig, cat and rabbit do not (Darsie *et al.,* 1945); even so, histamine causes dilatation of capillaries in cat and rabbit (Feldberg, 1927). Vasodilatation may therefore be considered a possible function of mosquito saliva.

Although much remains obscure about the skin reaction to mosquito bites certain conclusions can be drawn. Both the immediate and the delayed reactions are allergic in nature since both require sensitization of the host. Mosquito saliva is the source of the allergens, but whether the immediate and delayed reactions are caused by the same or dissimilar substances in the saliva is not known. Individuals differ in the nature and extent of their reactions to mosquito bites. In many cases this is due to different histories of sensitization but differences in susceptibility have been reported in rabbits (McKiel, 1959) and it is likely that they occur in man also. The frequency with which some individuals find themselves bitten and the apparent freedom of others from mosquito bites can probably be explained by a combination of factors: variation in attractiveness to mosquitoes (p. 289), history of sensitization and desensitization, and inherent susceptibility to the allergens.

CHAPTER 8

ADULT NUTRITION AND METABOLISM

Digestion

It appears that no digestive enzymes are secreted by the salivary glands of adult mosquitoes since tests for protease, lipase and amylase in the salivary glands of *Anopheles quadrimaculatus* females (Metcalf, 1945) and for protease and invertase in the salivary glands of *Aedes aegypti* females (Fisk, 1950; Fisk and Shambaugh, 1954) all gave negative results. However, a protease is present in the midgut of females of *Aedes aegypti* (Fisk, 1950) and a carbohydrase in the diverticula and midgut of females of the same species (Fisk and Shambaugh, 1954). Because the diverticula lack a secretory epithelium the carbohydrase is presumed to have been secreted elsewhere.

Carbohydrase activity has been investigated by incubating intestinal homogenates from female *Aedes aegypti* with starch or sucrose. Starch was not digested but sucrose was hydrolysed by both midgut and diverticula indicating the presence of invertase (β-fructosidase). Invertase activity was lower in the diverticula than in the midgut and activity in the diverticula declined after feeding on sugar or blood. Activity in the midgut showed little change after the insect had fed on 5 per cent sucrose but after a blood meal it increased threefold and remained high for about 2 hr (Fisk and Shambaugh, 1954). Homogenates of whole adults of *Aedes aegypti* digest several carbohydrates (Galun and Fraenkel, 1957) but this does not prove that the enzymes concerned are present in the intestine. However, the utilization of certain oligosaccharides by females of *Aedes aegypti* (p. 155) suggests that both an α-glucosidase and an α-galactosidase are present in the gut.

Proteolytic digestion was investigated in *Aedes aegypti* by allowing females to take a blood meal, removing the midgut at various intervals after feeding, homogenizing it and incubating with added substrate followed by colorimetric determination of the digestion products (Fisk and Shambaugh, 1952). Protease activity was confined to the midgut and it was not enhanced when homogenates of salivary glands or diverticula were incubated with the midgut. The protease activity of midguts dissected from mature, unfed females was very slight but it increased steadily after a blood meal reaching a maximum about 18 hr after feeding. After

48 hr there was still considerable activity (Fig. 52). In the first few minutes after feeding on blood the protease activity of the midgut dropped below the residual level characteristic of unfed mosquitoes, possibly due to an

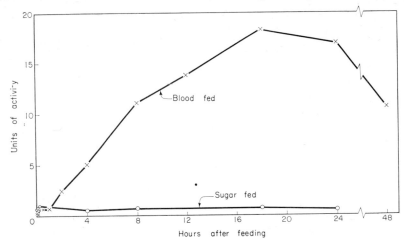

FIG. 52.   Activity of midgut proteolytic enzymes of *Aedes aegypti* females at intervals after feeding on blood or sugar. (After Fisk and Shambaugh, 1952).

inhibitor in the blood. Sugar feeding produced a twofold rise in protease activity during the first hour but this effect was transient.

The *p*H of the gut contents of male and female *Aedes aegypti* is 5·5–6·0 in the crop, 6·5 in the midgut and 5·8–6·0 in the rectum. After a blood meal the midgut contents are *p*H 7·3, the normal value of blood (Fisk, 1950). Similar results have been obtained with other species (Fisk, 1950; Micks *et al.*, 1948) but the contents of the diverticula sometimes become strongly acid through bacterial activity (Lea *et al.*, 1958). Digestion of serum albumin at 40°C by midgut homogenates of *Aedes aegypti* proceeds fastest at *p*H 7·8, corresponding fairly closely to the *p*H of the midgut contents of a blood-fed individual (Fisk, 1950).

Protease activity in midgut homogenates from *Aedes aegypti* 18 hr after gorging was found to be proportional to the amount of blood which had been ingested (Fig. 53) (Shambaugh, 1954). Control of enzyme secretion might be nervous, hormonal, or secretogogue—i.e. due to the presence of food or food products. Unfed mosquitoes injected with haemolymph taken from blood-fed mosquitoes showed no increase in enzyme activity 8–10 hr after injection, suggesting that control was not hormonal. After mosquitoes had fed on sheep erythrocytes suspended in saline protease activity was only a little higher than the residual level found in unfed mosquitoes. The activity was increased slightly by adding protein-free serum dialysate to the erythrocytes, and it was raised to the level obtained after feeding whole blood by feeding erythrocytes plus serum proteins. In the absence of evidence for nervous or hormonal control of protease secretion Shambaugh (1954) considered that the stimulation which resulted from feeding on certain fractions of blood indicated a secretogogue type of control, the most important stimulants being the non-dialysable plasma proteins.

In *Culex pipiens* digestion of blood begins next to the stomach wall and proceeds inwards. At an early stage in digestion a layer of pigment sur-

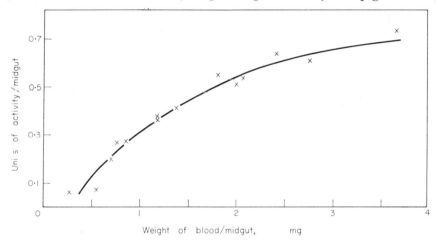

FIG. 53. Relationship between amount of blood ingested by *Aedes aegypti* females and protease activity of the midgut 18 hr after feeding. (From Shambaugh, 1954).

rounds the blood mass, within that is a layer of partially digested erythrocytes and in the centre a mass of blood of quite normal appearance (Fig. 49e). The mass of blood gradually decreases in size as it is digested (Huff, 1934). Analysis of the midgut contents of gorged *Aedes aegypti* showed practically no decrease in total nitrogen during the first 48 hr of digestion at 25°C, indicating that absorption had not progressed very far. Half of the blood protein was partially digested within 3 hr, as shown by the increased ultrafiltrate, and further analysis showed that the serum globulins were broken down first, being present only in traces after 6 hr, whereas serum albumins were still present after 18 hr (Williams, 1956). In *Aedes aegypti* and *Anopheles maculipennis* digestion of haemoglobin is complete and only a small black residue of protohaematin remains in the faeces. No formation of bile pigment can be detected (Wigglesworth, 1943).

Little is known of the absorption of digestion products, but iron lactate is said to be absorbed in the posterior part of the stomach (de Boissezon, 1930a, c).

The principal method of investigating rate of digestion has been the precipitin test; gut contents are mixed at intervals with suitable antisera and when a precipitate is no longer formed the serum proteins are assumed to have been digested. When gorged females of *Culex pipiens fatigans* were kept at 27°C and at a saturation deficit of 2 mm Hg the precipitin test first failed to give a positive reaction 52 hr after feeding, when slightly less than half of the abdomen was distended with blood. Haematin pigments remained in the gut long after digestion of proteins was complete (O'Gower, 1956). Digestion proceeds at different speeds in different species, for under the same conditions complete digestion of proteins in 50 per cent of the population requires 31 hr in *Aedes scutellaris,* 38 hr in *Aedes aegypti* and 48 hr in *Aedes australis* (O'Gower, 1956).

The rate of digestion is strongly dependent on temperature (Table 11) (Shlenova, 1938) and in *Aedes aegypti* has an average Q_{10} of 2·0 between

TABLE 11.   MEAN TIME REQUIRED FOR DIGESTION OF BLOOD BY FEMALES OF *Anopheles maculipennis messeae* UNDER DIFFERENT CONDITIONS OF TEMPERATURE AND HUMIDITY. (FROM SHLENOVA, 1938).

Relative humidity	10°C	15°C	20°C	25°C	30°C
30 – 40%	265	138	109	85	55 hr
70 – 80%	291	165	93	59	41 hr
90–100%	337	123	67	54	40 hr

15° and 35°C (Williams, 1956). There is some evidence that humidity also affects the rate of digestion. Observations on several Indian species of *Anopheles* showed that during the hot dry months digestion of blood took 3–5 days but that when the relative humidity increased the gut was cleared in 1–3 days (Mayne, 1928). In hibernating females of *Anopheles maculipennis messeae,* in which digestion proceeded as in normal females, at temperatures above 15°C digestion was much more rapid at higher relative humidities but at 10°C the opposite result was obtained (Table 11) (Shlenova, 1938). The rate of digestion in *Aedes notoscriptus* could be increased by reducing exposure of females to light (O'Gower, 1956).

Nutrition and Metabolic Activity

Although the principal food of female mosquitoes is blood, male and female mosquitoes both feed extensively on nectar of which the principal constituents are fructose, glucose and sucrose; maltose, melibiose and raffinose occasionally occur in low concentration (Wykes, 1952). Sugar alone is sufficient to maintain adult life and females are able to live for several weeks in the laboratory on sugar without undue reduction of tissue nitrogen (Terzian *et al.*, 1957). Galun and Fraenkel (1957) investigated the survival of females of *Aedes aegypti* fed various carbohydrates in 5 per cent solution. Survival was longest on sucrose, 50 per cent surviving 32 days, the longest-lived individual surviving 67 days, and in Table 12 survival

TABLE 12. THE NUTRITIVE VALUE TO FEMALES OF *Aedes aegypti* OF VARIOUS CARBOHYDRATES IN 5% SOLUTION, EXPRESSED AS LENGTH OF SURVIVAL ON EACH COMPOUND IN RELATION TO SURVIVAL ON WATER (0·0) AND ON 5% SUCROSE SOLUTION (1·0). (FROM GALUN AND FRAENKEL, 1957).

Pentoses		Trisaccharides	
Arabinose	0·0	Melizitose	0·9
Rhamnose	0·0	Raffinose	0·5
Ribose	0·0		
Xylose	0·0	Polysaccharides	
		Dextrin	0·2
Hexoses		Glycogen	0·0
Fructose	1·0	Inulin	0·0
Galactose	0·3	Starch	0·0
Glucose	0·8		
Mannose	0·0	Glycosides	
Sorbose	0·0	α-methyl-glucoside	0·0
		α-methyl-mannoside	0·0
Disaccharides			
Cellobiose	0·0	Sugar alcohols	
Lactose	0·0	Dulcitol	0·0
Maltose	0·8	Glycerol	0·0
Melibiose	0·3	Inositol	0·0
Sucrose	1·0	Mannitol	0·0
Trehalose	0·3	Sorbitol	0·5

on the other compounds is expressed in relation to survival on water alone and on 5 per cent sucrose, giving a measure of relative nutritive value. Glucose and fructose were highly nutritious, as would be expected, and oligosaccharides were utilized to a variable extent. Unfortunately it is not certain whether the carbohydrates which failed to prolong life were ingested. The larvae of *Aedes aegypti* utilize a number of carbohydrates which are apparently of no value to the adults (cf. p. 50).

The fat body stores of fat, glycogen and protein disappear during the first few days after emergence in *Culex pipiens* (Clements, 1956a), but feeding on sugar leads to the redevelopment of heavy deposits of fat and glycogen in the fat body and of small amounts of glycogen in the flight muscles (Clements, 1955). Females of *Aedes taeniorhynchus* and *Aedes sollicitans* which feed on glucose solution lay down extensive reserves of triglyceride, the fatty acids of which are very largely palmitic, palmitoleic and oleic acids. The males of these species show no increase in triglyceride level when fed glucose but only a slow fall (Van Handel and Lum, 1962). Wild specimens of *Aedes communis*, examined within 6 hr of emergence, contained only sparse deposits of fat and glycogen (Hocking, 1953a) so it is possible that the reserves of wild mosquitoes seldom reach the levels obtained in the laboratory. A histochemical examination of females of *Culex pipiens* var. *berbericus* which had been flown to exhaustion on a flight mill revealed that glycogen had almost disappeared from the fat body although there was no discernible change in fat content (Clements, 1955). In contrast, the fat content of hibernating *Culex pipiens pipiens* gradually declines during the winter, other solids remaining unchanged (Buxton, 1935). This suggests that glycogen alone can be used in flight but that fat and glycogen are used during rest, possibly fat alone being used during hibernation. However, the respiratory quotient of resting *Aedes aegypti* is always between 0·9 and 1·1 (Galun, 1960), characteristic of carbohydrate metabolism.

Owing to the small size of mosquitoes their tissues cannot easily be isolated for biochemical studies. Homogenates of whole adults of species of *Anopheles, Aedes* and *Culex* contain aldolase, an enzyme on the Embden–Meyerhof pathway of glycolysis which catalyzes the splitting of fructose-1,6-diphosphate to glyceraldehyde-3-phosphate and dihydroxy-acetone phosphate (Phifer, 1962). Respiratory particles from whole bodies of *Aedes aegypti* adults, of which flight muscle sarcosomes formed the largest part, oxidized all citric acid cycle intermediates and showed oxidative phosphorylation (Gonda, Traub and Avi-Dor, 1957). These particles contained DPNH-cytochrome *c* reductase (Avi-Dor, Traub and Mager, 1958) and adenosine triphosphate (Avi-Dor and Gonda, 1959). Homogenates of *Aedes aegypti* adults show high DPNH-cytochrome *c* reductase and succinate-cytochrome *c* reductase activity but low TPNH-cytochrome *c* reductase activity (Lang, 1959). Trehalose has not been recorded in mosquitoes but it would be surprising if it were not an important metabolite.

According to unpublished observations of A. O. Lea, resting autogenous females of *Aedes taeniorhynchus* held at 28°C show fluctuations in oxygen uptake, 3 periods of high uptake having peaks at approximately 27–29, 36–38 and 53–56 hr after emergence. The periods of increased oxygen consumption coincide with periods of follicle growth and yolk deposition, the first peak coinciding with deposition of yolk in stage IIb follicles and the second with the change from stage II to stage III. An anautogenous female showing no ovary development shows no peaks of oxygen uptake. In further unpublished work Lea showed that oxygen uptake increased nearly threefold half an hour after ingestion of 0·3 M-sucrose by females of *Aedes taeniorhynchus*, and that uptake fell steeply from this initial peak over the following 6–8 hr and then more gradually. The curve showing loss of body weight after the meal was almost identical with the curve of falling oxygen consumption and Lea considered that the increased oxygen uptake reflected the increased energy consumption of the Malpighian tubes in eliminating water. This was supported by the observation that a female which remained distended and failed to lose water showed no change in oxygen consumption.

Anautogenous females of *Culex pipiens* are able to fly considerable distances on a flight mill using reserves carried over from the pupal stage (Table 13, series C). When mosquitoes were flown to exhaustion and then fed glucose solution they could resume flight within a minute of starting to feed. Calculation showed that the flight reserves of an unfed female aged 48–72 hr must have been equivalent to about 0·12 mg glucose. To find whether ingested blood could be utilized for flight, the distances covered by unfed females flown to exhaustion on a flight mill on 5 successive days were compared with distances flown by females of the same age fed to repletion on human blood on the day before the first flight (Table 13,

TABLE 13.   DISTANCES FLOWN BY ANAUTOGENOUS FEMALES OF *Culex pipiens* ON A FLIGHT MILL. (FROM CLEMENTS, 1955).

Series	Conditions before flight	No. flown	Mean distance flown on five days (m)					Total
			1st	2nd	3rd	4th	5th	
A	Unfed; free in cage; aged 72–96 hr at first flight	10	1282	455	314	242	129	2422
B	Fed blood; free in cage; aged 72–96 hr at first flight	10	1564	1809	1055	410	225	5063
C	Unfed; confined in tube; aged 48–72 hr at first flight	10	2728	781	736	548	546	5339

series A and B). There was no significant difference between the distances flown on the 1st day. On the 2nd day the blood-fed females flew even further than on the 1st day whereas the unfed females could fly little more than a third of the distance they had covered on the 1st day. Over the 5 days the blood-fed females flew more than twice as far as the unfed, covering an additional distance for which the sugars contained in the blood meal were totally inadequate and for which digestion products of the blood proteins must have been used. Small amounts of glycogen were laid down in the flight muscles of both unfed and blood-fed mosquitoes between flights but only in the blood-fed mosquitoes was glycogen deposited in the fat body (Clements, 1955). Since the unfed females showed some recovery of flight ability after a rest of 24 hr it is possible that part of the fat reserve was converted to carbohydrate.

The normal range of dispersion of mosquitoes is very poorly known because the origin of captured mosquitoes can rarely be ascertained unless they are marked, and marked mosquitoes are very seldom recaptured in sufficient numbers. Some species of mosquitoes undoubtedly travel distances of several miles or more. These flights may occur regularly at a given stage of adult life, as in the dispersal of *Aedes taeniorhynchus* which occurs a few hours after emergence (Nielsen, 1958), the premating flight of *Anopheles labranchiae atroparvus* (Swellengrebel and de Buck, 1938) and the prehibernation flight of *Anopheles sacharovi* (Kligler, 1932), or they may occur irregularly, often over many miles but usually in the direction of strong winds (Garrett-Jones, 1950). Unfed females of *Culex pipiens* var. *berbericus* flew over 5000 m on a flight mill, and could have flown much further without the drag of the mill (Clements, 1955), and it has been calculated that females of various species of *Aedes* are able to fly over 20–50 km in still air without stopping to feed (Hocking, 1953a) (see p. 266).

Nutritional Requirements for Reproduction

The question of what nutrients are required by the female mosquito for egg production is one that has excited interest for many years. Early work in which blood fractions were fed to mosquitoes suggested that protein was the only essential requirement (Woke, 1937a; Yeoli and Mer, 1938) and this was confirmed when diets of amino acids were produced which would stimulate egg production when fed to females of *Aedes aegypti* (Table 14) (Dimond *et al.*, 1956; Singh and Brown, 1957). When any 1 of 8 amino acids was omitted from the diet no eggs were produced. These were arginine, isoleucine, leucine, lysine, phenylalanine, threonine, tryptophan and valine. When either histidine or methionine was omitted, a few eggs were laid during the first few days after the start of the experiment but none later. It was concluded that the deficient amino acid was carried over from the pupa in sufficient amount for the production of a few eggs but that when these stores were depleted the acid became indispensable since in its absence no further egg production occurred. Ten

TABLE 14. Two Diets Which Permit Egg Production in *Aedes aegypti* When Fed to the Adult Female. (From Dimond *et al.,* 1956).

		Medium A	Medium B
	Fructose	5·00 g/100 ml	5·00 g/100 ml
	Glucose	5·00	5·00
	Salts	0·15	0·15
*	L Arginine HCl	0·50 g/100 ml	0·38 g/100 ml
	L Cystine	0·20	0·15
	L Glutamic acid	1·00	1·00
	Glycine anyhydride	0·50	—
*	L Histidine HCl	0·70	0·15
*	DL Isoleucine	1·00	0·50
*	L Leucine	1·00	0·75
*	L Lysine HCl	0·90	0·75
*	DL Methionine	0·20	0·15
*	DL Phenylalanine	0·70	1·20
*	DL Threonine	0·80	0·30
*	L Tryptophan	0·40	0·30
*	DL Valine	1·00	1·00
	Total amino acids	8·90 g/100 ml	6·64 g/100 ml
	Egg production	7000 eggs/400 ♀♀	16000 eggs/400 ♀♀

* Essential for egg production.

amino acids were therefore essential for egg production and these were the same amino acids which were essential for larval development (p. 46). Citrulline could replace arginine in the diet, although fewer eggs were produced, but ornithine was ineffective (Dimond *et al.,* 1956).

Omission of either cystine or glutamic acid led to a fall in the number of eggs laid. Cystine could not be replaced by excess methionine. The stimulating effect of glutamic acid appeared to be due to its contribution of amino groups for the synthesis of non-essential amino acids, since it could be replaced with aspartic acid, which like glutamic acid is important in transamination in many animals, or by ammonium acetate. Moreover,

a-ketoglutaric acid, the deamination product of glutamate, had no stimulating effect (Dimond *et al.,* 1956). The D isomer of histidine was as effective as the L isomer in promoting egg production and the D isomers of methionine, phenylalanine and tryptophan could also be used although they were less effective than the corresponding L forms. No eggs were produced when the D isomers of isoleucine, leucine, threonine and valine were fed (Dimond *et al.,* 1956).

Attempts to find the optimum concentration of each amino acid led to the production of a series of diets, 2 of which are given in Table 14 (Dimond *et al.,* 1956). From the egg production of 400 females allowed continuous access to food for 14 days it can be seen that Medium B was far more satisfactory than Medium A although it contained a lower concentration of amino acids. Haemolysed blood gave an egg yield which was double that on Medium B, but if the blood was diluted to a nitrogen level equal to that of Medium B egg production dropped to one-tenth of that on the amino acid solution. It seems probable that in the artificial diet the amino acids were provided in proportions well suited for protein synthesis by the female (Dimond *et al.,* 1958).

Sugar was included in the diet to stimulate feeding but it seems unlikely to be an indispensable nutrient. Egg production was not increased when vitamins, nucleic acid or sterols were added to the diet (of non-sterile mosquitoes). Addition of salts containing sodium or potassium led to a doubling of egg production over that on salt-free diets (Dimond, Lea and DeLong, 1958). Sterile females from larvae reared on a chemically-defined medium were capable of laying eggs when fed only amino acids and sugar (Singh and Brown, 1957). It is characteristic that insects such as the Cimicidae and Pediculidae which feed on vertebrate blood alone throughout their lives require symbionts for normal growth and reproduction, whereas mosquitoes and other insects which feed on blood only in the adult stage do not need symbionts (Koch, 1956). Gut contents taken from adults of *Anopheles claviger* and *Aedes cinereus* had a lethal action on certain bacteria but had no bactericidal effect on most species (Duncan, 1926). Five species of bacteria have been recorded from the midgut lumens of adult *Culex pipiens fatigans* (Ferguson and Micks, 1961) and rickettsias are found within midgut cells of this and other species (Micks, Julian, Ferguson and Duncan, 1961).

It is generally considered that mosquitoes will develop more eggs after feeding on certain hosts than on others. Unfortunately, there is an almost complete lack of critical data on which to test this hypothesis, for not only must the number of eggs per mg of ingested blood be known, but also the average blood intake from the different hosts must be similar on account of the pronounced effect which size of blood meal has on the number of eggs formed per mg of blood ingested (p. 185). In one experiment which did fulfil these conditions *Culex pipiens* laid, on average, 40 eggs per mg of human blood and 82 eggs per mg of canary blood (Woke, 1937b). It may be that nucleated erythrocytes are more nourishing than anucleate erythrocytes but females of *Aedes aegypti* laid more eggs per mg of blood ingested from rabbit or guinea pig than from canary or turtle (Woke, 1937c), and as shown above addition of nucleic acids to an artificial diet of amino acids fed to *Aedes aegypti* did not raise egg production. The most likely explanation is that the amino acid balance is more suitable in the blood of some hosts than in others. In the experiments which appear to support this view insufficient critical data is given to provide proof but the evidence is worth considering nevertheless. *Aedes aegypti* fed a suspension of sheep erythrocytes laid only 5 eggs per female but when 1 per cent DL isoleucine was added egg production rose to 54 eggs per female compared to 61 per female after addition of 5 per cent egg albumin (Greenberg, 1951). Egg production was lower when females of *Aedes aegypti* were fed whole blood of man, sheep or ox, in which the haemoglobin has a singularly low isoleucine content, than when they were fed whole blood of pig or rabbit in which the isoleucine content of the haemoglobin is higher. Addition of isoleucine to the blood of pig and rabbit had no significant effect on egg production but addition to the blood of man, sheep or ox raised the level of egg production to that characteristic of pig and rabbit blood. The addition of 9 other essential amino acids had no effect (Lea, Dimond and DeLong, 1958).

Excretion

During the first hour or two after a blood meal a clear, watery fluid is discharged but when this has ceased nothing more is passed for about 12 hr. The excreta then consist of semi-solid masses of uric acid. Three or four hours after feeding the rectum is distended with a clear fluid with some uric acid granules in suspension, but the rectal contents become increasingly solid suggesting that water is absorbed by the rectal papillae (Wigglesworth, 1932).

Each gonotrophic cycle sees the build up of excretory matter in the Malpighian tube cells and its discharge from the organism (Bryukhanova, 1960). Uric acid is deposited in the cells of the fat body, which acts as a kidney of accumulation. In the young adult of *Culex pipiens* little uric acid is to be found in the fat body but the uric acid deposits increase with age and they are particularly extensive in the hibernating female (de Boissezon, 1930a).

Figure 54 presents total nitrogen and uric acid nitrogen in the excreta of *Aedes aegypti* females, fed on sucrose, during the first 72 hr after emergence and during each week thereafter. Immediately after emergence there is a high output of nitrogenous matter, the bulk of which is uric acid,

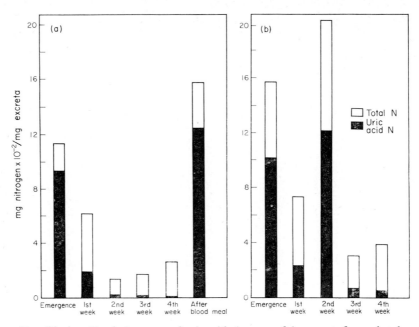

Fig. 54a–b.   Total nitrogen and uric acid nitrogen of the excreta from a batch of females of *Aedes aegypti* maintained on 4 per cent sucrose, collected during the first 72 hr after emergence and at weekly intervals thereafter.
(a) Blood meal given at end of 4th week; (b) blood meal given at end of 1st week. (From Terzian, Irreverre and Stahler, 1957).

and in the following week excretion is still high although the proportion of uric acid nitrogen is substantially reduced. In subsequent weeks excretion is low, at a level which effectively conserves the nitrogen resources of the adult in the absence of any protein intake, but the excretion of non-uric acid nitrogen slowly increases. Excretion increases very greatly in the 7-day period following a blood meal, with uric acid forming a high proportion of the nitrogenous matter, but the level is low again thereafter (Terzian *et al.*, 1957).

Analysis of excreta obtained over a 2-week period from females of 3 species, fed only 4 per cent sucrose, showed that uric acid, ammonia, urea, amino acids and protein were present (Table 15). On hydrolysis the protein yielded galactosamine and glucosamine, in addition to amino acids, indicating the presence of glycoprotein (Irreverre and Terzian, 1959).

Females of *Aedes aegypti* fed on solutions of chick plasma or of lysed chick erythrocytes excrete increased amounts of nitrogeneous matter of

TABLE 15. CONSTITUENTS OF THE EXCRETA OF FEMALE MOSQUITOES, FED ONLY 4% SUCROSE, COLLECTED DURING A 2-WEEK PERIOD. (FROM IRREVERRE AND TERZIAN 1959).

Species	% Nitrogen					Total nitrogen accounted for
	Uric Acid	Ammonia	Urea	Amino Acids	Protein	
Aedes aegypti	47·30	6·40	11·90	4·40	10·82	80·82%
Anopheles quadrimaculatus	42·50	7·80	9·50	4·70	9·22	73·72%
Culex pipiens	46·90	10·00	7·90	5·50	9·67	79·97%

which less than one-fifth is uric acid, and it appears that only during ovary development is ingested protein fully metabolized with extensive deamination (Terzian *et al.*, 1957).

CHAPTER 9

REPRODUCTION

Structure of the Reproductive Organs

The Male Reproductive System

Our knowledge of the structure of the internal reproductive organs is due principally to the studies of Prashad (1916b), Christophers (1960), Lum (1961a, b) and Hodapp and Jones (1961). The two testes are pear-shaped or elongate bodies, largely covered with fat body, situated dorso-laterally in the 5th and 6th abdominal segments, their anterior ends pointed and ending in terminal filaments of connective tissue which are attached to the heart and alary muscles (Fig. 55). As in other Diptera (Snodgrass, 1959) each testis consists of a single follicle enclosed in an investing sheath, and in newly-emerged males each is divided into cysts, of germ cells, in various stages of development. The posterior cyst in each testis contains spermatozoa and opens into the reproductive duct of its side.

According to Hodapp and Jones (1961) the anterior portions of the two reproductive ducts comprise the vasa efferentia and the posterior portions the vasa deferentia, which open into paired seminal vesicles. The vasa efferentia are thin-walled tubes without muscle fibres, whereas the vasa deferentia are thick-walled and muscular except in *Anopheles* where they are poorly defined. In *Aedes aegypti* and *Psorophora howardii* the vasa deferentia fuse into a common duct which supplies both seminal vesicles (Fig. 55b). The seminal vesicles are distensible regions of the efferent ducts, fused externally in many species although their lumina remain distinct. Their function is to store spermatozoa which may be found in them very soon after emergence. A pair of accessory glands flanks the seminal vesicles, being fused to them in certain *Anopheles,* and they consist of columnar cells packed with secretion and surrounding a central duct. The anterior region of each gland secretes large granules and these with the fluid component of the accessory-gland secretion accompany the sperm at copulation. The seminal vesicles and accessory glands discharge into an ejaculatory duct which penetrates the aedeagus and which is lined with cuticle, having arisen in the pupa as an invagination of the body wall. The walls of the seminal vesicles, accessory glands and ejaculatory duct all contain muscle fibres, the ejaculatory duct being especially strongly

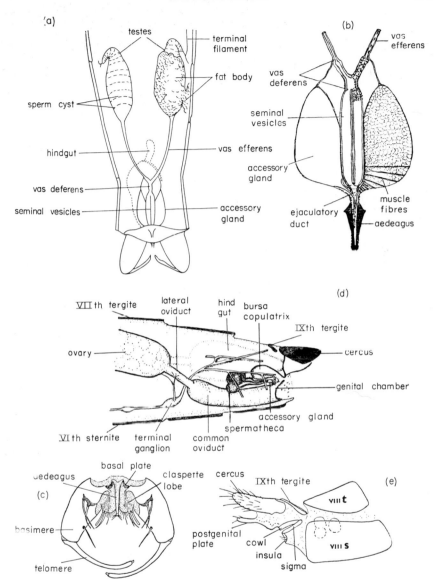

FIG. 55a–e. The male and female reproductive organs.
(a) Ventral aspect of the internal reproductive organs of a male *Aedes aegypti*
before rotation of the terminalia; (b) the efferent ducts in a male *Aedes aegypti;*
(c) the genitalia of a male *Anopheles quadrimaculatus;* (d) lateral aspect of the
internal reproductive organs of a female *Aedes aegypti;* (e) lateral aspect of
the terminalia of a female *Aedes pulchrithorax*. (a and b from Hodapp and
Jones (1961), c from Snodgrass (1957), d from Curtin and Jones (1961),
e from Edwards (1941)).

supplied with muscles in *Anopheles,* and these organs are innervated from the terminal abdominal ganglion.

The male genitalia are borne on the 9th abdominal segment and consist basically of an intromittent organ, the aedeagus, flanked by a pair of parameres (Snodgrass, 1957). The parameres take the form of claspers, each being divided into a large basimere and a slender telomere (Fig. 55c). Apodemes extend into the abdomen from the basimeres, and both segments of the claspers are independently movable by strong antagonistic muscles. Two claspette lobes arise from the inner surfaces of the basimeres and they assume a variety of forms in different species. The aedeagus (sometimes called the mesosome or phallosome) is a slender organ lying between the basimeres and connected to them by two small basal plates. The genitalia are innervated from the terminal abdominal ganglion (Snodgrass, 1959; Christophers, 1960).

During the first day or two after emergence the 8th and posterior segments rotate through 180° so that the positions of the sterna and terga are reversed, the anus coming to lie below the aedeagus and the true ventral surface of the genitalia facing upwards. This leads to a crossing of the vasa deferentia, the tracheal trunks and certain abdominal muscles. Rotation of the terminal segments occurs with equal frequency in clockwise and anti-clockwise directions, and in *Aedes aegypti* has been shown to be due entirely to a twisting of the hindgut for the hindgut always twists in the direction of rotation of the terminalia, and rotation of the terminalia fails to occur after removal of the hindgut but occurs more or less normally when the terminal segments are connected to the hindgut alone. The intersegmental membrane between the 7th and 8th abdominal segments is thought to have a special nature which permits rotation, for it has a glistening appearance unlike other intersegmental membranes and after rotation there is no visible twisting in the membrane (Hodapp, 1960).

The Female Reproductive System

The following account is based upon descriptions of the reproductive organs in various species of *Anopheles, Aedes, Culex, Culiseta* and *Mansonia* by Nicholson (1921), von der Brelje (1924), Giglioli (1959), Curtin and Jones (1961) and Bertram (1961). Two ovaries lie dorso-laterally in the posterior portion of the abdomen and are connected by lateral oviducts to a common oviduct which opens by the primary genital opening, the gonopore, into a genital chamber or vagina (Fig. 55d). The ovarioles, which are variable in number, are short and extremely numerous radiating about an extension of each lateral oviduct called the calyx (Fig. 56). In *Aedes aegypti* the number of ovarioles in the two ovaries ranges from 50 to 150 varying with the size of the female (Colless and Challapah,

1960), whereas in *Culex pipiens pipiens* the size of the egg raft indicates that there must be 400 ovarioles or more (Christophers, 1945) and in *Anopheles maculipennis melanoon* up to 500 (Shannon and Hadjinicalao, 1941). Each ovariole consists of an anterior germarium, a posterior vitellarium, and two sheaths, the tunica propria and the ovariole sheath (Fig. 56). The

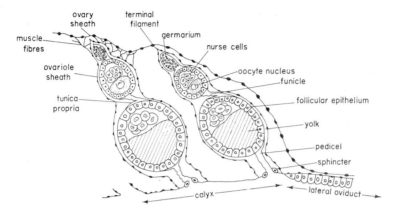

Fɪɢ. 56.   Two ovarioles from a nulliparous female in longitudinal section. (After an unpublished diagram of D. S. Bertram by kind permission).

germarium contains a central mass of large nuclei belonging to oogonia, oocytes and nurse cells (trophocytes), and a peripheral layer containing smaller nuclei which give rise to the follicular epithelium. The vitellarium comprises 2 or 3 follicles, each consisting of an oocyte and 7 nurse cells surrounded by follicular epithelium. The germarium and vitellarium are closely bounded by a very fine elastic membrane, the tunica propria, and less closely by the ovariole sheath, while an outer bag-like ovary sheath encloses the whole ovary and extends forwards as the terminal filament. A reticulum of anastomosing, striped muscle fibres is found on the outside of the ovariole sheath and on the inside of the ovary sheath, while other fibres traverse the cavity and link the 2 systems together. The outer layer of fibres is continuous with the circular muscles and the inner layer with the longitudinal muscles of the lateral oviduct. The follicles are connected to one another, to the germarium and to the calyx by narrow, tubular regions of the tunica propria called funicles. At its junction with the calyx the posterior funicle, which is also called the pedicel, is surrounded by a sphincter of 6–8 muscle fibres. Tracheae, variously described as arising from the 3rd and 4th or 4th and 5th abdominal spiracles, pass to the ovaries where they branch profusely before penetrating the ovarioles as tracheoles.

M

The epithelium of the common oviduct is glandular, and during gonotrophic cycles a secretion accumulates in its slightly bifurcated, anterior region, leading to swelling and the consequent more distinct appearance of two ampullae (Mer, 1932; Polovodova, 1949). The genital chamber has muscular walls and in *Anopheles* at least it becomes narrow posteriorly where it is encircled by a powerful sphincter. Spermathecae, an accessory gland and a bursa copulatrix (absent in most *Anopheles*) all open into the genital chamber through a small structure, the dorsal plate, in its dorsal surface. Anophelines have only 1 spermatheca but 1, 2 or 3 may be present in culicines, usually 3. *Uranotaenia, Aedeomyia* and certain *Aedes* have only 1 spermatheca (Edwards, 1941) and *Mansonioides* have 2 (Neveu-Lemaire, 1902). *Aedes aegypti* has a large median spermatheca, with its own duct, and 2 smaller lateral spermathecae whose ducts fuse before entering the genital chamber. A spermatheca consists of a sclerotized shell, which in inseminated females contains sperm, surrounded by a layer of cells. In *Anopheles maculipennis* these cells are large and cytoplasmic strands pass from them through pores in the shell, and it is thought that secretions from the surrounding cells possibly nourish the sperm (Polovodova, 1947). In *Aedes aegypti* the cell layer is thin and although the shell is said by Hayes (1953) to be perforated this is denied by Curtin and Jones (1961). In *Aedes aegypti* and other species glandular cells occur at the top of the spermathecal duct. The accessory gland is a globular body of variable size whose cells are filled with secretion. The bursa copulatrix is a large, distensible sac and like the genital chamber and the ducts of the accessory gland and spermathecae it is lined with cuticle. von der Brelje (1924) stated that a bursa copulatrix was present in *Aedes, Culex* and *Culiseta* but absent from *Anopheles*. Giglioli (1959) did not find a bursa in *Anopheles gambiae* but one has been described in *Anopheles sacharovi* by Mer (1932). The terminal abdominal ganglion innervates the ovary (in *Anopheles* at least), the oviducts and genital chamber as well as the hindgut and cerci (Polovodova, 1953; Curtin and Jones, 1961).

The female terminalia appear very simple (Fig. 55e). The last complete abdominal segment is the 8th and the small lobe beyond it consists of the 9th and 10th segments. The 9th segment bears a small tergite dorsally and a 10th tergite is also found in *Anopheles*. The gonotreme or opening of the genital chamber is behind the 8th sternite; in front of it there often lie 2 sclerites, the sigma and insula, and behind it another, the cowl. Behind the gonotreme is a moderate-sized sclerite, the postgenital plate, so-called because like the other ventral sclerites its homologies are obscure. The 10th segment bears the cerci and the anus (Christophers, 1923).

Growth of the Egg Follicle

At intervals a group of 8 large cells at the inner end of the germarium, consisting of an oocyte and 7 nurse cells formed from a single oogonium, becomes surrounded by the smaller, outer cells of the germarium and separates forming a follicle. Follicles may appear as early as the 4th instar larva in *Aedes aegypti* (Christophers, 1960). In the adult each ovariole contains 2 or 3 follicles, the posterior follicle in each ovariole being the farthest advanced, and as the female passes through a gonotrophic cycle the posterior follicle in each ovariole develops to maturity but the remaining follicles make very little growth. At emergence the oocytes of the posterior follicles may be distinguishable from their nurse cells and in exceptional cases they may contain a few granules of yolk (Mer, 1936), but normally the oocytes cannot be distinguished for several hours. The growth of the egg follicle falls naturally into 2 periods: development up to a resting stage which can be regarded as an ovarian diapause, and further development to the formation of a mature egg, which does not normally start until the mosquito has taken a meal of blood.

The cytoplasm of the oocyte and nurse cells increases as the young follicle starts to grow and a small amount of yolk is formed around the oocyte nucleus before it enters the resting stage. The cells of the follicular epithelium multiply rapidly at this time but after the resting stage they grow only by increase in size (Nicholson, 1921). In the first gonotrophic cycle deposition of yolk before the resting stage can be achieved at the expense of reserves accumulated during larval life or by feeding on sugar or blood. In *Anopheles sacharovi* and *Anopheles labranchiae atroparvus* only large females, from well-nourished larvae, are able to deposit yolk in the oocytes and reach the resting stage without feeding; females which have not formed yolk from their reserves before reaching the resting stage need 2 blood meals to produce mature eggs unless they are first given access to sugar (Mer, 1936; Detinova, 1944). Females of *Aedes aegypti* which have developed from undernourished larvae generally require 2 blood meals (Macdonald, 1956), and undernourishment may be the reason why most females of *Anopheles gambiae* and *Anopheles funestus* (Gillies, 1954, 1955) in nature need at least 2 blood meals to develop their first batch of eggs, but the regularity of this phenomenon in certain species suggests that under-nourishment is not the only cause. In each subsequent gonotrophic cycle, as 1 oocyte attains full development the one lying above it secretes a small amount of yolk around its nucleus and enters the resting stage and a new follicle breaks away from the germarium. Mosquitoes are therefore generally able to develop a batch of eggs after each of the later blood feeds.

After the mosquito has taken a blood meal the oocyte at the base of each ovariole grows rapidly forming a large amount of yolk and elongating to the shape of a mature egg; meanwhile the follicular epithelium secretes the chorion and micropyle apparatus. As the oocyte grows, in *Anopheles labranchiae atroparvus* and *Culiseta annulata,* its nucleus becomes very highly branched, the branches forming a cup-shaped structure which roughly follows the contours of the egg, occupying a median position between the centre of the egg and the periphery. The extensive branching of the nucleus is clearly associated with the rapid synthesis of yolk, and the nuclei of the nutritive cells are also very large (Nicholson, 1921). Similar branching of the oocyte nucleus occurs in *Aedes aegypti* (Bauer, 1933) but Nath (1924, 1929) was unable to find any branching of the oocyte nucleus in *Culex pipiens fatigans*. Nicholson (1921) considers that in *Anopheles labranchiae atroparvus* the greater part of the nutritive material reaches the egg through the nurse cells and that these in turn must receive it from the rosette cells, modified cells of the follicular epithelium overlying the nurse cells, since the rosette cells are the only part of the epithelium which is not secreting the chorion in the later stages of oogenesis. The bigger yolk granules are composed of protein. When the oocyte is approaching its full size the cytoplasm of the nurse cells begins to disappear; simultaneously, large masses of deeply-staining material appear in the branches of the oocyte nucleus. Subsequently, the nuclei of the degenerate nurse cells, surrounded by their cell membranes, pass into the follicular epithelium. When the oocyte has stopped secreting yolk the oocyte nucleus resumes its normal size (Nicholson, 1921). Golgi apparatus is visible in the cells of the youngest follicles of *Culex pipiens fatigans*, and later it is found extensively in the follicular epithelium, nurse cells and oocyte. The majority of the Golgi elements in the oocyte develop lipid contents during development but those of the follicular epithelium and nurse cells never do (Nath, 1929).

The chorion or egg shell consists of 2 layers, the endochorion and exochorion. When the oocyte of *Anopheles labranchiae atroparvus* has reached about a third of its ultimate size the follicular epithelium secretes globules which fuse forming a coat around the entire egg except for a circular area below the future micropyle. This layer is the endochorion and it remains soft until some time after the egg has been laid, when it hardens to form a thin, dark membrane (Nicholson, 1921). According to Nath (1924) the inner layer is not part of the chorion but is a thick vitelline membrane secreted by the oocyte. The first parts of the exochorion to appear in *Anopheles* are the floats, corrugated, balloon-like expansions on either side of the egg. In 2 lateral regions of the follicle groups of very elongate epithelial cells appear, lying at right angles to the main axis of the egg, and the epithelium becomes folded so that some of the elongated cells overlie others. The floats are secreted between the outer cells and those lying immediately under them, each corrugation of the floats being formed over the surface of one of the elongated cells. Shortly afterwards the remainder of the exochorion appears in the form of a very thin membrane, from which processes extend into the follicular epithelium, a number penetrating each cell. The exochorion does not increase in thickness but the processes grow far into the cytoplasm of the epithelial cells until they reach their final size and form. The epithelium then undergoes degeneration and separates from the processes until it consists simply of a thin membrane to which irregular masses of flattened nuclei are attached, forming a sheath around the whole egg. At the stage when the endochorion is being formed the epithelial cells at the base of the anterior funicle enlarge and protrude inwards and come to lie between the nutritive cells and the epithelium, radiating in the form of a rosette. They appear to secrete the micropyle plug (Nicholson, 1921). Subsequently, the nurse cells degenerate and the micropyle apparatus is secreted under the rosette cells at the time when the exochorion is being layed down. In *Psorophora*, follicle cells in the same position as the rosette cells secrete the micropyle apparatus but they are not arranged so systematically (Harwood and Horsfall, 1957). In *Culex* the micropyle cup is secreted around the degenerating nurse cells (Nath, 1924).

The degeneration of a certain number of egg follicles in each gonotrophic cycle seems to be a normal occurrence in mosquitoes (Nicholson, 1921; Detinova, 1949; Hosoi, 1954a). The degeneration is first apparent in the follicular epithelium and develops later in the central mass. It appears to take place principally among follicles just resuming growth after the mosquito has taken a meal of blood but it also occurs, in older females at least, among follicles which have not reached the resting stage (Polovodova, 1949). The number of follicles degenerating is greater after a meal which is nutritionally inadequate (Hosoi, 1954a) and it is also high in females which have passed through several gonotrophic cycles (Detinova, 1949). Degeneration of a follicle within any ovariole does not prevent development of another follicle in that ovariole in the next cycle (Detinova, 1949).

It appears that after a sufficiently large blood meal the majority of follicles in the resting stage start to develop, although a few do not, but a number of the developing follicles degenerate during the early stages of oocyte development. Detinova (1949) suggested that after feeding only those follicles proceed to develop which have a sufficiently low threshold of sensitivity to the stimuli initiating oogenesis. If later on the material needed for ripening the eggs is not sufficient for all the follicles which have started to develop then some of the follicles degenerate, this double regulatory process allowing the remainder to develop fully. When development of one ovary is prevented experimentally it is found that the remaining ovary develops many more follicles than usual so that egg production is not reduced (Hosoi, 1954a).

Further evidence of competition between follicles is provided by an experiment of Larsen and Bodenstein (1959) in which ovaries at the resting stage were transplanted from *Culex pipiens pipiens* and *Aedes aegypti* into the abdomens of females of the autogenous mosquito *Culex pipiens* var. *molestus* (in which the ovaries develop automatically after emergence without blood feeding). As Table 16 shows, when the host was less than

TABLE 16. THE DEGREE OF DEVELOPMENT OF TRANSPLANTED OVARIES AND HOST'S OVARIES 4 TO 5 DAYS AFTER OVARIES IN THE RESTING STAGE (STAGE IIb) WERE TRANSPLANTED FROM *Culex pipiens pipiens* AND *Aedes aegypti* INTO *Culex pipiens* VAR. *molestus* OF DIFFERENT AGES. (FROM LARSEN AND BODENSTEIN, 1959).

Condition of host at time of transplantation		Number of Experiments	Number of experiments in which	
Age (hr)	Ovary stage		Host's ovaries develop	Donor's ovaries develop
0–16	Ia– Ib	19	0	19
24–48	IIIa–IIIb	18	18	18
50–65	IIIb–IVa	19	19	0

16 hr old the transplanted ovaries developed to maturity and suppressed development in the host's ovaries, but when the host was 50–65 hr old its own ovaries continued developing to maturity and suppressed development in those of the donor. The nature of the competition is not clear but it could involve competition for foodstuffs or active inhibition of the less advanced follicles.

Development of the follicle beyond the resting stage is stimulated by a gonadotrophic hormone secreted by the corpora allata after the female has taken a blood meal (p. 177). It has been claimed that the presence of sperm in the spermathecae is a prerequisite of ovary development in *Anopheles subpictus*, on the grounds that captive females which never mate in the laboratory never develop their ovaries after feeding and that unmated females in nature are found never to have developed their ovaries whereas mated females have always done so (Roy, 1940); this evidence is inadequate. It has been found in many species that virgin females develop their ovaries in the normal manner after feeding but that in many cases they will not lay these eggs until they have mated (p. 184), and it is probably either this fact or the difficulty of stimulating ovary development in some species in the laboratory which has led to claims that insemination is a prerequisite of ovary development, for example in *Anopheles minimus* (Muirhead Thomson, 1941b) and *Anopheles gambiae* (Muirhead Thomson, 1948).

The rate at which developing oocytes pass from the resting stage to maturity is controlled by the temperature which presumably acts both indirectly, by affecting the rate of digestion of blood, and directly on the growth of the oocyte. The speed of ovary development differs between species. *Anopheles gambiae* will oviposit within 2 days of feeding when the temperature is above 74°F (23·3°C); *Anopheles funestus,* on the other hand, requires 3 days for ovary development at temperatures below 76·5°F (24·7°C) and not until the temperature is raised to 78°F (25·5°C) will all females oviposit within 2 days of feeding (Gillies, 1953). In Assam females of *Anopheles vagus* are ready to lay their eggs 24 hr after taking a blood meal (Muirhead-Thomson, 1951b). In southern Russia, in Stalingrad Oblast, females of *Anopheles maculipennis* could complete 12 gonotrophic cycles in 42 days whereas in the Moscow Oblast the same number of cycles took 79 days (Detinova, 1962). Ovarian development in autogenous females of *Culex pipiens* could be suspended for periods of 10 days or more by lowering the temperature to 40°F (4·4°C), but development was resumed with the return to normal temperatures (Spielman, 1957). It seems that the gonotrophic cycle lasts 2 days for most species under tropical conditions, but that in cooler regions the gonotrophic cycle will be longer and will vary more widely owing to the wider fluctuations of temperature.

In laboratory studies and in field work it is often convenient to classify the stage of development of the ovaries according to a somewhat artificial scheme. The scheme devised by Christophers (1911) has been widely used and is given in a slightly modified form below incorporating some of the changes suggested by Mer (1936) and Macan (1950).

Stage Ia   the follicle is spherical and the oocyte is not differentiated from the nurse cells

Ib   the follicle is oval and consists of an oocyte and 7 nurse cells surrounded by a distinct follicular epithelium

Stage IIa   a few very fine yolk granules, visible only under a $\frac{1}{6}$ in. objective, appear around the oocyte nucleus

IIb   a few coarse yolk granules, visible under a $\frac{2}{3}$ in. objective, appear around the oocyte nucleus; the follicle is in the resting stage

Stage IIIa   the follicle has left the resting stage; the oocyte cytoplasm is cloudy with yolk granules visible under a low-power, binocular microscope and the oocyte occupies about half the follicle

IIIb   the yolk obscures the oocyte nucleus and the oocyte occupies two-thirds to three-quarters of the follicle

Stage IVa   the follicle starts to elongate and the nurse cells occupy only about one-tenth of it

IVb   the follicle assumes the shape of the mature egg

Stage V   chorionic structures such as the floats (*Anopheles*) and micropyle cup (*Culex*) are visible; the egg becomes ready for laying.

Autogeny

Theobald (1901) appears to have been the first to notice that some individuals of *Culex pipiens* can lay eggs without feeding on blood. Roubaud (1929, 1933) showed that this ability is restricted to certain genetically-distinct populations, now called *Culex pipiens* var. *molestus,* and he coined the word autogeny to describe it. Autogenous mosquitoes are able to lay a single egg raft without feeding but require blood before they can develop more eggs. The autogenous females clearly use reserves carried over from the larval stage in maturing their first batch of eggs and most early workers thought that the basic difference between the autogenous and anautogenous races of *Culex pipiens* was the amount of reserves available to the adult. There was certain evidence against this view for some workers found that poor larval nutrition reduced the number of eggs laid by autogenous mosquitoes but did not prevent their developing such eggs (Gaschen, 1932; Hecht, 1933), and even larvae reared near the starvation limit produced females which were all autogenous (de Buck, 1935). Other workers, however, found that poor larval nutrition not only lowered the egg yield of laying females but also reduced the number of laying females in an autogenous population (Boissezon, 1930d; Shute, 1951; Déduit, 1957).

A detailed investigation of the reserves of newly-emerged autogenous and anautogenous females of *Culex pipiens* was made by Clements (1956a) who concluded that there was no great difference in the type or amount of the reserves and that the young anautogenous female contained sufficient reserves in the fat body and autolysed abdominal muscles for the formation of a number of eggs. Broadly similar conclusions were reached by Twohy and Rozeboom (1957). Clements (1956a) suggested that the difference between the autogenous and anautogenous races of *Culex pipiens* was not in the reserves but lay in the hormonal control of ovary growth. It was postulated that a gonadotrophic hormone was secreted automatically after emergence in autogenous mosquitoes but was not secreted by anautogenous mosquitoes without the stimulus of a blood meal; this hypothesis has proved correct (p. 179).

Experiments by A. O. Lea (unpublished), however, indicate that larval nutrition is in some way connected with the appearance of autogeny in a population. Lea reared larvae of *Aedes aegypti* on a rich diet of liver and yeast and fed the adults 1 per cent albumen solution. Over successive generations the albumen solution was progressively diluted and after a number of generations autogeny appeared in a colony in which it had previously been unknown. It appears that the combination of extremely rich larval food and poor adult diet somehow led to a change in reproductive physiology or allowed a mutation to become established. Weyer (1934) had noticed that when larvae of *Aedes aegypti* and *Anopheles maculipennis* were fed a particularly rich diet the ovarian follicles would develop beyond the resting stage without adult feeding.

The details of autogeny are clearly not the same in all species which show this character. Certain populations of *Aedes communis* obtain the materials required for autogenous ovary development from their fat body and abdominal muscles (Beckel, 1954) whereas other populations of that species also histolyse their indirect flight muscles (Hocking, 1954).

After early crossing experiments between autogenous and anautogenous strains of *Culex pipiens* in which autogeny disappeared from the F_1 generation and reappeared in the F_2 it was postulated that autogeny was the result of a single recessive gene in a homozygous condition, and that the anautogenous character was a simple Mendelian dominant (Roubaud, 1930, 1933). However, autogenous females occasionally appear in the F_1 generation, and the F_2 generation usually does not have the 3 : 1 ratio which would be expected (Kitzmiller, 1953; Krishnamurthy and Laven, 1961). It seems to be characteristic of all crosses between the 2 strains that autogeny appears irregularly in the succeeding generations. Spielman (1957) considers it most probable that factors controlling autogeny occur on 2 chromosomes. Autogeny is now known to occur very widely and has been recorded in the following genera: *Anopheles* (Markovitch, 1941), *Aedes* (Vermeil, 1953), *Culex* (Roubaud, 1929), *Culiseta* (Marshall and Staley, 1936), *Deinocerites* (Haeger and Phinizee, 1959), *Mansonia* (Anon, 1960), *Toxorhynchites* (Muspratt, 1952), *Tripteroides* (Dobrotworsky, 1955) and *Wyeomyia* (Price, 1958b). Circumstantial evidence suggests that it may also occur in other genera including *Malaya, Opifex* and *Uranotaenia.*

Hormonal Control of Ovary Development

The Stomatogastric System and Endocrine Organs

The stomatogastric system has been described by Cazal (1948) (Fig. 57a). From the frontal ganglion a pair of connectives run to the front of the brain and a recurrent nerve runs back, between the aorta and pharynx,

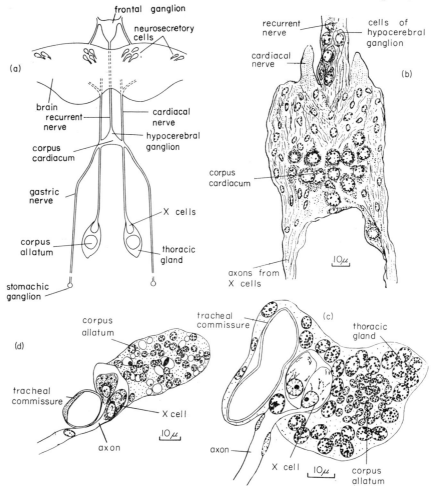

Fig. 57a–d.   The stomatogastric system and endocrine organs.
(a) The stomatogastric system and endocrine organs of a *Culex* pupa; (b) horizontal section through the fused corpora cardiaca, the hypocerebral ganglion is situated below the corpus cardiacum and a few of its cells can be seen in the recurrent nerve; (c) longitudinal section through a thoracic gland, corpus allatum and X cells of a *Culex* pupa; (d) longitudinal section through a corpus allatum and X cells of a *Culex* adult. (a after Cazal (1948) with additions, b from Cazal (1948), c original, d from Clements (1956a)).

to end in the hypocerebral ganglion a short distance behind the brain. Two gastric nerves connect the hypocerebral ganglion with a pair of stomachic ganglia lying on either side of the gut. The cibarial pump is innervated from the frontal ganglion (Day, 1954).

Neurosecretory cells are present in the brain and in the ganglia of the ventral nerve cord but their axons can be traced for only short distances (Clements, 1956a). According to Cazal (1948) a pair of cardiacal nerves, each with 2 roots in the brain which are presumably composed of the axons of neurosecretory cells as in other insects, run back from the brain to join an unpaired corpus cardiacum which is fused to the hypocerebral ganglion below the aorta in the neck (Fig. 57b). Clements (1956a) failed to find the corpus cardiacum in this position and considered that it occurred elsewhere, but the description of a corpus cardiacum fused to the hypocerebral ganglion in *Chaoborus* (Chaoboridae) (Füller, 1960) suggests that this must be the condition in mosquitoes also.

Paired endocrine organs are found behind a transverse tracheal commissure in the front of the thorax (Fig. 57c, d) (Bodenstein, 1945b; Cazal, 1948; Clements, 1956a). Each contains an oval corpus allatum, apparently syncytial, consisting of a number of rather small nuclei dispersed in cytoplasm. The corpora allata grow in size and in number of nuclei after emergence, decreasing in size after the female has taken a blood meal (Detinova, 1945a; Mednikova, 1952). Each corpus allatum is surrounded by a tissue containing very large nuclei and rather sparse cytoplasm; since this tissue degenerates early in adult life it is almost certainly thoracic gland. Two nerves run back from the corpus cardiacum to end just in front of the corpora allata, not as nerve endings but as cell bodies with large nuclei and extensive cytoplasm containing granular material which stains with Gomori's chrome haematoxylin, a stain for neurosecretory material (Figs. 57c, d) (Clements, 1956a). Until the structure of the endocrine organs of mosquitoes is reinvestigated the homology of these cells must remain in doubt and they are here called X cells. Somewhat similar cells with forward-directed axons are found, with other cells, in the corpora cardiaca of *Ptychoptera* (Ptychopteridae) (Thomsen, 1951), and it is an interesting possibility that the corpora cardiaca of mosquitoes have become divided into separate parts.

Experimental Evidence of Hormonal Control

From knowledge of the physiology of other blood-sucking insects it has long seemed likely that gorging by female mosquitoes stimulates secretion of a gonadotrophic hormone resulting in the development of the ovaries, the hormone conveniently linking ovary growth to the supply of nourishment. Data from other insects indicate that the corpora allata and the neurosecretory cells of the brain are probable sources of hormone.

Larsen and Bodenstein (1959) brought about maturation of the ovaries of anautogenous females of *Culex pipiens* and *Aedes aegypti* by injecting blood into the stomach via the anus, showing that the stimulus for secretion of the postulated gonadotrophic hormone was not dependent on blood passing through the foregut. Milk injected by the same route clotted in the stomach and stimulated ovary development but the injection of saline or gelatine solution, which produced no long-term distension of the midgut, failed to stimulate ovary development. When mosquitoes which had been sealed at the anus and fed apple slices were dissected several days later it was found that the midgut was greatly distended and that the ovaries had developed at the expense of protein reserves carried over from the larva. This was thought to provide conclusive evidence that distension of the abdomen, probably of the midgut itself, for a sufficient period stimulates afferent nervous impulses leading directly or indirectly to the release of gonadotrophic hormone. Detinova (1953b, 1962) arrived at the same conclusion from rather similar experiments with *Anopheles maculipennis*. This conclusion certainly seems correct but it does not account for the stimulation of ovary development in *Aedes aegypti* by a solution of amino acids and sugars which is stored in the diverticulum (Dimond *et al.*, 1956).

Indirect evidence of hormonal control has accumulated over a number of years: Detinova (1945a) showed that ligaturing *Anopheles maculipennis* across the metathorax within 6 hr of gorging prevented ovary development; Clements (1956a) showed that ligation at the base of the abdomen prevented development of the ovaries in *Anopheles stephensi* when performed within 1 hr of gorging, and that decapitation or ligation prevented ovary development in the autogenous mosquito *Culex pipiens* var. *molestus* when performed within a few hours of emergence (Fig. 58); Gillett (1958) decapitated females of *Aedes aegypti* a few hours after gorging so that some but not all could be expected to develop their oocytes, and found that injection into these females of haemolymph taken from other individuals which were at a slightly later stage of ovary development significantly increased the proportion which developed their oocytes to maturity; Larsen and Bodenstein (1959) transplanted ovaries from unfed, anautogenous females of *Culex pipiens pipiens* and *Aedes aegypti* into other anautogenous females, which were subsequently fed on either blood or apple slices, and found that the transplanted ovaries developed when the host fed on blood but not when it fed on apple slices; they also showed that ovaries transplanted from unfed anautogenous females of *Culex pipiens pipiens* and *Aedes aegypti* into the autogenous females of *Culex pipiens* var.

molestus developed to maturity but that ovaries transplanted from auto-genous females into unfed, anautogenous females remained in diapause.

Proof of hormonal control was given by Larsen (1958) and Larsen and Bodenstein (1959) who transplanted the corpora allata (and X cells) from autogenous females of *Culex pipiens* var. *molestus* aged less than 24 hr into anautogenous females of *Culex pipiens pipiens* and *Aedes aegypti* which

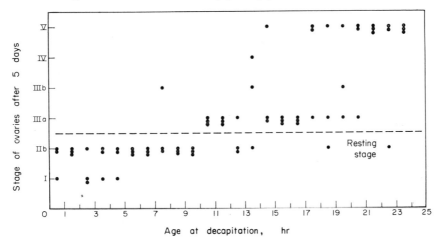

F<small>IG</small>. 58.   The stage of development of the ovaries of *Culex pipiens* var. *molestus* aged 5 days which had been decapitated at different times after emergence.   Each point represents 1 female.   (From Clements, 1956a).

had never taken a blood meal. In a small number of cases the host's ovaries developed almost to maturity. The same workers produced maturation of the ovaries in unfed anautogenous females of *Culex pipiens pipiens* and *Aedes aegypti* by injecting extracts of corpora allata of the cockroaches *Periplaneta* and *Blaberus*. In all these cases the ovaries developed at the expense of protein reserves carried over from the larval stage.

The corpora allata decrease in volume and their cells show changes in appearance following a blood meal in *Anopheles maculipennis* (Detinova, 1945a) and *Culex pipiens pipiens* (Larsen and Bodenstein, 1959) and similar changes appear to take place in *Anopheles claviger* (Mednikova, 1952). In the autogenous females of *Culex pipiens* var. *molestus* the corpora allata almost double in size through increase in cytoplasm during the first day of adult life but shrink very considerably during the next 24 hr simultaneous with the early stages of ovary development (Larsen and Bodenstein, 1959).

In the females of *Aedes aegypti* studied by Larsen and Bodenstein (1959) the critical period after gorging for development to maturity was about 50 min in the case of decapitation and about 180 min in the case of ligation at the base of the abdomen, so one might deduce that 50 min were required for activation of the corpora allata, possibly by the neuro-secretory cells of the brain, and that a further 2 hr were required for the corpora allata to secrete their hormone in high enough titre to produce maturation of the ovaries. Larsen and Bodenstein (1959) showed that individual ovarioles transplanted from *Culex pipiens* var. *molestus* into *Culex pipiens pipiens* would develop to maturity if transplanted at stage IIIb but not if transplanted earlier and they concluded that the follicles needed to remain in the presence of hormone up to stage IIIb in order to develop to maturity.

From observations on decapitated *Aedes aegypti* Gillett (1956b) postulated that the development of the follicles from the resting stage to maturity took place in two steps. When females were decapitated within 2 min of taking a blood meal the follicles made no growth but when decapitation was delayed for 2 min to 8 hr the follicles in a proportion of the females developed to stages IIIa or IIIb (of the classification given on p. 173) and a delay of over 8 hr permitted development to maturity in a proportion of cases, in all if the delay lasted for 14 hr. This might be interpreted as indicating a gradual release of hormone but Gillett found that when development occurred at all the follicles developed either to stages IIIa or IIIb or to stage V and that development never stopped at stage IV. Similar results were obtained with *Aedes aegypti* and *Culex pipiens pipiens*, although with a different time scale, by Larsen and Boden-stein (1959); no ovary development occurred in females decapitated within 17 min of feeding whereas development to stage IIIb occurred when decapitation was delayed for 30–40 min and to stage V when decapitation was delayed for 50–60 min. In females of *Culex pipiens* var. *molestus* decapitated at intervals after emergence follicle development tended to proceed only a short way or to maturity, with only one individual stopping at stage IV (Fig. 58) (Clements, 1956a); Larsen and Bodenstein (1959) also found 2 steps in follicle development in *Culex pipiens* var. *molestus*. In *Anopheles* the importance of the nurse cells rapidly diminishes after stage III (Christophers, 1911; Nicholson, 1921) and it is possible, as Gillett (1956b) has suggested, that in the first step of follicle growth the nurse cells are of major importance and in the second step the follicular epithel-ium or more probably the oocyte itself. Gillett (1956b) noticed that those decapitated females of *Aedes aegypti* which developed their ovaries only to stage III usually eliminated the blood meal by defaecation 28–32 hr after feeding, whereas in females which developed their ovaries to maturity elimination of the blood meal was delayed for a further 7–10 hr.

As we have seen, the transplantation of active corpora allata (and X cells) from autogenous females into unfed, anautogenous females leads to maturation of the host's follicles indicating that the corpora allata (and X cells) may stimulate both the early and late stages of follicle development. Since the follicles will develop to stage IIIb in females of *Culex pipiens* var. *berbericus* and *Aedes aegypti* ligatured at the base of the abdomen within 2 or 3 min of starting to feed (Clements, 1956a) it seems probable that the early stages of follicle development can take place without corpus allatum hormone, although what the stimulus for development is in this case is not known. It is not the experimental procedure itself since no follicle growth is made in unfed controls which are ligatured (Clements, unpublished). Of females of *Anopheles labranchiae atroparvus* ligatured at the base of the abdomen within 2–4 min of starting to feed a considerable proportion had developed their ovaries to stage IV when examined 3 days later and it is possible that if left they would have developed their follicles to maturity (Clements, 1956a). This result differs from that of Detinova (1945a) who found that a ligature tied around the metathorax of *Anopheles maculipennis* sensu lato within 6 hr of feeding would prevent ovary development, but Detinova also found that decapitation did not interfere with ovary development. It is possible that these closely-related species differ in their reproductive physiology from species such as *Culex pipiens* and *Aedes aegypti*, and a detailed experimental investigation of their reproduction would probably be rewarding.

Despite the fairly intensive studies which have been made on the humoral control of ovary development in mosquitoes relatively little has been established. We know that in anautogenous females the stretching of the abdomen by a blood meal probably triggers the controlling mechanism leading some time later to secretion of a gonadotrophic hormone by the corpora allata, and decapitation experiments have shown that the head must be present for a certain period for the corpora allata to become activated. In autogenous females the corpora allata appear to secrete the gonadotrophic hormone a few hours after emergence without the stimulus of a blood meal but what activates the corpora allata in this case is not known.

In the decapitation and ligation experiments of Clements (1956a), Gillett (1956b) and Larsen and Bodenstein (1959) there is a consistency in the timing of the critical period established by each worker for different species or strains that is absent when the results of the different workers with the same species are considered. This suggests that details of the experimental procedures may have had important effects on the outcome of the experiments; genetic differences may also have been involved. The effect of experimental conditions has been demonstrated by Gillett (1957a) who found that the critical period for the development of follicles to maturity occurred 4–8 hr after the blood meal in females of *Aedes aegypti* which had had no other access to food, but occurred 6–12 hr after the blood meal when the females had previously imbibed fruit juice.

Ovulation and Oviposition

The muscular activity of the reproductive organs was investigated by Curtin and Jones (1961) in females of *Aedes aegypti* from which a portion of the body wall had been removed. In non-gravid females the ampullae twitched, the lateral oviducts contracted vigorously and waves of contraction swept forwards over the ovaries, the sheaths of the two ovaries contracting asynchronously. The frequency of contraction of the ovarian sheaths and oviducts varied from one strain to another but it was not affected by age, insemination, isolation from the nervous system or from the endocrine organs of the head and thorax, or by the earlier stages of ovary development, but in gravid females the distension of the ovaries prevented the large contraction waves of the ovarian sheath.

The follicular epithelium breaks down as the developing eggs reach maturity so that the space in which the eggs lie becomes continuous with the lumen of the oviducts (Giglioli, 1959). Observations of Curtin and Jones (1961) on gravid females of *Aedes aegypti* showed that the vigorous, rhythmical contractions of the lateral oviducts were much more important for ovulation (the passage of the egg from the ovary into the oviduct) than were the relatively weak movements of the ovary sheath. At oviposition the 8th abdominal segment was extended causing the common oviduct to straighten out, and when females were forced to lay by decapitation it could be seen that oviposition also was due to the contractions of the lateral oviducts, the common oviduct remaining quite impassive. The genital chamber also appears to play a passive role in oviposition, for in *Aedes aegypti* and *Aedes polynesiensis* an egg issuing from the genital chamber is wiped on to the substratum by movements of the abdomen and if one sticks in the breech it is removed by the hind legs (Wallis, 1954a), while an egg laid by *Anopheles* first protrudes from the genital chamber and is then discharged by a flick of the abdomen (Rozeboom, 1936; Keener, 1945). It is therefore probably true to say that the movement of the egg from the ovariole to the lips of the genital chamber is caused predominantly by movements of the lateral oviducts whereas in the final act of deposition movements of the whole abdomen play a part. Such movements are particularly developed in *Sabethes chloropterus* in which the female while in flight suddenly jerks the head and thorax back and thrusts the abdomen forward, forcibly ejecting 1 or 2 eggs. The eggs are accurately aimed to pass through a small aperture, which may be up to 6 cm away, leading to one of the enclosed tree holes which form the larval habitat of this species (Galindo, 1958). In mosquitoes the posterior pole of the egg is first to issue from the genital chamber and the egg is thought to be penetrated by sperm when the micropyle at the anterior pole passes the openings of the spermathecal ducts (Polovodova, 1947). From the structure of the egg it has been suggested that in *Anopheles* (Nicholson, 1921) and *Culex* (Nath, 1924) compression of the egg as it passes through the genital chamber causes the micropyle apparatus to bulge outwards and later retract drawing sperm into it. However, this can only be regarded as speculative.

The muscle systems of the ovary sheath and lateral oviducts are capable of rhythmic contractions after isolation of the reproductive system indicating that these contractions are myogenic. However, ovulation and oviposition appear to be under nervous control, for they do not take place under adverse conditions such as the absence of water although a severe shock such as stunning, decapitation, ether poisoning or insecticide poisoning leads to oviposition in many species (Shute, 1933b; DeCoursey and Webster, 1952; Curtin and Jones, 1961). Females of *Anopheles quadrimaculatus* discharge their eggs when treated with insecticides but not after decapitation (DeCoursey *et al.*, 1953). That great distension of the ovaries is not the stimulus leading to ovulation and oviposition is suggested by the fact that *Aedes aegypti* do not always lay all their eggs at one time but may lay them over several days (Gillett, 1955b; Curtin and Jones, 1961). Eggs are discharged from both ovaries at about the same rate so that the ovaries are emptied of mature eggs almost simultaneously (Polovodova, 1947; Curtin and Jones, 1961).

Mosquitoes usually lay their eggs shortly after they have matured but oviposition may be delayed or prevented by cold (Nicholson, 1921; Mayne, 1926a), absence of water (Fielding, 1919; Holstein, 1952; Woke, 1955) or by failure to mate (Macfie, 1915; Mer, 1936; Tate and Vincent, 1936). Females of *Aedes aegypti* which had been given 1 blood meal and which had subsequently been fed on sugar solution and kept away from open water retained their eggs up to 90 days, laying when provided with water. The viability of the eggs declined rapidly when they had been retained for more than 15 days after blood feeding; 30 days after the blood meal only 38 per cent were viable although 98 per cent of the eggs formed were deposited, while after the 45th day none of the eggs laid was viable. With the passage of time a decreasing proportion of eggs formed was deposited so that after 60–90 days retention 30 per cent or less were deposited and many eggs were abnormal in appearance. There was no evidence that eggs were resorbed (Woke, 1955). Very similar results have been obtained with *Culex pusillus* but in that species the eggs remained

N

viable for a rather longer period and after 58 days retention 8 per cent of the eggs laid were still viable (Shalaby, 1959). The mortality rate was normal among females of *Aedes aegypti* and *Culex pusillus* fed blood once and retaining their eggs in the absence of water (Woke, 1955; Shalaby, 1959) but it has been reported to be slightly higher than normal among females of *Aedes aegypti* which retained their eggs because they had not been inseminated and which took frequent blood meals (Lavoipierre, 1958a).

Gillett (1955c, 1956a) has investigated the effect of mating on oviposition in 2 strains of *Aedes aegypti*. Eighty-six per cent of unmated females from Lagos laid within 5 days of feeding whereas only 8 per cent of unmated females from Newala laid during this period although they contained mature oocytes in their ovaries. When virgin females of the Newala strain were mated up to 3 weeks after feeding 80 per cent laid within 2 or 3 days. The differences of oviposition behaviour between the two strains were found to have a genetic basis.

Gillett (1955c) was able to show that it was the presence of semen in the female, rather than the act of copulation, which led to oviposition by females of the Newala strain of *Aedes aegypti* since oviposition did not ensue when females were mated with infertile males. When groups of 8 Newala females were mated in quick succession to single males fertile eggs were laid by the first 3 or 4 mates, a few infertile eggs were laid by some of the 4th and 5th mates, but no eggs were laid by the 6th, 7th or 8th mates. Males were able to inseminate females again after a rest of 36 hr whereas copulation after a shorter period resulted in the females laying full batches of infertile eggs. Gillett concluded that in the latter case seminal fluid had been transferred but not sperm and that this also accounted for the small numbers of infertile eggs laid by some of the 4th and 5th mates. Terzian and Stahler (1958) irradiated male mosquitoes and found that this sometimes affected the oviposition of the females to which they were mated. When males of *Aedes aegypti* were exposed to 20,000 r and mated the following day the females oviposited like normal fertile females but the eggs did not hatch although the spermathecae contained motile sperm. When mating was deferred for 15 days after irradiation the pattern of oviposition resembled that of virgin females and it was found that in only half the females did the spermathecae contain motile sperm.

It may be concluded that ovulation and oviposition are effected principally by the movements of the lateral oviducts and of the abdomen as a whole, and that the process is controlled by the nervous system. In some mosquitoes seminal fluid must be present in the spermathecae before ovulation and oviposition can proceed but the mechanism linking this stimulus with the eventual muscular activity remains unknown although it has been suggested that a hormone is involved (Gillett, 1955c).

Fecundity

The number of eggs laid in a batch, i.e. laid by a single female during 1 gonotrophic cycle, varies greatly between species. In the first gonotrophic cycle *Anopheles maculipennis melanoon* lays up to 500 eggs (Shannon and Hadjinicalao, 1941); *Culex pipiens pipiens* lays 250–400 (Christophers, 1945; Möllring, 1956); *Culiseta annulata* and *Culiseta subochrea* lay up to 300 (Marshall, 1938); *Anopheles maculipennis messeae* lays about 280 (Detinova, 1955); *Aedes detritus* lays up to 260 (Marshall, 1938) but other species of *Aedes* usually lay fewer than this and the batch size is normally below 100 in *Aedes aegypti* and *Aedes polynesiensis* (Woke *et al.*, 1956; Ingram, 1954). *Culex pipiens* var. *molestus* lays a raft of 50–80 eggs without feeding and may subsequently lay 80–100 eggs after each blood meal (Christophers, 1945).

Several factors may affect the size of the egg batch in any species. The number of eggs laid shows a positive correlation with the size of the female in several species of *Anopheles* (Roy, 1931; Shannon and Hadjinicalao, 1941; Detinova, 1955), in *Aedes hexodontus* (Barlow, 1955) and in *Aedes aegypti* (Colless and Chellapah, 1960), and this is thought to account for the greater egg production in *Anopheles maculipennis messeae* than in *Anopheles labranchiae atroparvus* (Detinova, 1955). Some workers failed to find this correlation in *Aedes aegypti* (Roy, 1936; Woke *et al.*, 1956) but that was probably because they did not exclude from their calculations females which had failed to lay at all (Colless and Chellapah, 1960). The number of eggs laid in a batch by *Aedes aegypti* shows a positive correlation with the amount of blood ingested (Roy, 1936; Woke *et al.*, 1956; Colless and Chellapah, 1960), but as Fig. 59 shows this is only the case with medium-sized and small blood meals and there is no increase in egg production after 3 mg of blood have been ingested. In *Aedes hexodontus,* however, the number of eggs laid is proportional to size of blood meal between 1 and 5 mg (Barlow, 1955). Woke *et al.* (1956) and Colless and Chellapah (1960) failed to find any significant correlation between the volume of blood ingested and the size of the female in *Aedes aegypti*, but Bar-Zeev (1957a) found that females of this species derived from well nourished larvae ingested over twice as much blood as females reared under conditions of starvation and Barlow (1955) found that heavier females of *Aedes hexodontus* ingested more blood. The number of ovarioles in the 2 ovaries of *Aedes aegypti* shows a positive correlation with the size of the female, numbers varying beween 50 and 150 (Colless and Chellapah,

1960). Within any species, therefore, the size of the individual female, which varies with the larval breeding conditions, will have a pronounced effect on the number of eggs she lays, acting partly through the number of ovarioles available for development. In *Aedes aegypti* the size of the blood meal does not affect fecundity unless it falls below about 2 mg. In wild *Aedes hexodontus* it was observed that a seasonal fall in blood meal weight from 3·5 to 1·5 mg was not accompanied by a reduction in mosquito weight and caused no reduction in fecundity and it was con-

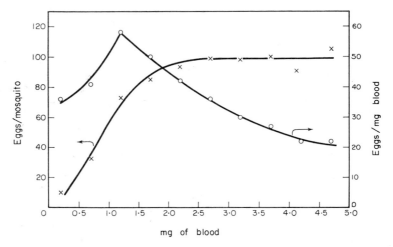

Fig. 59. The relationship between size of blood meal (as measured by weighing the mosquito before and within 15 min after feeding on man) and number of eggs developed by females of *Aedes aegypti* fed for the first time. (After Woke *et al.* (1956), modified to exclude females which developed no eggs).

cluded that adult size was the dominant factor controlling fecundity in this species (Barlow, 1955). The nature of the blood ingested exerts a strong effect on the number of eggs laid (p. 160) and the removal of water, by concentrating the blood during feeding (p. 129), may exert some effect also. According to Shannon and Hadjinicalao (1941) the size of the egg does not vary with the size of the female in *Anopheles* but does vary considerably between species, as the following average egg lengths show: *Anopheles superpictus* 0·53 mm, *Anopheles sacharovi* 0·61 mm, *Anopheles maculipennis melanoon* 0·63 mm, *Anopheles maculipennis maculipennis* 0·67 mm. Autogenous females of *Culex pipiens* var. *molestus* from undernourished larvae lay not only fewer but also smaller eggs than usual (Oelhafen, 1961).

Mosquitoes usually survive to lay a number of batches of eggs in the laboratory. Females of *Anopheles labranchiae atroparvus* which survived long enough to lay more than 10 batches were estimated to have laid approximately 2500 eggs each, and one female laid 17 times (Shute, 1936). Three females of *Aedes aegypti* laid 22 times in 87 days, laying on average 1360 eggs each (Mathis, 1935). A small proportion of females of *Anopheles maculipennis messeae* survive in nature to lay 10 times (Detinova, 1955) and females have been taken whose ovaries show a history of 13 gonotrophic cycles (Detinova, 1953c, 1955; Kozhevnikova, 1953). In all mosquitoes which have been studied, the number of eggs laid in each batch decreases with successive gonotrophic cycles (Roubaud, 1934; Putnam and Shannon, 1934; Detinova, 1949). This results from the increase in the number of follicles which degenerate during the later gonotrophic cycles and this factor eliminates the relationship between body weight and size of egg batch which is found during the first 2 cycles in *Anopheles maculipennis messeae* (Detinova, 1955). With *Aedes aegypti* it was estimated that each successive egg batch contained 15 per cent fewer eggs than the one which preceded it (Putnam and Shannon, 1934).

Seasonal variations in size of egg batch have been reported in a number of species of *Anopheles* (Mer, 1931; Shannon and Hadjinicalao, 1941; Detinova, 1955). Shannon and Hadjinicalao (1941) showed that the temperature prevailing during larval development affected adult size in *Anopheles* and hence size of egg batch and Detinova (1955) showed how the progressive decline in size of egg batches with increasing age affected results at various seasons.

These seasonal variations are well illustrated by studies made in the Soviet Union on egg-batch size in *Anopheles maculipennis*. Females which have overwintered lay an average of 195 eggs in their first egg batch in April. In May, when they have passed through 2–3 gonotrophic cycles the average batch size drops to 172 and this again drops to 149 in June. The offspring of these overwintering mosquitoes are flying in June and as they have developed at low temperatures they are larger than the over-wintered females and the average size of their first egg batch is 289 eggs. During July and August these females will continue to lay but will pro-duce progressively smaller egg batches. At the same time other females are emerging and laying their first egg batches, but since these females developed at progressively higher temperatures it is found that they diminish in size as they emerge through July and August and that their first egg batches are also smaller than those produced in June, consisting of 263 eggs in July and 256 in August. From the middle of August the emerging females start to enter diapause (Detinova, 1955). It can be seen that the conditions of temperature and nourishment during larval develop-ment affect the size of the female and consequently the size of the egg batch and that fecundity falls with age, while the simultaneous occurrence of females of different generations leads to a population whose members vary widely in reproductive potential.

Determination of Reproductive History

Because mosquitoes must feed twice to acquire and transmit pathogens it is often important to know the proportions of females in a population which are nulliparous, i.e. which have yet to lay their first batch of eggs, and which are parous, having laid one or more egg batches, especially if the latter can be classified as uniparous, biparous, and so on. The first character to be used in distinguishing parous from nulliparous females was described by Mer (1932) who showed that the ampullae at the anterior end of the common oviduct swell during the first gonotrophic cycle and do not return to their original size after oviposition. Subsequently, Detinova (1945b) described how the fine tracheae and tracheoles of the ovary are coiled in tight spirals in nulliparous females, and that they open up permanently during the first gonotrophic cycle. Unfortunately, this method cannot be applied with certainty when the ovaries have passed stage II (Gillies, 1958).

A great advance was made by Polovodova (1949) who discovered changes in the ovariole. When an egg about to be laid passes into the oviduct it leaves the pedicel and the region of the tunica propria which had previously surrounded it highly distended. The pedicel later returns to its normal size but the swollen region of tunica propria within 48 hr forms a small, sac-like dilatation which usually contains remnants of the nurse cells and follicular epithelium, called the follicular relic (Fig. 60). When a second egg is ovulated from the same ovariole the process is repeated and a second dilatation appears anterior to the first, and although the original follicular relic is swept out by the passage of the egg the original dilatation remains. When a female has passed through several gonotrophic cycles her ovarioles bear chains of dilatations, the most posterior dilatations marking the places where eggs of the first batch developed, the most anterior the places where the last batch developed. The ovariole sheath remains as a wide, outer sleeve, unaffected by the development of the eggs.

Follicles which degenerate also form dilatations with follicular relics and these characteristically appear pigmented, at least until the passage of an egg from an overlying follicle discharges the pigment. It sometimes happens that a number of eggs are retained in the ovarioles at oviposition. They may be laid with the next batch of eggs or may be resorbed, but in either case during the following gonotrophic cycle the follicle anterior to the retained egg, which would normally have developed, degenerates and leaves a dilatation (Detinova, 1953a). A female of *Anopheles maculipennis messeae* examined by Detinova (1949) had laid 104, 98 and 103 eggs in 3 batches, a total of 305. Dissection showed that the ovarioles bore 377 dilatations of which 25 were pigmented, having formed from follicles which degenerated in the third cycle. Of the 377 dilatations, 305 had formed from the passage of normally-developed eggs whereas the remaining 72 must have formed from degenerated follicles, an average of 24 per cycle. The two ovaries contained 160 ovarioles so that development

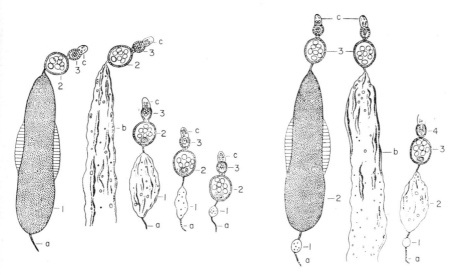

FIG. 60. The formation of dilatations and follicular relics in an ovariole of a mosquito during 2 gonotrophic cycles. 1, 1st follicle and subsequent dilatation; 2, 2nd follicle and subsequent dilatation; 3 and 4, 3rd and 4th follicles; a, pedicel; b, pedicel, tunica propria and ovariole sheath distended after ovulation; c, germarium. (From Beklemishev *et al.*, 1959).

of all ovarioles in each cycle would have produced 480 dilatations. Thus in the 3 cycles 103 ovarioles failed to develop, an average of 34 per cycle.

In determining the reproductive history of a female it is necessary to examine a number of ovarioles since not all produce an egg in each cycle, but if this precaution is taken the number of gonotrophic cycles which the female has passed through can be determined with certainty. Although examination of the ovarioles is difficult in small species it has been carried out successfully on various species of *Anopheles* (Polovodova, 1949; Detinova, 1949), *Culex*, *Aedes* (Colless, 1958) and *Mansonia* (Bertram and Samarawickrema, 1958; Wharton, 1959). Large samples can be analysed more rapidly by identifying the nulliparous individuals on external characters such as extent of wear, colour of integument, and presence of meconium, or by examining the ovarian tracheae (Corbet, 1959, 1960). The examination of *Anopheles maculipennis* in Russia showed that wild populations contained a considerable proportion of females which had passed through 2 or more gonotrophic cycles (Gillies, 1958; Detinova, 1962) and which could therefore have acted as vectors (Fig. 47).

CHAPTER 10

SENSE ORGANS

The Compound Eyes

Structure of the Compound Eyes

The structure of the compound eyes has been described in several species, and it is found to vary only slightly (Constantineaunu, 1930; Satô, 1950, 1953a, b, 1957, 1959, 1960; Christophers, 1960). The 2 eyes cover much of the front and sides of the head and almost meet each other above and below. Ommatidia are directed forwards, sideways, upwards, downwards and, to a slight extent, backwards, the visual angle in the horizontal plane being nearly 225° (Rao, 1947). The eyes are of approximately the same size relative to the body in the 2 sexes although those of the male are more emarginated anteriorly to accommodate the larger antennal pedicels. Recorded numbers of ommatidia in a single eye range from 358–369 ♂ and 421–492 ♀ in *Aedes aegypti* (Christophers, 1960) to 779–824 ♂ and 878–963♀ in *Armigeres subalbatus* (Satô, 1960). The ommatidia differ in size and proportions from one region of the eye to another although not in a uniform manner among the different species; however, in each species the facets are always larger in the female eye than in the corresponding region of the male eye.

In its basic structure of dioptric apparatus and retinula the mosquito ommatidium resembles that of other insects but there are several important specializations of detail. The structure of an ommatidium in its light-adapted condition is shown in Fig. 61b. The dioptric apparatus consists of 'cornea', corneal lens and cone (or crystal) cells. The biconvex corneal lens is covered by a transparent, hemispherical cuticle, about 1μ thick, which has unfortunately been called the 'cornea', while below the corneal lens are 4 cone cells which replace the crystalline cone of other insects, the eye consequently being classified as acone in type. Satô (1950) stated that the corneal lens changed shape during dark adaptation. He later (1957) admitted that variability between individuals in the size of the corneal lens threw doubt on this assertion, but it is interesting that Constantineaunu (1930) described the inner surface of the corneal lens as being unhardened, at least in the young adult.

The retinula is composed of 8 pigmented retinula cells and a rhabdom. One of the retinula cells occupies a central position and is surrounded by

191

the rhabdom which consists of 8 rhabdomeres, each rhabdomere presumably being secreted by one of the retinula cells as in other insects. The rhabdom is transparent and apparently soft in constituency since it is capable of changing shape. Seven retinula cells surround the rhabdom, one of them smaller than the others. Immediately outside the rhabdom the cytoplasm is free of pigment granules, forming the intermediate zone, but just outside this most of the pigment granules of the retinula cells are concentrated into a dense band. The pigment granules of the central

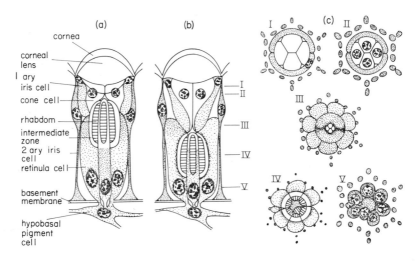

Fig. 61a–c.   Diagram of light- and dark-adapted ommatidia.
(a) L.S. through an ommatidium in the dark-adapted condition; (b) L.S. through an ommatidium in the light-adapted condition; (c) transverse sections through a light-adapted ommatidium at the levels indicated in (b). (From Satô, 1950).

retinula cell are peculiar in being motile. The retinula cells are primary sense cells giving rise to axons which traverse the intermediate zone and penetrate the basement membrane, under which they form a plexus before passing to the outer synaptic region of the optic lobe.

Two primary iris cells surround the cone cells while a number of secondary iris cells, usually 12–18 in number, surround the ommatidium over practically the whole of its length stretching from the edge of the cornea to the basement membrane. The iris cells and another cell, the hypobasal pigment cell which lies under the basement membrane, are packed with black pigment granules. Pigment granules also load the basement membrane and the nerve plexus.

Since the retinula is situated immediately below the dioptric apparatus and pigment cells surround the whole ommatidium, the images formed are of the apposition type, only perpendicular rays which have passed through the dioptric unit of the same ommatidium falling on the retinula, and not, as in some insects, of the superposition type in which oblique rays from several lenses also fall on each retinula.

In the process of dark adaptation the rhabdom moves outwards, separating the cone cells and coming to lie between them (Fig. 61a). Although it has a similar shape in its fully light- and dark-adapted conditions the rhabdom changes shape to a considerable extent during its migration. The 2 primary iris cells retract their proximal borders so that the opening over the retinula, the so-called 'pupil', becomes greatly enlarged. The corneal lens is said to thicken so that it almost touches the rhabdom, but this is doubtful. In the dark-adapted condition the pigment granules of the central retinula cell become concentrated at the base of the cell so that the crescent-shaped pigment mass found within the rhabdom in the light-adapted eye is no longer in that position. Movement of the rhabdom in dark adaptation takes 10–20 min but changes in the primary iris cells and the central retinular cell take 2–3 hr. In the dark-adapted eye images are still formed by apposition.

Changes of this type are found on dark adaptation in the eyes of *Culex pipiens* var. *pallens, Culex vorax* and *Anopheles sinensis*. Similar changes occur in *Aedes japonicus* except that there is only slight migration of the rhabdom; in *Armigeres subalbatus* the primary iris cells contract causing enlargement of the 'pupil' but little migration of the rhabdom occurs and no concentration of pigment in the central retinula cell. It is interesting that the last 2 species are active in relatively bright light (Satô, 1950, 1953a, b, 1957, 1959, 1960; Satô, Katô and Toriumi, 1957).

Dorsal ocelli which are present in the adults of some insects are not found in mosquitoes but the lateral ocelli of the larvae can still be found in a degenerate condition at the posterior margins of the compound eyes.

Physiology of the Compound Eyes

In experiments upon the responses of resting *Culex pipiens* var. *pallens* and *Aedes vexans* to the movement of vertical stripes Suzuki (1960) found that the strength of the optomotor response varied with the velocity of stripe movement and with the width, number and arrangement of the stripes. The minimum ommatidial angle was about 3° and it was observed that mosquitoes could perceive movement of stripes submitting an angle greater than 2°. Experiments performed by Kennedy (1939) showed that visual stimulation of females of *Aedes aegypti* in free flight by moving stripes produced different responses depending on which regions of the compound eyes were affected. When the moving stripes were below the mosquito, in the field of the ventral ommatidia, the mosquito's line of flight was directed parallel to the line of stripe movement, whereas movement of vertical stripes in the field of the lateral ommatidia caused an ipsilateral turning movement after which the mosquito kept facing one of the moving black stripes. Kennedy also noticed that the mosquitoes would orientate to objects above them. Rao (1947) observed that *Anopheles labranchiae atroparvus* and *Culex pipiens* var. *molestus* rendered flightless would walk away from a horizontal light source and towards a dark vertical stripe. After being blinded in 1 eye and enclosed in a white-walled cylinder the insects performed circus movements, turning towards the blinded side, but when enclosed in a cylinder with a black vertical stripe the circus movements stopped as soon as the stripe came into the field of vision of the functional eye when the mosquitoes turned sharply and walked towards the stripe in a practically straight line. Orientation with a single compound eye is probably due to the presence of two functionally different regions, one initiating turning towards its own side of the body and the other towards the opposite side (Fraenkel and Gunn, 1940). From the experiments of Kennedy (1939) and Rao (1947) we may conclude that there are at least 3 or 4 functionally different regions in each eye.

Kalmus (1958) found that males of *Aedes aegypti* gave optomotor responses to the rotation of polarized light. Optomotor responses were not given by mosquitoes on a white substrate reflecting largely depolarized light but only on a dark, reflecting substrate which reflected a great deal of light in the plane of vibration but very little vertical to it, so producing a brightness pattern. Kalmus concluded that mosquitoes do not possess any special powers of analysis but respond to brightness patterns. More critical experiments will have to be performed, however, before it is proved that mosquitoes cannot perceive the plane of vibration of polarized light.

Several studies have been made of the responses of mosquitoes to light of different wavelengths but in only a few cases has the relative brightness of the different colours been taken into account. Gilbert and Gouck (1957) measured the rate at which caged mosquitoes landed on discs of different colours. When all the discs produced 40-ft candles of reflected light the attractiveness of the colours was in the following order, the groupings showing differences significant at the 5 per cent level:

Aedes aegypti   —yellow>orange and red>green, violet, black, blue and white

Aedes taeniorhynchus—white>orange, green, yellow and blue>violet, red and black

Aedes sollicitans   —black, blue, orange and green>yellow, violet, red and white.

Using a brightness of 20 ft-c the relative attractiveness of certain colours differed from that found at 40 ft-c to a significant extent in each species. Brett (1938) measured the landing rate of females of *Aedes aegypti* on gloved hands and found that although the mosquitoes generally preferred dark surfaces, red was more attractive than several colours which reflected less light whereas blue was more repellent than several colours which reflected more light. These experiments showed a differential response by mosquitoes to different colours of the same brightness, but although the physical intensities of the different wavelengths were equalized the physiological intensities may have been different because of differential wavelength absorption by the photosensitive substance of the eye (Roeder, 1953), so the results have not proved that mosquitoes are capable of colour discrimination. Studies by Suzuki (1961) on the optomotor responses of female *Culex pipiens* var. *pallens* to moving coloured stripes have confirmed

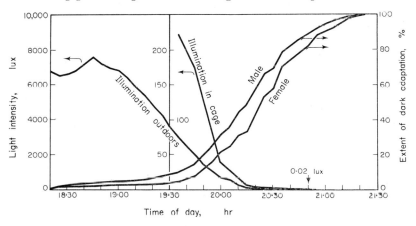

FIG. 62. The course of dark adaptation in the eyes of *Culex pipiens* var. *pallens* at dusk. (From Satô, Katô and Toriumi, 1957).

that colours reflecting equal amounts of light may have strikingly different physiological intensities to the mosquito and that this plays an important part in the apparent discrimination of colour.

The attractiveness of different coloured surfaces as landing surfaces for female *Aedes aegypti* is an inverse function of the intensity of reflected light between 4750 and 6250Å; no correlation with intensity is found outside these limits (Brown, 1954). This indicates an insensitivity to the deeper shades of red, to infra-red and to violet and ultraviolet light. Many insects are known to be insensitive to red light but insensitivity to ultraviolet is unusual.

Contour and movement have been shown to be important in the visual responses of *Aedes aegypti* (Sippell and Brown, 1953; Haufe and Burgess, 1960), very probably due to the flicker effect which they produce (Roeder, 1953). The presence of the iris pigments is necessary for perception of contour and movement since white-eyed mutants of *Culex pipiens* var. *molestus* did not show the usual flight reaction when an opaque object passed between them and a light source, nor would they show optomotor reactions to moving stripes although they would show quite normal phototaxis, moving into the light at dusk (Kalmus, 1946; Gilchrist and Haldane, 1947). Satô, Katô and Toriumi (1957) collected and fixed males and females of *Culex pipiens* var. *pallens* at dusk as they flew towards the light from a shaded cage standing in front of a window, and found by measurement of such factors as 'pupil' width and rhabdom movement that mosquitoes caught later in the evening showed a progressive increase in dark adaptation (Fig. 62). The change in 'pupil' width occurred 10 min earlier in males than in females, and in both sexes this change occurred about 10 min earlier in the ventral than in the dorsal ommatidia.

The Antennae

As in all insects, mosquito antennae bear some of the most important sense organs; the female antennae almost certainly play an important role in host finding while those of the male are modified for locating the female. In both sexes each antenna consists of 2 large, basal segments, the scape and pedicel, and a flagellum of 13 or 14 segments. The scape is the proximal segment, ring-like and largely sunk within the head. The pedicel is a large, globular segment containing Johnston's organ, and it is larger in the male than in the female.

Each antenna is moved by 3 muscles arising on the tentorium or the head capsule and inserted on the base of the scape, and by other muscles which arise on the wall of the scape and which are inserted on the base of the pedicel. Movement in the transverse plane is controlled by 2 articulations between head capsule and scape, and in the vertical plane by 2 further articulations, approximately at right angles to the others, between scape and pedicel. Nerves, tracheae and a blood vessel from a pulsating organ run through the scape and pedicel, supplying these segments and the flagellum (Risler, 1953, 1955; Christophers, 1960).

Structure of the Flagellum

There is disagreement over the number of segments in the flagellum, for according to Roth and Willis (1952) and Christophers (1960) there are 13 in the flagella of males and females of *Aedes aegypti* but Risler (1955) has described 14 segments in the flagella of males of *Aedes aegypti*, *Culex pipiens* and *Anopheles stephensi*. The point of disagreement is probably whether the most distal of the large hair wreaths in the male is part of the long penultimate segment, or whether it arises on another small segment which is fused to the penultimate segment. The female antenna has 13 distinct sections but it is possible that the basal section consists of 2 fused segments. A detailed study is necessary to settle this point, but for present purposes the flagella of male and female mosquitoes will be taken to consist of 13 segments.

In the female of *Aedes aegypti* the flagellar segments are of approximately equal length. Each segment except the first is composed of a narrow, basal, sclerotised ring followed by a clear membranous section and then by a sclerotised section which forms the main length of the segment. A whorl of 5 or 6 long hairs arises from the membranous section, and smaller hairs arise towards the distal end of the segment, while small, thin-walled sensilla are distributed over the whole segment. In the first flagellar segment the long hairs spring from the body of the segment (Christophers, 1960).

In the males of *Aedes aegypti* and other species the 2 distal segments are long and form about half the length of the flagellum, whereas the remaining segments are all short (Fig. 63a–c). The small, thin-walled sensilla are restricted to the 2 distal segments. Twelve wreaths of extremely long, slender hairs or fibrillae arise from sockets borne on two crescent-shaped projections on each of the 12 basal segments, the fibrillae steadily decreasing in length towards the tip of the flagellum. The crescents bearing the fibrillae occupy a subapical position in each segment except possibly in the case of the terminal crescent, the segmentation of which is in doubt. A few short hairs arise at the base of the distal segment. The fibrillae increase the surface area of the male flagellum to approximately ten times that of the female. The fibrillae are innervated by neurones which lie close to their insertions and which send axons to the 2 flagellar nerves (Roth and Willis, 1952; Risler, 1953, 1955). In *Culex pipiens fatigans* each fibril is a hollow tapering shaft bearing at least 16 rows of projections which appear like the teeth of a saw. Each segment bears 30 to 35 fibrillae arising from collarlike sockets on the crescents, and as the sockets are of larger diameter than the bases of the fibrillae the fibrillae are thought to have freedom of movement at their insertions (Tulloch and Shapiro, 1951).

At emergence the fibrillae of the male are recumbent, lying flattened against the shaft of the flagellum. The fibrils are gradually erected after emergence and in males 2 days old all of the fibrils are normally more or less perpendicular to the shaft. In males of *Aedes aegypti* and *Culex pipiens* the fibrillae remain permanently erected, but in males of *Anopheles quadrimaculatus, Culex theileri, Aedes caspius* and *Aedes taeniorhynchus* they remain recumbent during most of the day and are erected only during periods of

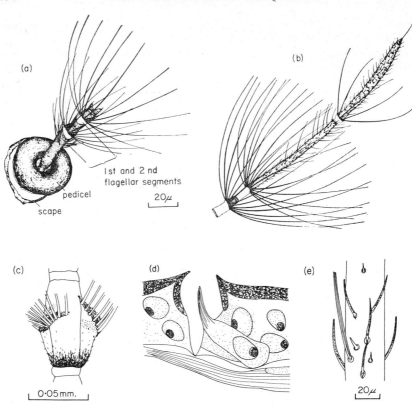

FIG. 63a–e.   The structure of the antenna.
(a) The first 4 segments of the antenna of a male *Aedes aegypti;* (b) the terminal
segments of the antenna of a male *Aedes aegypti;* (c) a single flagellar segment
of a male of *Aedes aegypti;* (d) section through a pit organ on the flagellum of
a female *Anopheles labranchiae atroparvus;* (e) part of the penultimate segment
of the antenna of a male *Aedes aegypti* stained with crystal violet. (a and b from
Roth, 1948; c from Christophers, 1960; d from Ismail, 1962; e drawn from a
photograph by Slifer and Brescia, 1960).

activity at dusk and dawn, being retracted again when the insects come to
rest (Roth, 1948; Nielsen and Nielsen, 1958, 1962).

In a number of species the male antennae lack long fibrillae and
resemble those of the female. These include *Culiseta inornata, Uranotaenia
lowii, Deinocerites cancer, Opifex fuscus,* and certain species of Sabethini.
Associated with the reduction of the antennae is a loss or reduction of the
sense of hearing. In male *Deinocerites cancer* minute sensilla of the chemosensory type are said to be distributed on all flagellar segments, making
the antennae even more like those of the female (Howard, Dyar and Knab,
1912; Roth, 1948; Marks, 1958).

In males of *Aedes aegypti* and *Anopheles stephensi* the flagellum is strength-
ened by an endoskeleton which is in the form of a cylinder running through
the flagellum (Fig. 64). The cylinder is fused to the outer wall of the
flagellum at certain points, and in each segment the cavity of the endoskeleton is continuous with the blood space surrounding it through holes

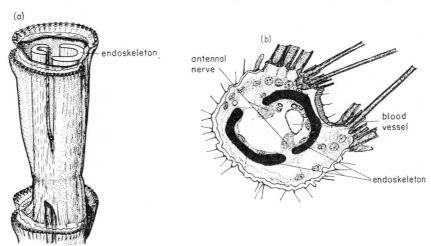

FIG. 64a–b.   The endoskeleton of the flagellum.
(a) Reconstruction of a single flagellar segment of a male *Anopheles stephensi*
(omitting the fibrillae). (From Risler, 1953); (b) T.S. through the flagellum
of a male *Anopheles stephensi*. (From Risler, 1955).

in the cylinder. In males of *Culex pipiens* the endoskeleton is reduced to 2
slender half cylinders fused to the wall of the flagellum, but in this
species the outer wall of the flagellum is reinforced on 1 side. In each
species a blood vessel runs inside the endoskeleton, and axons from
flagellar sense cells join the 2 flagellar nerves which run with the blood
vessel and tracheoles through the endoskeleton (Risler, 1953, 1955).
Nothing is known of the internal structure of the female flagellum.

Probable chemosensory organs are found on the flagella of *Aedes
aegypti*, on all flagellar segments in the female but restricted to the 2 long,
distal segments in the male (Roth and Willis, 1952; Bässler, 1958; Christophers, 1960; Slifer and Brescia, 1960). There are 3 types of sensilla: thin-
walled hairs, peg organs, and a pair of thin-walled papillae at the tip of the
antenna. Approximately 30–40 hairs and less than 15 peg organs are
present on each flagellar segment in the female, rather more on each of the
2 distal segments in the male. Each thin-walled hair is 40–50 μ long and
without a fully-articulated base although arising from thin membrane
surrounded by a semi-circular ridge of cuticle. A neurone is found at the

o

base of the hair within the epidermis. Slifer and Brescia (1960) have shown that 2 types of short hair are present, one with a heavier wall and pointed tip and the other with a thinner wall and rounded tip. The hairs with thinner walls were shown to be permeable in certain regions to a solution of crystal violet, a characteristic of organs known to be chemoreceptors in certain other insects, organs which they also resemble in structure (Fig. 63e). Bar-Zeev (1960b) has shown that the antennae mediate the response of female *Aedes aegypti* to water vapour. The evidence that the antennae are involved in location of the host by females is rather equivocal (p. 284), but in the absence of firm evidence to the contrary it may be supposed that the antennae are used for this purpose and that the sensilla which they bear are sensitive to host odour, carbon dioxide, and possibly heat.

Ismail (1962) has described 7 types of sensilla on the flagella of *Anopheles labranchiae atroparvus:* long and short articulated tactile bristles, long and short thin-walled hairs, peg organs, olfactory pits and campaniform sensilla. In the male the sensilla are restricted to the 2 terminal segments except for a small number of tactile hairs and 2 campaniform sensilla which occur on the 1st segment. In the female the basal flagellar segment bears very few sensilla but sensilla are abundant on the other segments although the different types are not evenly dispersed. The pit organs appear externally as dark rings of cuticle; in section each pit, which is about 5μ wide, is seen to have thick cuticular sides and a membranous floor from which arises a single peg organ (Fig. 63d). A group of about 6 sense cells lies at the base of the sensillum and fibres pass from the cells to the apex of the peg. The campaniform sensilla appear externally as bell-shaped domes about 4μ long and 3μ wide; internally each contains a sense rod and sense cells. If they are correctly identified as campaniform sensilla they must function as proprioceptors.

Structure of Johnston's Organ

The pedicel is almost filled by a large sense organ which was correctly described as an organ of hearing by Johnston (1855), partly due to the misconception that organs of hearing were always situated on the antennae in insects, but also because he considered that the flagellum was able to transmit sound waves to the nervous elements in the pedicel. Detailed descriptions of the structure of Johnston's organ have been given by Eggers (1924) for the male and female of *Culex pipiens*, and by Risler (1953, 1955) for the males of *Anopheles stephensi, Aedes aegypti* and *Culex pipiens*.

The following description of Johnston's organ and the structures associated with it refers to the male mosquito and is based upon the accounts of Eggers (1924) and Risler (1953, 1955). The outer surface of the pedicel is deeply invaginated forming an approximately dumbbell-shaped depression, the apical pit (Fig. 65). In *Anopheles stephensi* the cuticle is considerably thickened at a point half way down the depression, forming

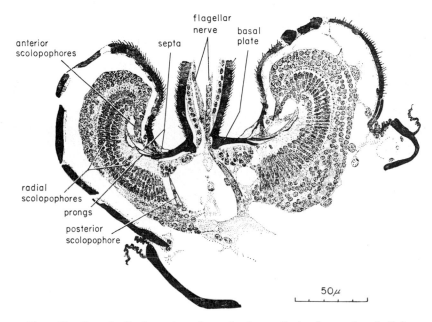

FIG. 65. Longitudinal section through the pedicel of a male of *Culex pipiens* showing Johnston's organ and its relationship to the base of the flagellum. (From Risler, 1955).

a band called the sclerotized ring (Fig. 66), but in all species the cuticle below this region becomes thin, turning to articular membrane at the base of the apical pit. The articular membrane is attached to a circular basal plate at the bottom of the pit, and in an opening in the centre of the plate is set the base of the flagellum.

The basal plate is not sclerotized; it is thick medially but becomes thin towards the edge. The articular membrane is attached halfway between the centre and the edge of the plate, and for some distance above the plate the articular membrane is reinforced with rib-like thickenings (Fig. 66). Radiating from the basal plate is a series of over 60 cuticular prongs which curve upwards within the pedicel, ending at about the height of the sclerotized ring. The nature of the connection between the basal plate and the prongs is not clear. Septa radiate from the inner wall of the pedicel and interdigitate with the prongs (Figs. 66 and 67).

Johnston's organ itself consists of a large number of scolopophores, organs sensitive to tension, arranged in anterior, posterior and radial series. The great majority of the scolopophores are in the radial series, arranged in numerous bundles of 3 in a large, thick ring which occupies most of the cavity of the pedicel. A blood space visible in the living animal

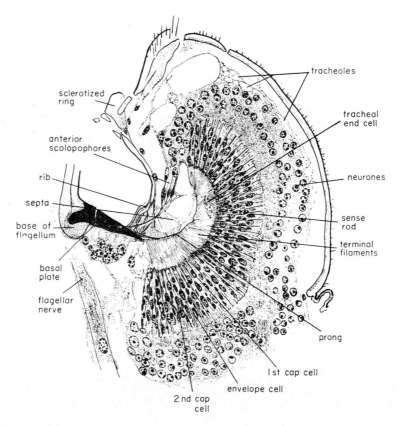

FIG. 66. Longitudinal section through Johnston's organ of the male of *Anopheles stephensi.* (From Risler, 1953).

separates the outer wall of the pedicel from the scolopophores, although it is traversed by a number of connective tissue fibres. The scolopophores of the radial series are attached by their terminal filaments to the prongs which arise from the basal plate.

The scolopophores do not show the structure, usually considered typical, of sense cell and sense rod, envelope cell and cap cell. In longitudinal section (Figs. 66 and 67), the radial series of scolopophores is seen to consist of a band composed of the terminal filaments joined to sense rods, a band of cells in which the nuclei are arranged in 3 rows, a narrow band of nerve fibres, and a band of neurones 2 or more cells thick. The band containing 3 rows of nuclei is thought to consist of first and second cap cells and envelope cells, and the outer layer of neurones is thought to comprise the sense cells of the scolopophores.

The anterior series of scolopophores consists of bundles of 4 to 5 units disposed in a ring in the space between the radial series and the articular membrane (Figs. 65 and 66). Their sense cells are situated about the level of the sclerotized ring and their terminal filaments are inserted on the bases of the prongs, passing between the septa (Figs. 66 and 67). The posterior series of scolopophores consists of relatively few units in

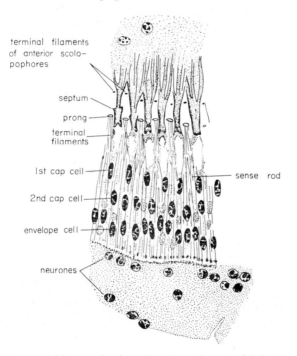

FIG. 67.   Tangential-longitudinal section through part of Johnston's organ of the male of *Anopheles stephensi*. (From Risler, 1953).

medial, dorso-lateral and ventro-lateral positions below the basal plate, orientated along the longitudinal axis of the antenna with their terminal filaments running into the epidermal cells which line the plate (Fig. 65). The axons from the 3 series of scolopophores collect in a massive, funnel-shaped nerve which passes through the scape to enter the deutocerebrum at the base of the antenna. An opening in the antennal nerve permits tracheae and a blood vessel to penetrate to the centre of the antenna and it is from this point that the 2 flagellar nerves arise from the inner surface of the antennal nerve (Christophers, 1960).

The 3 series of scolopophores are undoubtedly stimulated by movements of the flagellum on its longitudinal axis, the movements being transmitted to the scolopophores by the plate and prongs. Movements of this nature occur when the male flagellum resonates in response to the flight tone of the female, and it is thought that the scolopophores also serve to distinguish more complex movements of the flagellum which may be used in directional hearing. The electrophysiological characteristics of the organ are described in the next section.

Eggers (1924) has shown that the structure of the pedicel and of Johnston's organ in the female of *Culex pipiens* differs in several ways from that in the male. In the female, the apical pit is shallower and the point of attachment of the flagellum consequently more superficial. No prongs

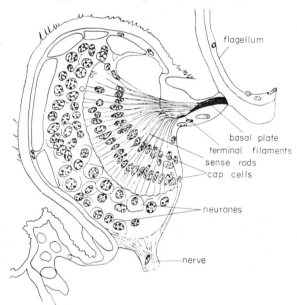

FIG. 68.   Longitudinal section through Johnston's organ of the female of *Culex pipiens*. (From von Buddenbrock, 1952, after Eggers, 1924).

radiate from the basal plate and the terminal filaments of the radial series of scolopophores appears to be inserted on the plate at about its point of attachment to the flagellum (Fig. 68). The sense cells and sense rods are larger in the female but fewer in number. In addition to the sense-cell nuclei there are 2 other layers of nuclei and these Eggers homologizes with the 2 layers of cap-cell nuclei in the male. Whether the anterior and posterior series of scolopophores are present is not clear. Johnston's organ is highly developed in females but it is not known whether sound reception plays any part in the life of the female.

The Sense of Hearing

Male mosquitoes give a mating response to a female flying nearby or to any artificial sound source whose frequency is close to the wing-beat frequency of the female. Roth (1948) performed a number of experiments which proved the antennae to be the organs of sound perception. Amputation of both antennal flagella made males of *Aedes aegypti* unresponsive to females, although this might have been because they were reluctant to fly at all. However, when the bases of the antennae were covered with shellac so that the flagellar shafts were not free to vibrate, the males failed to respond to flying females or to tuning forks. When drops of shellac were placed on the tips of the flagella very few males responded to a tuning fork or to females, although when the tips of their antennae were later cut off the males showed normal mating responses once more. Males would respond to a tuning fork after practically all the fibrillae had been stripped from their flagella but they would not respond to flying females, a far less powerful stimulus.

Mayer (1874) had previously found that the fibrillae in the antenna of a *Culex* male showed sympathetic vibrations in response to the vibrations of tuning forks, each fibril vibrating weakly over a range of frequencies but very strongly to a particular tuning fork, the different fibrillae differing in the frequencies to which they responded most strongly. The fibrillae are innervated directly, but Roth's experiment of cementing the bases of the flagella with shellac showed that resonance of the fibrillae alone was insufficient to produce attraction to a sound source. It therefore appears that the fibrillae are set in motion by sound waves emanating from a flying female and that the motion of the fibrillae is transmitted to Johnston's organ by the shaft of the flagellum. The pitch of the female flight tone rises with increasing temperature (Sotavalta, 1947), but the resonance frequency of the male antenna shows a similar tendency to rise so that it always remains in tune with the fundamental of the female flight tone, independent of temperature (Tischner and Schief, 1955).

The electrical characteristics of Johnston's organ have been investigated by Tischner (1953), Tischner and Schief (1955) and Keppler (1958a, b). These workers inserted 1 electrode into the cavity of the pedicel of a male mosquito and a second elsewhere in the body, and recorded the electrical changes which occurred. When the mosquito was stimulated with sound a change of potential occurred between the pedicel and the body of the animal. The potential changes were not action potentials for the electrode was not near a nerve. The potentials in fact reproduced the wave form of the acoustic stimulus (Fig. 69) and, as Keppler (1958a) has pointed out, they resembled the microphonic potentials found in the cochlea of the mammalian ear, in the lateral line of fish, and other organs of hearing. It is worth listing here the characteristics of the microphonic potential of the mammalian cochlea. It is an alternating electrical potential of the same frequency as the acoustic stimulus; the response is continuously graded

(a)   (b)

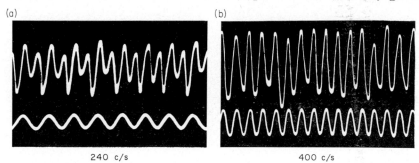

240 c/s   400 c/s

FIG. 69a–b.   Microphonic potentials recorded from the antenna of a male *Anopheles subpictus* on stimulation with pure tones.

(a) The microphonic potential (above) contains both the fundamental and 1st harmonic of the stimulus (240 c/s); (b) the microphonic potential reproduces the wave form of the stimulus (400 c/s). (From Tischner, 1953).

and there is no true threshold and no refractory period; it shows no adaptation or fatigue; at moderate intensities of acoustic stimulus the output voltage is proportional to the amplitude of the stimulus, but after reaching a maximum which rarely exceeds 5 mV it levels off or declines. The source of the cochlear microphonic is the hair cells and the potential is a measure of the displacement of the tentorial membrane relative to the reticular lamina. The microphonics are thought to be involved in the production of action potentials in the cochlear nerve (Davis, 1957).

The microphonic potential of the mosquito antenna is an alternating potential of the same frequency (except under certain conditions) as the acoustic stimulus (Fig. 69). The amplitude of the microphonic potential is proportional to the intensity of the stimulus up to a maximum not exceeding 200 μV, above which saturation occurs (Fig. 70). For sound of a given intensity, the amplitude of the microphonic potential is a function of the frequency and in fact the curve of microphonic potential at different frequencies closely resembles the resonance curve of the flagellum obtained by measuring the displacement of the flagellum at different frequencies of

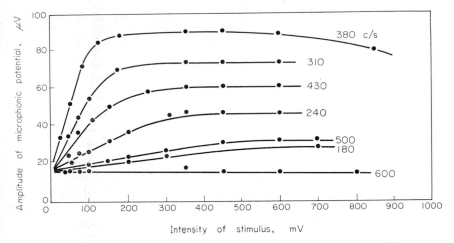

FIG. 70. The amplitude of the antennal microphonic potential in a male of *Anopheles subpictus* at different intensities of stimulation with pure tones and at different frequencies. (From Tischner, 1953).

acoustic stimulus under stroboscopic illumination (Fig. 71). Anything impeding movement of the flagellum relative to the pedicel stops the appearance of microphonics on acoustic stimulation. The source of the antennal microphonic potentials is thought to be the scolopophores of Johnston's organ. No recordings of action potentials have been obtained

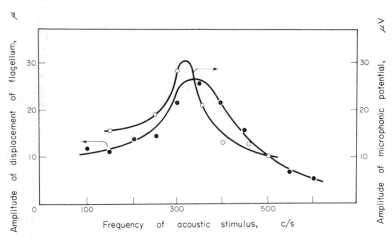

FIG. 71. The effects of stimulating with pure tones of different frequencies on the amplitude of displacement of the antennal flagella of an *Aedes aegypti* male at 21°C (resonance curve) and on the amplitude of the antennal microphonic. (From Tischner and Schief, 1955).

from the antennal nerve but Keppler (1958a) stated that if an electrode hit the antennal nerve summated spikes were seen.

Antennal microphonics have been obtained in males in *Aedes aegypti* over the frequency range of 150–450 c/s with a maximum amplitude at about 320 c/s (Fig. 71) (Tischner and Schief, 1955; Keppler, 1958b), and in males of *Anopheles subpictus* over the range 150–600 c/s with a peak at 380 c/s (Tischner, 1953). In each case the greatest sensitivity to sound was close to the fundamental of the female flight tone, whereas the frequency of the male flight tone was outside this range or only bordered on it, and it is clear that neither the male's own flight tone nor the harmonics of the female flight tone would normally stimulate the production of microphonics in the antenna of the male.

Roth (1948) found that males of *Aedes aegypti* showed habituation on continuous stimulation with one frequency at high intensity, apparent in the loss of the mating response. Habituation was much slower when stimulation was discontinuous, and the response always reappeared after habituation if the mosquito was stimulated with a different frequency.

We may conclude that the male antennal flagella are displacement receptors which resonate in a sound field at a given frequency, at other frequencies remaining more or less at rest. In this way they act as a band-pass filter, separating the fundamental of the female flight tone from the male's own flight tone and other background noises. Vibrations of the flagella apparently cause displacement of the terminal filaments of the scolopophores of Johnston's organ producing potential changes, recognized as the antennal microphonics, which may be generator potentials leading to the formation of action potentials in fibres of the antennal nerves.

A male mosquito stimulated by the sound of a flying female will fly straight towards the female showing that it has the ability to locate the source of a sound. Sound localization in vertebrates depends largely upon differences of intensity and phase as the sound waves strike the 2 ears, but in the mosquito the organs of hearing are exposed and very close together so that a different mechanism of sound localization must be used. Theories on the mechanism of directional hearing in mosquitoes have been proposed by Mayer (1874), Tischner (1953, 1954, 1955), Risler (1955) and Keppler (1958a). Mayer (1874) observed that when sound waves fell upon a fibril in the antenna of a *Culex* male so that the direction of movement of the sound waves was along the long axis of the fibril, the fibril was not set in motion, but that when the direction of movement of the sound waves was changed the fibril started to vibrate reaching a maximum amplitude of movement when the wave front was parallel to the fibril. Mayer suggested that the flight tone of the female would normally stimulate the fibrillae of one antenna more strongly than those of the other because the antennae were set at angles to the body, and he considered that the male would turn in the direction of the antenna which was more strongly stimulated. When the antennae were equally stimulated the male would be facing in the direction of the female. Risler (1955) also considered that obtaining equal stimulation of the 2 antennae was an important aspect of directional hearing, and he thought that the ventral series of scolopophores, which are arranged in medial, dorso-lateral and ventrol-lateral positions, would assist orientation by indicating the direction in which the flagella were tipped by the sound waves. Roth (1948) found that unilateral amputation of a flagellum in males of *Aedes*

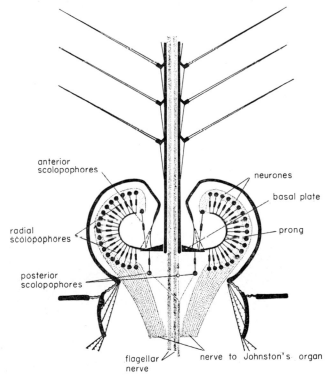

FIG. 72. Diagram of Johnston's organ showing its relationship to the flagellum. (From Risler, 1955).

aegypti reduced the rate of successful copulation but did not prevent it, and that these males would fly to the vibrating prongs of a tuning fork. He pointed out that Mayer's theory involved tropotaxis, i.e. the comparison of the intensity of stimulation of 2 symmetrically-placed receptor organs, and that in such responses unilateral amputation of a receptor normally led to circus movements. Since continuous-turning movements were not observed on stimulating the males with a single flagellum with a tuning fork, and since such males were able to copulate successfully, Roth (1948) considered the tropotactic explanation of directional hearing to be wrong. However, the circus movements performed by a mosquito blinded in 1 eye cease when it sees a black, vertical stripe to which it can orientate using functionally-different regions in its remaining eye (p. 194), so before the tropotactic theory can be disproved it must be shown that Johnston's organ does not contain functionally-different regions, or another mechanism must be demonstrated.

In a series of papers Tischner (1953, 1954, 1955) discussed a possible mechanism of directional hearing in mosquitoes based on the observation that the antennal microphonic frequently contains not only the fundamental of a pure tone stimulus but also the first harmonic. The relationship of the amplitude of the first harmonic to the fundamental was called the *Klirrfaktor*. He suggested (1953, 1955) that sound waves passing in the direction of the longitudinal axis of the mosquito caused the basal plate to vibrate parallel to itself, on its downstroke pressing on the posterior scolopophores of the radial series and on its upstroke pressing on the anterior scolopophores of that series (Fig. 72), so producing a microphonic of twice the frequency of the stimulus. The small number of scolopophores of the anterior series were also considered to be stimulated on the upstroke, making the first harmonic of the microphonic of slightly greater amplitude than the fundamental. Sound waves travelling at right angles to the insect were considered to rock the flagellum and its basal plate in such a way that the anterior series of scolopophores was stimulated twice in each cycle, first those on one side of Johnston's organ being stimulated and then those on the other, thus producing a change in the *Klirrfaktor*. The flagella were seen to vibrate in the manner suggested when sound waves fell on them from different angles, and Tischner considered that the *Klirrfaktor* provided a means of orientation towards the source of the sound.

In 1954 Tischner stated that sound waves travelling in the direction of the longitudinal axis of the flagellum caused it to vibrate in that direction producing only the fundamental of the acoustic stimulus, whereas sound waves travelling at right angles to the flagellum caused it to vibrate at right angles to its longitudinal axis, producing both the fundamental and the first harmonic of the acoustic stimulus in the antennal microphonics. Keppler (1958a) investigated the relationship between the *Klirrfaktor* and the angle at which sound waves struck the flagellum by stiffening the flagellum of a male of *Aedes aegypti*, thus abolishing its resonant properties, and touching it with a rod which was moved to and fro in *sine* form by a magnetic coil. It was found that when the flagellum was moved on its longitudinal axis a microphonic appeared containing only the fundamental frequency of the stimulus. When the rod was placed at an angle to the flagellum producing a certain lateral movement the first harmonic appeared in addition to the fundamental and increased in amplitude as the rod subtended a greater angle to the flagellum (Fig. 73). These results

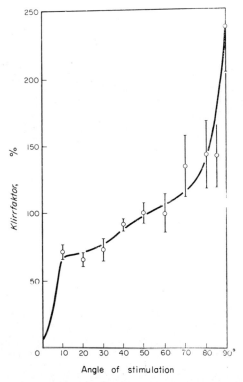

FIG. 73. The variation in *Klirrfaktor* (ratio between amplitudes of 1st harmonic and fundamental of the antennal microphonic) with the angle subtended to the antenna by the stimulus. (From Keppler, 1958a).

confirmed the existence of the *Klirrfaktor*, and Keppler (1958a) suggested ways in which different movements of the flagellum and basal plate would affect the production of fundamental and first harmonic in the microphonic potentials (Fig. 74). He supposed that when the flagellum vibrated in the plane of its longitudinal axis all the scolopophores of the radial series would be under tension on the downstroke of the plate and would be freed from tension on the upstroke, producing a microphonic potential of the same frequency as the stimulus. Movement of the flagellum at right angles to its longitudinal axis would stimulate 2 different regions of scolopophores one after the other in each cycle giving a microphonic of double the frequency of the stimulus, whereas movements of the flagellum containing both longitudinal and transverse components would also produce microphonics at the frequencies of the fundamental and first harmonic but with a *Klirrfaktor* proportional to the angle of incidence of the sound waves.

The mechanism of directional hearing in mosquitoes has not been fully elucidated but the experiments and observations of the German authors have provided some information on the probable mechanism. The flagellum has been seen to vibrate in different planes according to the direction of the sound source and in such a way as to produce differential stimulation of the scolopophores of Johnston's organ. The microphonics

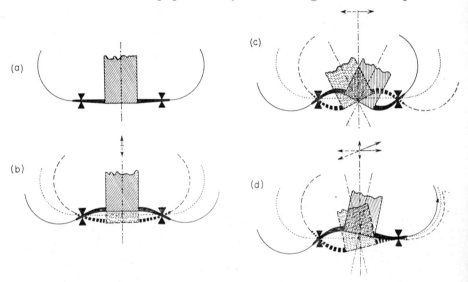

FIG. 74. The possible manner of movement of the basal plate of the antenna when the flagellum is caused to vibrate by sound waves travelling in the directions of the arrows. (From Keppler, 1958a).

originating in Johnston's organ have been shown to vary according to the direction of the sound source, and it seems not unlikely that this variation in antennal microphonics is an important part of the orientating mechanism of the mosquito. Such a mechanism would account for the observed ability of mosquitoes to locate a sound source after unilateral amputation of a flagellum. Clearly, mosquitoes possess a hearing organ which differs in its mechanism from all others previously described in animals.

Johnston's organ is less developed in the female mosquito than in the male and the female's flagellum is not modified to any great extent as a sound receptor; nevertheless, Keppler (1958a) recorded antennal microphonic potentials from the female of *Aedes aegypti*, slightly smaller than those of the male and appearing at a lower stimulus frequency corresponding to the lower resonance frequency of the female flagellum, and showed the existence of a *Klirrfaktor* which varied with the angle of stimulation. There is no evidence, however, that sound perception plays any part in the life of the female.

Contact Chemoreceptors of the Mouthparts and Legs

The insect contact chemoreceptors which have been most intensively investigated are on the labella and tarsi of the blowfly. These are medium-sized, curved hairs, each with a small papilla at its tip and with 2 cavities running throughout its length, 1 cavity thin-walled and the other thick-walled. At the base of the hair is a sac containing several cells, 2 being the trichogen and tormogen cells which secrete the hair and its socket, and the others being neurones, each with a distal fibre. Three fibres, possibly sometimes 4, pass up the thick-walled cavity to end in the papilla which is

TABLE 17. ACCEPTANCE THRESHOLDS FOR TARSAL AND LABELLAR CHEMORECEPTORS. THE LOWEST CONCENTRATIONS OF GLUCOSE AND SUCROSE TO WHICH 50% RESPONDED. (DATA FOR *Culiseta inornata* FROM FEIR *et al.*, 1961, AND FOR THE BLOWFLIES *Calliphora* AND *Phormia* FROM HASSETT *et al.*, 1950).

Species	Organ	Taste Thresholds	
		Glucose	Sucrose
Culiseta	tarsus	2·095 M	0·135 M
Calliphora	tarsus	0·125 M	0·0006 M
Phormia	tarsus	0·132 M	0·0098 M
Culiseta	labella	0·425 M	0·0107 M
Calliphora	labella	0·04 M	0·0035 M

the receptor site of the sense organ. Action potentials of different sizes can be recorded if the hair is stimulated mechanically or if the receptor site is stimulated with distilled water or with sugar, salt or protein solutions (Dethier, 1955; Hodgson, 1957; Wallis, 1961; Evans and Mellon, 1962).

Somewhat similar contact chemoreceptors are found in mosquitoes. In males and females of *Culiseta inornata* the 2 labellar lobes at the tip of the proboscis bear hairs averaging 70 μ in length which contain 2 lumina, and which experiments have proved to be chemosensory (Feir, Lengy and Owen, 1961). Hairs containing 2 lumina occur on the tarsi of various species of *Anopheles, Culex* and *Aedes* (Grabowski and Dethier, 1954) and although they have not been implicated directly as chemoreceptors it is known that the tarsi mediate responses to sugar and salt solutions (Frings and Hamrum, 1950; Feir, Lengy and Owen, 1961; Wallis, 1954a).

The physiology of these contact chemoreceptors has been investigated in *Culiseta inornata* by Feir, Lengy and Owen (1961). Males and females which were held by the thorax and which had drunk water to satiation were stimulated with sugar solutions applied to individual hairs or to a part bearing sense organs. A downward movement of the proboscis towards the test solution was taken as an index of tarsal stimulation and spreading of the labella as the criterion for stimulation of sensilla on that organ, both being normal responses in a feeding mosquito. Responses were given when the labella or individual labellar hairs were touched with 1 M sucrose and also when the 2nd, 3rd, 4th or 5th tarsal segments were stimulated in this way, but no responses were given on stimulation of the 1st tarsal segment or the distal end of the tibia. The mean threshold

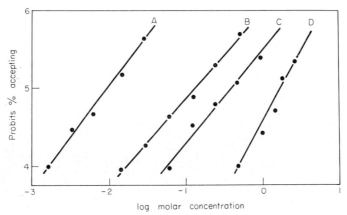

Fig. 75.   Probit regression lines showing the percentage of *Culiseta inornata* adults responding when different concentrations of sugars were applied to the labella or tarsi. A=sucrose on labella; B=sucrose on tarsi; C=glucose on labella; D=glucose on tarsi. (From Feir, Lengy and Owen, 1961).

concentrations at which glucose and sucrose elicited these responses are given in Table 17 where values for the blowflies *Phormia* and *Calliphora* are also give. In *Culiseta inornata* the labellar sense organs are 5–10 times more sensitive to glucose and sucrose than those on the tarsi, but both sets are far less sensitive than in the blowflies. Sucrose is 15 times more stimulating to the mosquito's tarsi and 40 times more stimulating to the mosquito's labella than glucose. Figure 75 shows that the scatter of the thresholds obtained with different individuals is normal with respect to the logarithm of the concentration, a result which is obtained with many insects (Dethier and Chadwick, 1948). It is likely that, as in the blowfly (Dethier, 1955), the thresholds measured by behavioural responses actually represent a central nervous system threshold or central excitatory state.

Frings and Hamrum (1950) showed that contact chemoreceptors sensitive to sucrose solution were present on the labella and tarsi of *Aedes aegypti* but absent from the palps and antennae, and that application of 2M-ammonium chloride to the labella led to withdrawal of the proboscis. Four types of hairs were present on the labella of males and females of *Aedes aegypti*, microtrichia 7 μ long, pointed hairs 40 μ long, thought to be tactile, curved hairs 20 μ long, thought to be a contact chemoreceptors, and short peg-like hairs about 6 μ long. Bar-Zeev (1960b) showed that the tarsi of *Aedes aegypti* were sensitive to contact with water. Observations of mosquito behaviour suggest that the females use their tarsal sense organs in selecting an oviposition site (Chapter 16). These organs are sensitive to a number of inorganic ions, and females of *Aedes aegypti* will select certain concentrations of sodium chloride from others for oviposition (Wallis, 1954a, b; Hudson, 1956).

The only organs on the stylets are a pair of peg organs near the tip of the labrum, described in the female of *Anopheles maculipennis* (Robinson, 1939) and in both sexes of *Aedes aegypti* (Christophers, 1960). The inner surface of the cibarial pump in both males and females bears a number of sense organs, some of which are almost certainly contact chemoreceptors. In *Aedes aegypti* they comprise a number of short spines and fine hairs, and 2 campaniform sensilla, all innervated from the frontal ganglion (Day, 1954).

Experiments of Hosoi (1954c) with *Culex pipiens* var. *pallens* showed that the labellar chemoreceptors mediated the drinking response on stimulation with glucose, and that the sense organs of the labrum and cibarial pump were only very slightly, if at all, sensitive to glucose, but that certain of them were sensitive to blood, mediating the gorging response (see Table 9, p. 141).

Other Adult Sense Organs

In all Diptera the hind wings are modified as halteres, gyroscopic organs of equilibrium which oscillate rapidly during flight and which give an indication to the fly of rotations in the yawing plane through the sensitivity of mechanoreceptors to stresses in the cuticle (Pringle, 1948). Stable flight is prevented in *Aedes aegypti* when the halteres are sealed to

P

the body (Christophers, 1960), and it is clear from their structure that they function in the same way in mosquitoes as in higher Diptera (Prashad, 1916a; Christophers, 1960). The mosquito haltere (Fig. 76a) consists of a knob-like head, the capitellum, joined by a narrow neck, the scape, to a dilated basal portion, the scabellum, and it articulates with the metathorax by a hinge-like joint, vibrating up and down through the contractions of 2

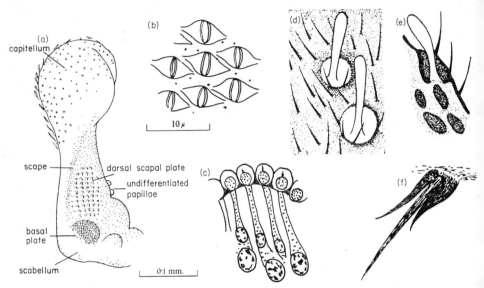

Fig. 76a–f.   Sense organs of the halteres and other appendages.
(a) Dorsal aspect of the left haltere of a female *Aedes aegypti;* (b) chordotonal sensilla of the dorsal scapal plate of *Aedes aegypti* in surface view; (c) chordotonal sensilla of the basal plate of *Aedes aegypti* in section (from Christophers, 1960); (d) blunt, thin-walled hairs on the palp of a female *Aedes aegypti;* (e) section through d (from Roth and Willis, 1952); (f) sensilla, probably tactile, from the tarsus of *Culex bitaeniorhynchus* (From Menon, 1951).

muscles inserted in its base. As in the higher Diptera the sense organs occur in groups in different areas of the scape and scabellum. The 'dorsal scapal plate' consists of about 12 long rows of campaniform sensilla in each of which the distal process of a single sense cell is inserted on the underside of an oval area of thin cuticle, situated between two thickened, cuticular crests (Fig. 76b). The 'ventral scapal plate' consists of 9 or 10 short rows of similar campaniform sensilla. The 'basal plate' is a tri-angular area, situated on the dorsal surface of the scabellum, containing 9 or 10 rows of campaniform sensilla in which the distal fibres of the sense cells are inserted in thin, dome-shaped elevations of the cuticle (Fig. 76c). Two 'undifferentiated papillae' are present on the posterior edge of the scape. The 'Hicks' papillae' found in higher Diptera are not present in the mosquito, unless they have been confused with those already described, and it is not known whether the chordotonal organs which occur inside the haltere in higher Diptera are present or not.

Large, blunt, thin-walled, sunken hairs, 20 or 30 μ long, are present on the maxillary palps in the female of *Aedes aegypti* (Fig. 76d, e). They number about 30 on each palp and are normally restricted to the terminal segment (Roth and Willis, 1952; Bässler, 1958; Christophers, 1960). Bässler (1958) described similar sense organs on the palps of the male but Christophers (1960) stated that they were lacking. The palp of female *Aedes aegypti* is said to end in a large circular area of membrane bearing a short peg (Christophers, 1960). The thin-walled hairs on the palps are possibly olfactory chemoreceptors, or may be sensitive to water vapour.

Christophers (1960) described the presence of numerous sensory pits on the ventral surface of the thorax and on the bases of the legs and the wings in *Aedes aegypti*. Other types of sensilla were described above the prosternum and on the bases of the legs.

Possible tactile receptors have been described on the tarsi of male and female mosquitoes. They are found on the foretarsi of anophelines and on the fore- and midtarsi of culicines, except in the Toxorhynchitinae where they are absent. When present they invariaby occur on the 1st tarsal segment and sometimes on the 2nd also. Each sense organ consists of a hinged hair, 40–100 μ long with a nerve fibre ending on the hinge, flanked by 2 foliate outgrowths of the cuticle (Fig. 76f). The hairs are said not to come into contact with surfaces except when the insect settles on water (Menon, 1951; Halcrow, 1953).

Larval Sense Organs

Constantineaunu (1930) described in detail the structure of the lateral ocelli in larvae of *Culex, Aedes* and *Anopheles*. Further descriptions have been given for *Culex pipiens* var. *pallens* (Satô, 1951b) and *Aedes aegypti* (Christophers, 1960). The elements of the lateral ocelli are concentrated in 1–5 groups on either side of the head and lie below unmodified regions of the head capsule. Some sort of lens is present between the cuticle and the sense cells but accounts of it differ. Constantineaunu (1930) described up to 16 large, clear refraction cells in the ocellus in *Culex pipiens* situated under the cuticle (Fig. 77c) but Satô (1951b) described a single lens-like body present in that position in some but not all ocelli of the same species (Fig. 77b). Christophers (1960) appears to describe both structures together in *Aedes aegypti*, a lens overlying a number of small, transparent bodies. Each ocellus contains a variable number of retinal cells whose

outer ends are modified into rhabdomeres and whose inner ends extend as
axons which run with those from the other ocelli to the optic lobe. The
rhabdomeres are frequently arranged in a circle pointing towards the surface, often surrounding a single median rhabdomere (Fig. 77d). Pigment
granules are present within the retinal cells and they show some movement
outwards in light and inwards in the dark (Satô, 1951b). White-eyed
mutants of *Culex pipiens* surprisingly show the normal diving response to
a shadow, possibly because they are responding to change of intensity
and not to movement of contour (Gilchrist and Haldane, 1947). The

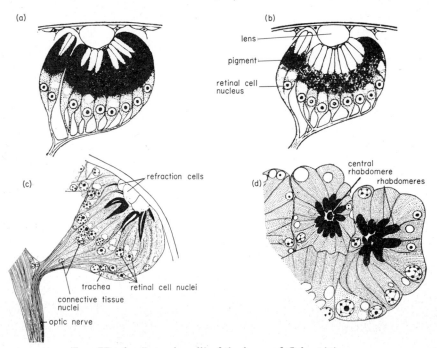

FIG. 77a–d. Lateral ocelli of the larva of *Culex pipiens*.
(a) Longitudinal section through ocelli in the light-adapted condition; (b)
L.S. through ocelli in the dark-adapted condition (from Satô, 1951b); (c)
L.S. through ocellus after removal of pigments; (d) T.S. through 2 ocelli
after removal of pigments. (From Constantineaunu, 1930).

lateral ocelli show little change of structure in the pupal stage and they are
still present in the adult, behind the compound eyes, although in a
degenerate condition.

During most of the larval stage the adult compound eyes are present
in an incompletely-developed form just anterior to the lateral ocelli, the
nerve from each compound eye joining that from the lateral ocelli of its

side. It seems quite possible that the compound eyes mediate the submergence reflex to change in light intensity.

Under a vertical beam of polarized light mosquito larvae glide in any direction but they will turn when the plane of vibration is rotated. This may be due not to perception of the plane of polarization but to intensity discrimination since light-scattering material in water scatters light from a vertical, polarized source, so that it is most intense at right angles to the plane of polarization (Baylor and Smith, 1953). The larvae appear to be sensitive to ultraviolet light since they submerge when a bottle containing carbon disulphide, a strong absorber of ultraviolet light, is placed between them and a light source (Leftwich, 1954).

Only a few other sense organs have been described in the mosquito larva. In *Aedes aegypti* sensory papillae occur on the tips of the antennae and maxillary palps, on the labium and at the apex of the respiratory siphon, while proprioceptors in the form of scolopophores occur in pairs in the abdominal segments, and 3 pairs and a further single scolopophore are found in the respiratory siphon (Christophers, 1960).

CHAPTER 11

DIAPAUSE

Diapause and Quiescence in the Egg Stage

Occurrence and Characteristics

All species of the aedine genera *Aedes, Psorophora* and *Haemagogus* are capable of arresting development at the egg stage. These mosquitoes lay their eggs either in moist soil in situations subject to flooding or just above the water level in tree holes or other small receptacles which collect rain water. Embryonic development proceeds to completion and the eggs must be kept moist during the first hours of this period until the shell becomes impermeable to water (p. 28), but subsequently the eggs of many species will retain their viability out of water for several months or more. For example, a hatch of 62 per cent was obtained from *Aedes aegypti* eggs held at 0 per cent R.H. and 28°C for 3 weeks (Buxton and Hopkins, 1927) and eggs of this species will survive for about 1 year provided the relative humidity does not drop below 70 per cent (Geigy and Gander, 1949). *Aedes squamiger* eggs remain alive in soil without flooding for at least 2 seasons (Telford, 1958) and *Aedes vexans* and *Aedes sticticus* eggs survive in large numbers for 3 years, a few even for 4 years, when kept moist, but fail to hatch after being kept in dry air for 9 months (Gjullin, Yates and Stage, 1950). Most species appear unable to survive for long at low humidities, i.e., below 70 per cent or 80 per cent R.H., but eggs laid in soil are deposited in interstices below the surface of soil rich in plant debris where the relative humidity probably remains high. This ability to arrest development in the egg stage and to survive in the absence of free water allows some aedine mosquitoes to hibernate and others to aestivate or to colonize niches which are only occasionally flooded. The same habit is found in the unrelated genus *Heizmannia* and in the subgenera *Armigeres* and *Culicella*. Eggs of *Culiseta (Culicella) morsitans,* for example, are laid on soil subject to flooding and are able to resist drying for many weeks (Shute, 1933a). Eggs of *Heizmannia stonei* survive drying for at least 3 weeks, those of various *Armigeres* species for an unspecified period (Macdonald and Traub, 1960). *Anopheles walkeri* passes the winter in the egg stage (Hurlbut, 1938) but it is not known whether its eggs can resist drying.

The arrest of development in insects can take the form of quiescence or of diapause. Quiescence is a state of inactivity induced by an unfavourable environment and it ceases on amelioration of the environment. Diapause is terminated only after reactivation, i.e., exposure to a factor such as cold for a period of time; when diapause occurs in univoltine species, those with only 1 generation a year, it is obligatory, when it occurs in multivoltine species it is facultative being induced by the environment. Diapause is quite distinct from quiescence but in some cases insufficient knowledge makes it difficult to distinguish between the two phenomena (Lees, 1955).

The eggs of most aedine mosquitoes show 2 peculiarities: they will hatch only when submerged in deoxygenated water, and those which have been dried require a short period of 'conditioning' (see below) before they will hatch. Once these 2 peculiarities are understood, the different aedine species fall fairly clearly into those whose eggs enter diapause and require reactivation, and those whose eggs become quiescent and hatch shortly after exposure to an adequate hatching stimulus, although they may require a few hours conditioning. The unfavourable environments which induce quiescence are absence of water or presence of oxygenated water. Typical quiescent eggs are those of *Aedes aegypti* (Gillett, 1955a), *Psorophora cingulata* and *Haemagogus spegazzinii* (Bates, 1949) which normally become inactive at the completion of embryonic development if free, deoxygenated water is not present but which will subsequently hatch at any time if they are submerged in water which is sufficiently deoxygenated. Obligatory diapause is found in *Aedes hexodontus,* a univoltine species which enters diapause spontaneously at the end of embryonic development and which will not hatch despite strong stimulation until it has been suitably reactivated (Beckel, 1958a). *Aedes canadensis, Aedes fitchii* and *Aedes stimulans* are other species with an obligatory diapause in the egg stage (Horsfall, Lum and Henderson, 1958). *Aedes dorsalis* is a multivoltine species exhibiting facultative diapause, only eggs laid in the autumn requiring reactivation (Khelevin, 1958a).

The manner of induction of egg diapause is hardly known. Eggs of *Anopheles walkeri* laid in late August and September become dormant after embryonic development is complete, although summer eggs would hatch at the prevailing temperature, and normally hatch during April at a lower temperature than that at which they were laid (Hurlbut, 1938). The winter eggs differ in structure from the summer eggs and a female of *Anopheles walkeri* has been recorded laying a batch of summer eggs on August 12 and a batch of winter eggs on August 28 (Matheson and Hurlbut, 1937). It is possible that the photoperiod experienced by the adult female determines the type of egg laid.

Khelevin (1958a) considered that the temperature prevailing during the late stages of embryonic development determines the onset of diapause in *Aedes dorsalis* which shows facultative diapause, since eggs laid by females captured in the autumn and held at room temperature (16–17°C) for 11 days after laying and then transferred to a higher temperature enter diapause, whereas autumn eggs held at room temperature for a shorter period, 6 days, and then transferred to 25 or 30°C fail to enter diapause. However, exposure of gravid females caught in May and June and their eggs to low temperatures (10–13°C) fails to induce diapause and the eggs hatch immediately after submergence. The effect of a short day on the spring generation or of a long day on the autumn generation has not been investigated.

It may be concluded that in univoltine species which pass the winter in the egg stage the eggs enter an obligatory diapause, whereas in multivoltine species which pass the winter as eggs the diapause is facultative and eggs only enter diapause if laid in late summer or autumn. Certain species aestivate in the egg stage. The factor inducing diapause is not known in most cases but from the importance of photoperiod in the reactivation of some diapausing eggs it seems possible that it sometimes controls induction also, acting either on the mother or directly on the egg. Eggs of all aedine mosquitoes become quiescent if conditions are unfavourable for hatching, including eggs which have broken diapause but remain in unfavourable conditions. Quiescence and diapause in the egg stage enable larvae to occupy transient bodies of water.

Hatching Stimulus

Practically all aedine eggs require a hatching stimulus in addition to submergence in water before the larvae which they contain will burst from their shells. Atkin and Bacot (1917) showed that quiescent eggs of *Aedes aegypti* would hatch when placed in water containing live bacteria but that few eggs would hatch in water containing dead bacteria or sterile bacterial extracts. Other workers have shown that solutions of many organic and inorganic compounds stimulate *Aedes* and *Psorophora* eggs to hatch under sterile conditions, larvae often appearing within 10 min of submergence (Gjullin, Yates and Stage, 1939; Gjullin, Hegarty and Bollen, 1941; Geigy and Gander, 1949; Travis, 1953). Gjullin, Hegarty and Bollen (1941) and Geigy and Gander (1949) showed that a fall in dissolved oxygen from 7 ppm to below 3 ppm stimulates *Aedes* eggs to hatch whether it is caused by physical, chemical or biological means. Changes in reduction potential independent of oxygen tension do not stimulate hatching (Gjullin, Hegarty and Bollen, 1941) and the impermeability of the egg shell makes it unlikely that reduction potential as such could affect the embryo. It therefore appears that anaerobiosis is the stimulating factor. This would account for the irregular hatching of floating eggs (Buxton and Hopkins, 1927; Shannon and Putnam, 1934) and would explain the stimulating effect on hatching of the crowding of eggs (Thomas, 1943). Other factors which stimulate hatching in the laboratory are mechanical agitation (Young, 1922; Hearle, 1929) and fall in temperature (Fielding, 1919; Gillett, 1955a) but these are much less powerful stimuli.

It is generally held that all compounds which stimulate hatching of aedine eggs do so by lowering the oxygen tension of the solution. A disappearance of oxygen has been demonstrated in ascorbic acid solution (Judson, 1960), in enzyme preparations and bacterial infusions (Gjullin, Hegarty and Bollen, 1941), and it would certainly occur in solutions of cysteine, thioglycollate, hydroquinone and pyrogallol, all of which stimulate hatching. It is not clear, however, how active compounds such as the weak reducing sugars maltose and lactose, the amino acids alanine, aspartate, glycine and leucine, or the amine asparagine can remove oxygen from solution. It is important that the mechanism of stimulation by these compounds should be investigated. Bacterial contamination is a possibility.

Horsfall, Henderson and Lum (1957) observed that unhatched larvae of *Aedes trivittatus* removed from their shells would become active when placed in saline at 4°C but not if glucose or acids of the tricarboxylic acid cycle were added to the medium. Other compounds including inositol, mannitol, sorbitol, galactose, gelatine and bovine albumin had slight or no effect. This observation is difficult to interpret but the importance of the inhibitory compounds in respiration is interesting.

It is characteristic of the hatching stimulus that all eggs can be caused to hatch by a strong stimulus but that progressive weakening of the stimulus causes progressively fewer eggs to hatch. The rate of hatching of *Aedes aegypti* eggs in a bacterial infusion is proportional to the number of bacteria present (Borg and Horsfall, 1953) and the percentage of *aegypti* eggs hatching in maltose solution is directly proportional to the concentration (Fig. 78) (Gander, 1951). Judson (1960) recorded an inverse relationship between percentage hatch and oxygen tension when *Aedes aegypti* and *Aedes nigromaculis* eggs were added to water of constant oxygen tension, very low tensions being needed to induce a high degree of hatch, but when eggs were already submerged even a slight lowering of oxygen tension proved a powerful hatching stimulus. For example, a fall in oxygen concentration from 8·3 to 6·7 ppm in 1 hr gave an average hatch of 52 per cent with *Aedes aegypti* eggs whereas only 12·5 per cent hatched when transferred directly to water containing 6·7 ppm oxygen. Experiments with irrigated pasture showed that the amount of oxygen in solution at the soil–water interface fell by 1·39 to 2·85 ppm in the first hour after flooding, leading Judson (1960) to conclude that falling oxygen tension is the effective stimulus in nature, rather than absolute tension, since hatching in the field usually occurs shortly after flooding. When 20-day-old eggs of 3 strains of *Aedes aegypti* were placed in water of low oxygen tension it was found in each case that male larvae hatched appreciably faster than female larvae (Elzinga, 1961).

Many workers have reported great variability in the hatching responses of eggs of the same species. For example, repeated flooding and drying of the same eggs produced successive hatches of larvae from eggs of *Aedes*

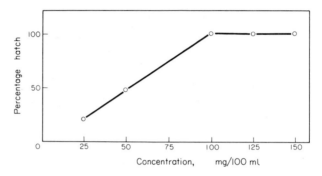

Fig. 78.   Relationship between concentration of maltose and percentage hatch of *Aedes aegypti* eggs. (From Gander, 1951).

sollicitans, Aedes taeniorhynchus and *Psorophora confinnis* (Travis, 1953). It has been seen that eggs vary in the strength of hatching stimulus which they require and this probably accounts for much of the variability of hatching in the field although not for all. Hatching in response to falling temperature in *Aedes aegypti* is an inherited character (Gillett, 1955b) and genetic control of hatching has also been postulated in *Haemagogus* (Hovanitz, 1946). A high proportion of recently-laid eggs of *Aedes aegypti* will hatch without any apparent fall in dissolved oxygen or other stimulus whereas other recently-laid eggs and all older eggs need a stimulus (Gjullin, Hegarty and Bollen, 1941; Gillet, 1959; Judson, 1960). When eggs of a West African strain of *Aedes aegypti* were submerged in water on the day of laying about half would hatch spontaneously on the 3rd and 4th days but none hatched subsequently unless a hatching stimulus was applied. On placing in the same container groups of eggs laid on 2 successive days, it was found that an average of 51 per cent hatched spontaneously in the older batch of eggs, but only 30 per cent in the younger. Further experiments showed that this was due to inhibition of spontaneous hatching in the younger eggs and not stimulation of hatching in the older. The mechanism of inhibition is not known (Gillett, 1959). Another factor causing a spread in hatching is the occasional need for conditioning, described in the next section. Variation in time of hatching within a species presumably has survival value in such transient larval habitats.

Conditioning

It has frequently been found that eggs respond more readily to a hatching stimulus if they have previously been held at a high humidity. For example, *Aedes aegypti* eggs kept at 98 per cent R.H. for 1–2 days gave a 70 per cent hatch within 15 min of submergence but only 12·5 per cent hatched within 15 min after storage at 74 per cent R.H. Hatching ability was restored to eggs which had been kept at 7 per cent R.H. for 24 hr by exposure to 100 per cent R.H. for the same period (Harwood and Horsfall, 1959). It has been suggested that drying affects the structure of the egg shell in *Aedes aegypti* and its resistance to escape of the larva in a manner which can be corrected by conditioning with water vapour (Harwood and

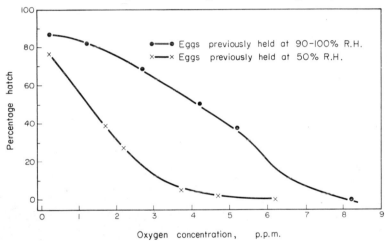

FIG. 79. The effectiveness of various "static" concentrations of dissolved oxygen as hatching stimuli for *Aedes aegypti* eggs previously held at high and low relative humidities. (From Judson, 1960).

Horsfall, 1959) but it is difficult to uphold this theory since Judson (1960) showed that the percentage hatch of *Aedes aegypti* eggs previously held at high and low relative humidities differed widely when submaximal hatching stimuli were applied but differed hardly at all after maximum stimulation (Fig. 79).

Aedes vexans eggs which have been exposed to dry air need a similar type of conditioning but in this case it cannot occur in a saturated atmosphere but only in free water (Horsfall, 1956). Eggs of this species which are submerged shortly after laying require conditioning by exposure to warm, moist air before they can be stimulated to hatch (Horsfall, 1956; Khelevin, 1961). Horsfall (1956) studied hatching of *Aedes vexans* eggs in a natural site which was continuously submerged from January to mid-June 1952 and in a site nearby which was dry until early April. All eggs in the dry site hatched during the April flooding but none hatched at that time in the continuously-submerged site, although eggs taken from that site hatched in the laboratory after a short exposure to air at room temperature. Eggs remaining in that site hatched naturally in mid-summer when flooding followed a period of drying.

A need for conditioning does not imply that eggs are in diapause, for conditioning is a short-term process which, when needed, will occur after a few hours exposure or submergence. It is an important factor in experiments, however, and as Judson (1960) has pointed out, is probably responsible for many ambiguous reports.

Reactivation

Diapausing eggs will respond to a hatching stimulus only after passing through a period of reactivation by a factor such as cold or light. In contrast to conditioning, reactivation may take many days.

In nature the eggs of *Aedes hexodontus* are inundated by autumn rains and usually spend the autumn under water and the winter under ice. They are still submerged in the spring and hatch without exposure to air when the water temperature rises a few degrees above zero Centigrade. Of a number of factors tested in the laboratory only cold led to the cessation of diapause. Exposure to 1° or −3°C for 100 days led to a rather low hatch and exposure for 200 days to a hatch which averaged about half the eggs. Only 2 per cent of eggs held at 20°C for 200 days could be stimulated to hatch (Beckel, 1958a). *Aedes stimulans* eggs in obligatory diapause require at least 180 days reactivation to give a high percentage hatch. Reactivation consists of exposure to summer temperatures followed by exposure to winter temperatures, and after such treatment the eggs hatch within 1 or 2 days of return to high temperature. No eggs hatched after continuous exposure for 6 months to 24° or 4°C. When eggs were first exposed to summer temperatures for 120 days, 60 days exposure to cold led to a high percentage hatch; when exposed to summer temperatures for 40 days, even 120 days exposure to cold led to only a moderate hatch (Horsfall and Fowler, 1961).

Circumstantial evidence suggests that low temperature breaks the diapause of several other species. Eggs of *Aedes vexans* and *Aedes sticticus* obtained in mid-winter hatch after conditioning by exposure to warm air but eggs obtained in the autumn and conditioned cannot be stimulated to hatch (Gjullin, Yates and Stage, 1950). Diapausing eggs of *Aedes dorsalis* which had been exposed to subzero temperatures gave a hatch in late autumn and early winter which was low but slightly higher than that of eggs which had been held at room temperature. Cold is not essential for reactivation in this species since eggs exposed to 30° or 35° break diapause within 2 months (Khelevin, 1959). Freshly-laid diapausing eggs of *Aedes flavescens* refuse to hatch after cooling or freezing but eggs which have passed the winter under laboratory conditions hatch after even a short period of cooling (Khelevin, 1958b). Winter eggs of *Anopheles walkeri* hatch only after a period of chilling (Matheson and Hurlbut, 1937).

In contrast to these species with a winter diapause it is interesting to consider a species with aestivating eggs. *Aedes squamiger* is univoltine and passes the summer in the egg stage. The eggs fail to hatch when covered by summer high tides but hatch if inundated between October and March, adults emerging in the spring. In the laboratory eggs had to be subjected to temperatures below 8°C before they would hatch (Telford, 1958). It is remarkable that low temperature breaks the diapause of both hibernating and aestivating eggs.

Day length controls development in the tree-hole mosquito *Aedes triseriatus*. A group of eggs from the area of New York could not be stimulated to hatch during October and November. The group was then split into 2 parts kept in air at 60–90 per cent R.H. for 5 weeks, one receiving normal daylight for approximately 10 hours per day and the other receiving illumination for 16 hr per day. When the eggs were placed in filtered tree-hole water at the end of this period 2 larvae hatched from the short-day eggs whereas the water containing the eggs subjected to a long day teemed with 1st instar larvae (Baker, 1935). Eggs of the same species from Georgia, USA, laid and maintained under a short-day regime or in darkness gave rise to larvae most of which entered diapause in the 4th instar (Love and Whelchel, 1955). This conforms with the observation that *Aedes triseriatus* passes the winter in the egg stage in the northern United States and in the larval stage further south (King *et al.*, 1960).

Eggs of *Aedes stimulans*, a few weeks old and in obligatory diapause, could not be made to hatch by normal hatching stimuli, but if their chorions were removed with hypochlorite solution the larvae would hatch from their serosal cuticles within 24 hr of submergence in water, although they would not fill their tracheae with air or feed for some days (Newkirk, 1955).

The mechanism of reactivation, like that of conditioning, remains largely unknown but it is important to distinguish between these two processes. Conditioning may be required by both quiescent and diapausing eggs and is a short-term process which will need repeating if the eggs become deconditioned. Reactivation is essential for hatching of diapausing eggs and is normally a long-term process but one which never needs to be repeated.

Diapause in the Larval Stage

A large proportion of the mosquitoes of temperate regions pass the winter in the larval stage. Certain species are known to be in diapause at this time but there is insufficient evidence to show whether the other species are in diapause or are simply quiescent and able to continue development at any time after a rise in temperature.

In certain species, hibernating larvae are reactivated by an increase in day length. The rate of pupation in a laboratory colony of the tree-hole mosquito *Aedes triseriatus* in Georgia, USA, was found to fall during the autumn. In a series of experiments, no development occurred among 4th instar larvae kept in darkness at 27°C or in natural winter light at 7° and 39°C but larvae kept in constant light at 29°C all pupated within 9 days. When larvae which had been kept in darkness at 27°C and 7°C were subjected to continuous illumination, those at 27° all pupated within 9 days but no development took place in the larvae at 7° (Love and Whelchel, 1955).

When hibernating larvae of 2 other tree-hole species, *Orthopodomyia signifera* and *Anopheles barberi,* were divided into 2 lots, one receiving a day length normal to a northern latitude in winter and the other a day length of 16 hr, the short-day larvae remained photonegative and did not feed or develop while the long-day larvae became photopositive, fed and pupated (Baker, 1935). Day length is possibly important in the tree-hole mosquito *Anopheles plumbeus* also, for larvae of the first 2 generations each year pupate within 29 days at room temperature, but larvae from eggs laid in September and October need at least 135 days under the same conditions of temperature and nourishment (Roubaud and Colas-Belcour, 1933).

Anopheles pulcherrimus normally hibernates in the larval stage in the USSR. Larvae reared at 28°C pupated within 16 days whether exposed to a short day of 10–12 hr light or a long day of 14 hr light. Larvae kept at 18°C and 10–12 hr light per day passed through the first 2 instars rapidly but subsequently showed considerable delay in development, the majority pupating by the 39th day but a few still remaining as 3rd or 4th instar larvae (Vinogradova, 1960). J. S. Kennedy (cited by Andrewartha, 1952) collected hibernating 2nd instar larvae of *Anopheles claviger* and reared them in 3 groups at an unspecified temperature and with 14, 8 and

TABLE 18. SUMMARY OF DATA CONCERNING INDUCTION OF DIAPAUSE AND REACTIVATION.

Species	Diapausing Stage	Factor Inducing Diapause	Reactivating Factor	Reference
Aedes hexodontus	egg	(obligatory)	cold	Beckel (1958a)
Aedes squamiger	egg	(obligatory)	cold	Telford (1958)
Aedes stimulans	egg	(obligatory)	heat then cold	Horsfall and Fowler (1961)
Anopheles walkeri	egg	?	cold	Matheson and Hurlbut (1937)
Aedes triseriatus (New York)	egg	?short day on ♀	long day	Baker (1935)
Aedes triseriatus (Georgia)	larva	short day on ♀	long day	Love and Whelchel (1955)
Orthopodomyia signifera	larva	?	long day	Baker (1935)
Anopheles barberi	larva	?	long day	Baker (1935)
Anopheles palcberrimus	larva	?	long day	Vinogradova (1960)
Anopheles claviger	larva	?	long day	Andrewartha (1952)
Anopheles maculipennis messeae	adult	short day on early stages	?	Vinogradova (1960)
Anopheles byrcanus	adult	short day on early stages	?	Vinogradova (1960)
Culex pipiens pipiens	adult	short day on early stages	?	Vinogradova (1960)

0 hours light per day. Within 3 weeks almost all larvae exposed to a long day had pupated but only 45 per cent of those in darkness and 15 per cent of those exposed to 8 hr light per day had pupated. It seems that short day and low temperature are both necessary to maintain diapause in *Anopheles pulcherrimus,* and probably in *Anopheles claviger* also, but that winter day length alone is sufficient to keep *Aedes triseriatus* in diapause, even at 39°C.

Photoperiod is involved in the induction of diapause in *Aedes triseriatus.* Although larvae obtained during the winter would pupate only when the photoperiod was lengthened, eggs laid in the summer gave rise to larvae which would pupate when exposed to 2, 7 or 9 hr light per day or to continuous darkness. Experiments were therefore performed to examine the effect of the day length experienced by adult mosquitoes on the development of their progeny. When females were given an additional 4 hr light each day in the winter most of their larvae pupated under conditions of continuous darkness, although the production of pupae was retarded at that time in the laboratory colony which was exposed to normal winter light. During the summer eggs were collected from females which had been kept in darkness for 2 weeks and from females exposed to natural light fluctuations. Larvae obtained from these eggs were reared in the dark, and while larvae whose parents had been exposed to normal summer daylight all pupated, most larvae whose parents had been kept in the dark did not pupate until exposed to a long day. It was concluded that shortening of day length with the approach of winter must result in the production of a different type of egg, only the short-day eggs producing larvae which respond to variations of photoperiod (Love and Whelchel, 1955).

The thoracic glands of hibernating larvae of *Anopheles claviger* differ in structure from those of active larvae according to Mednikova (1952), who considers that the arrested development of hibernating larvae stems from the absence of growth hormone.

No species is known to pass the winter in the pupal stage.

Hibernation of Adults

Hibernation in the adult stage is found in one or more species of most genera occurring in the temperate and arctic regions. It is the most usual stage of hibernation in anophelines but is rare among aedine mosquitoes. Most species hibernating as adults pass through more than one generation each year but the Alaskan mosquito *Culiseta impatiens* enters diapause soon after emerging in the summer and the adult females may live over a year (Frohne, 1953). In all species only the females survive to enter hibernation, having previously been inseminated. General observations suggest that females which emerge in spring or summer and which pass through one or more gonotrophic cycles never subsequently enter hibernation. The hibernating generation emerges in late summer or autumn while earlier generations are still active, and ovary development is held in abeyance in the hibernating females until spring. Mosquitoes vary in the activity they display during hibernation, but even species which do not feed move about to some extent and will quickly take to flight if disturbed (Berg and Lang, 1948) Females of *Culex pipiens pipiens* removed from hibernation during December and placed on a flight mill at room temperature would fly readily, covering an average distance of 4300 m, maximum 8674 m (Clements, 1955). The lipid content of hibernating *Culex pipiens pipiens* falls by the spring to one-seventh of that in September and October (Buxton, 1935).

The reproductive physiology of hibernating mosquitoes varies considerably from one species to another. Females of *Culex pipiens pipiens* which emerge in the autumn are not attracted by their normal hosts and do not feed on blood, but feed readily on plant juices and lay down large fat-body deposits of fat and glycogen from this source before entering hibernation. These females do not take a blood meal until they leave hibernation in the spring (Tate and Vincent, 1936; Lacour, 1937). According to these authors, females taken from hibernation and stimulated to feed by raised temperatures or strong illumination develop their ovaries, suggesting that there is no disruption of normal reproductive processes in hibernating females beyond the failure to gorge. However, Vinogradova (1960) reported a lack of ovary development in hibernating females of *Culex pipens pipiens* which fed, so it is possible that when ovary development has followed blood feeding the females had left the diapause state.

Females of *Anopheles labranchiae atroparvus* shelter in the winter in cattle sheds kept warm by animals. They do not develop a large fat body by feeding on plant juices in the autumn but take occasional blood meals during the winter, developing their fat bodies to some extent but not sufficiently to withstand a long period of fasting. The ovaries do not develop after blood meals taken in the winter so that the sequence of events which normally follows a blood meal is broken in some way (Swellengrebel, 1929). If the mosquitoes are kept at 26°C they will develop their ovaries after 3 or 4 blood meals in October and November and after 1 blood meal in February (de Buck and Swellengrebel, 1934; Swellengrebel and de Buck, 1938).

Anopheles maculipennis messeae does not feed on blood during the winter. However, if it is stimulated to feed by raising the temperature at least 3 blood meals are necessary in October and November before the ovaries will develop, although later in the winter or after prolonged warming the ovaries will develop after a single meal (de Buck and Swellengrebel,

Q

1934). There is clearly a dissociation of ovarian development and feeding, but digestion is also known to be abnormal in this mosquito in the early months of the winter (de Buck and Swellengrebel, 1934).

In Israel the hibernating generation of *Anopheles sacharovi* appears in October and blood feeding leads to growth of fat body reserves but not to ovary development. Owing to the high temperatures still prevailing the whole of the reserves become depleted in about eight days so that frequent blood meals must be taken until the temperature drops in November (Mer, 1931).

It is most likely that the failure of ovary development after blood feeding by hibernating mosquitoes results from a failure in hormone production. The corpora allata of hibernating females of *Anopheles maculipennis* are said to differ in staining properties from those of actively-reproducing females. They increase in size during diapause but shrink rapidly after the first intake of blood in spring, assuming the size and staining properties of those of summer females (Detinova, 1945a). The terms gonotrophic concordance, gonotrophic dissociation and gonotrophic discordance have been used to describe different types of reproductive physiology in hibernating mosquitoes (Swellengrebel, 1929; Rao, 1947), but as so little is known of the physiology of hibernating mosquitoes it is probably better not to use them.

Studies of Vinogradova (1960) on the effect of different regimes of light and dark on several species of mosquito show that photoperiod has a major role in the induction of diapause in adult females. Mosquitoes were reared from egg to adult under a particular light regime and at constant temperature, and females were considered to have entered diapause if they failed to develop their ovaries after one or two blood meals. Populations of *Anopheles maculipennis messeae* were studied at Leningrad (60°N) and Astrakhan (46°N). Exposure to different light regimes had no effect on the duration of larval development or on the blood-sucking activity of the females, which was usually slight. However, of the females which did bite those reared and maintained under short-day conditions mostly failed to develop their ovaries and those reared under long-day conditions mostly developed their ovaries (Fig. 80). The response to day length was much less sharp than in many insects. Vinogradova (1960) associated this with the slow appearance of diapausing individuals in wild populations which may last 15–30 days, suggesting that individual mosquitoes vary considerably in their response to photoperiod. The absence of a sharp response may also have been due to the high temperatures employed (22°–24°C). In many insects thresholds of photoperiod can be raised or lowered by temperature and in some the effect of day length is partially or completely masked except at medium temperatures (Lees, 1955).

Anopheles hyrcanus was investigated by Vinogradova (1960) at Astrakhan (46°N) and in southern Tadzhikistan (37°N). Differences in length of daylight had no effect on duration of development but controlled the entry of females into diapause as judged by ovary development (Fig. 80).

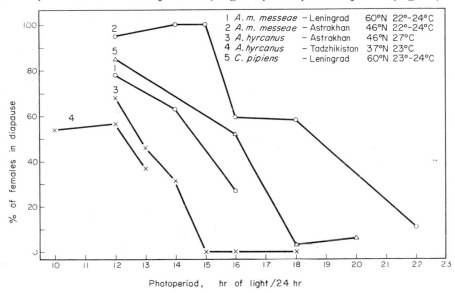

FIG. 80. Relationship between photoperiod (experienced throughout life) and percentage of females entering diapause. (From Vinogradova, 1960, 1961).

Long-day females were more aggressive in blood-sucking than short-day females and in nature a sharp drop has been observed in the number of *Anopheles hyrcanus* attacking man in August and September in Astrakhan. *Anopheles superpictus* at Stalinabad (38°N) showed a weak response to photoperiod, 67 per cent of females diapausing in 15 hr daylight, 100 per cent at 13 hr daylight. In nature, larvae which will give rise to hibernating females start life at a day length of $14\frac{1}{2}$ hr or less (Vinogradova, 1960). *Culex pipiens pipiens* shows a clear association between photoperiod and diapause (Fig. 80). Females are reluctant to bite under all conditions of day length but the proportion biting is significantly higher among females reared under long-day conditions. *Culex pipiens* var. *molestus* develops its ovaries autogenously whatever light conditions it has experienced. Hybrids of the F_1 generation are all non-diapausing but diapause occurs in 25 per cent of the F_2 generation (Vinogradova, 1960, 1961).

When short-day larvae of *Anopheles maculipennis messeae* are transferred to a long day at the beginning of the 3rd instar none give rise to diapausing females, but transfer at the beginning of the 4th instar produces a small proportion of diapausing individuals (Fig. 81). Exposure to a short day from the beginning of the 4th instar causes diapause in 57 per cent and from the beginning of the 3rd instar in all females (Vinogradova, 1960). Exposure of adult females of *Culex pipiens pipiens* to a short day is said to lead to diapause irrespective of the conditions of larval development (Danilevskii and Glinyanaya, 1958).

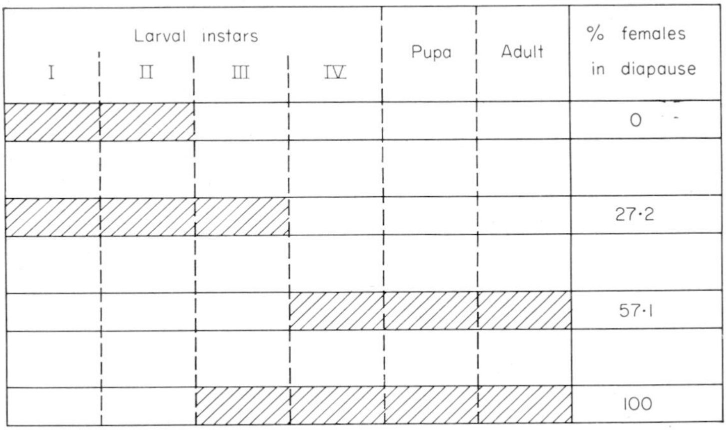

Larval instars				Pupa	Adult	% females in diapause
I	II	III	IV			
/////	/////					0
/////	/////	/////				27·2
			/////	/////	/////	57·1
		/////	/////	/////	/////	100

FIG. 81. The effect of different exposures to long and short day on the induction of diapause in females of *Anopheles maculipennis messeae* from Leningrad, reared at 22° to 23°C. (Hatching indicates exposure to short day). (Redrawn from Vinogradova, 1960).

A distinct difference can be seen between the thresholds of photoperiod needed for diapause in northern and southern populations of *Anopheles maculipennis messeae* (Fig. 80). Sixteen hours daylight induces diapause in 60 per cent of females in Leningrad (60°N) but for the Astrakhan population (46°N) 16 hr is a long day and induces diapause in only 27 per cent (Vinogradova, 1960). Similar results are obtained with ecological data (Table 19), wild *Anopheles maculipennis messeae* in northern Russia entering diapause at longer day length than wild populations in southern Russia. The higher threshold of the northern populations is easily understood, for not only does cold weather arrive sooner in the north but also daylight lasts considerably longer in summer in northern than in southern latitudes. Shipitsina (1959) surveyed the dates on which females of *Anopheles maculipennis* (presumably *messeae*) enter diapause in different parts of the Soviet Union. Diapause sets in during the period of high summer temperatures, and a close correspondence was noted between the appearance of diapausing females in different regions and the length of daylight.

TABLE 19. PHOTOPERIOD AT THE DATE OF EMERGENCE OF DIAPAUSING FEMALES OF *Anopheles maculipennis messeae* AND AT THE DATE WHEN THESE FEMALES HAD COMPLETED HALF THEIR LARVAL LIFE. (FROM VINOGRADOVA, 1960).

Locality	Photoperiod — hours of light per 24 hr.			
	when first diapausing females to appear have completed half of larval life	when diapausing females first appear	when most of diapausing generation have completed half of larval life	when most of diapausing females appear
Leningrad (60°N)	21 hr 20 min (July 9)	19 hr 44 min (July 24)	19 hr 44 min (July 24)	18 hr 10 min (August 8)
Astrakhan (46°N)	16 hr 32 min (July 19)	16 hr 08 min (July 29)	15 hr 11 min (August 17)	14 hr 26 min (August 27)

Variations in temperature cause only slight differences, not exceeding $2\frac{1}{2}$ weeks, in the dates of mass appearance of diapausing mosquitoes in each area. In many areas of similar latitude but different longitude diapausing females appear at the same time, but in some localities there is slight variation due to climate, diapause occurring earlier in regions of severer climate such as mountainous regions.

There is no clear evidence on the mechanism terminating hibernation but mosquitoes differ from many other insects in the relative ease with which they can be caused to resume activity. Hibernating females of *Culex pipiens pipiens* can be stimulated to gorge and to develop their ovaries by exposure to light for 5–10 days at 20°C (Tate and Vincent, 1936). Hibernating females of *Anopheles maculipennis messeae* and *Anopheles labranchiae atroparvus* will develop their ovaries after feeding if they have first been kept at 26°C for 3 weeks (de Buck and Swellengrebel, 1934). Ovary development has been stimulated in the autumn in hibernating females of *Culex pipiens* (Lacour, 1937) and *Culiseta impatiens* (Frohne, 1953) showing that, in these species at least, a period of chilling is not necessary for reactivation. It is generally held that reactivation is brought about by the rise of temperature in the spring (Mer, 1931; Bennington, Blackmore and Sooter, 1958) although the mosquitoes resume activity at a lower temperature than that at which they laid down their reserves the previous autumn (de Buck and Swellengrebel, 1934).

Our knowledge of the physiology of diapause in adult mosquitoes can be summarized quite briefly. In the few species which have been investigated the induction of diapause is due to exposure of the developing insects to a short day. The hibernating females lay down extensive fat body reserves after feeding on plant juices or on blood and, at least in those taking blood meals, there is some disruption of reproductive processes so that ovary development does not follow blood feeding.

Aestivation of Adults

In hot regions certain species of *Anopheles* are able to survive the dry season as adult females. Holstein (1952) has cited observations made by other workers on the occurrence of *Anopheles gambiae* in the dry season, gravid females being found taking blood meals, and he also describes his own observations on the presence of females of this species in crevices and other small niches during the dry season in West Africa. Of females caught away from human habitations 87 per cent had ovaries at stages IV or V and 6 per cent contained blood, whereas 89 per cent of females caught within habitations had ovaries at stages IV or V and 63 per cent contained blood. The fat bodies were not hypertrophied. Holstein concluded that females of *Anopheles gambiae* can pass the dry season in the absence of water, ready to lay and continuing to feed on blood when able to do so. Females kept under similar conditions of temperature and humidity in the laboratory and offered blood every 2 days lived up to 156 days, laying 2 or 3 times. At 27°C and 35 per cent R.H. average survival was 112 days, at 29·5°C and 63 per cent R.H. 87 days. When blood and sugar solution were withheld females survived up to 70 days. In the laboratory aestivating females showed a reluctance to lay when provided with water, but they were stimulated to lay when the relative humidity was raised to 80 per cent.

Adults of *Anopheles funestus* have been found in the dry season in Southern Rhodesia deep among the rocks of river beds. The mosquitoes, which were in a state of torpor, were in damp dark crevices protected from the drying effects of sun and wind. Very few males were found and the great majority of the females were gravid (Leeson, 1931). In the Taman peninsula, southern USSR, the larval habitats of *Anopheles maculipennis messeae* dry up in the summer. The females then defer oviposition for some weeks but continue to take occasional blood meals to support their basal metabolism. If the mosquitoes are offered water in the laboratory they begin to lay after 3 days (Eichler, 1951).

When a number of eggs are retained in the ovarioles of *Anopheles maculipennis* after oviposition, the follicles above the retained eggs degenerate during the following gonotrophic cycle (Detinova, 1953a). It appears quite possible, therefore, that aestivating females can retain a batch of mature eggs in their ovaries and yet feed when chance allows. In the laboratory virgin females of *Aedes aegypti,* which tend not to lay their eggs, will take repeated meals of blood (Lavoipierre, 1958a).

In India in the hot dry months digestion of blood by *Anopheles* requires 3–5 days, but when the relative humidity increases the intestinal tract is cleared in 1–3 days (Mayne, 1928). Büttiker (1958) found females of *Anopheles culicifacies* and *A. aconitus* in the dry season in Ceylon and Burma. A high proportion of the females which were engorged had stomach contents which were coagulated, very hard and almost completely desiccated, but undeveloped fat body and ovaries. He considered this a case of quiescence, the females maintaining themselves during the dry season on their last blood meal.

There is no doubt that females of certain species of *Anopheles* can survive prolonged periods of hot dry weather, and the survival of gravid females possibly accounts for the sudden appearance of mosquito larvae with the first rains. Aestivation apparently involves modifications of digestion or reproduction but little else is known of the physiology of these mosquitoes.

CHAPTER 12

BEHAVIOUR OF LARVAE AND PUPAE

Mosquito larvae and pupae show a number of behaviour patterns, some of them peculiar to particular species, and in each case they can be analysed into tactic and kinetic responses.

When larvae of *Anopheles labranchiae atroparvus* are placed in water with a horizontal temperature gradient most of them accumulate at a particular temperature by orthokinesis. The larvae swim actively at temperatures above and below a preferred temperature and when by chance they enter the preferred zone of 27–29°C their swimming movements cease (Ivanova, 1940). The larvae and pupae of *Aedes aegypti* show similar behaviour. When placed in a horizontal temperature gradient of 8–42°C 2nd instar larvae accumulate by orthokinesis in the range 23–32°C, whereas 3rd and 4th instar larvae and pupae show a preference for the range 28–32°C (Omardeen, 1957). In the field, larvae of *Aedes communis* select the surface layer of water until the surface temperature rises above 16°C when they aggregate at lower levels, except for occasional sorties to the surface (Haufe and Burgess, 1956).

When subjected to a light gradient of 1·08–1·25 log ft-lamberts 2nd and 3rd instar larvae of *Aedes aegypti* show no marked preference for any one light intensity but 4th instar larvae tend to avoid the stronger light and pupae show a strong negative phototaxis (Omardeen, 1957). Fourth instar larvae of *Anopheles maculipennis* swim almost incessantly when in a bright light but become inactive on accidentally entering shade. Their accumulation in shade is due to kinesis since they do not turn back on entering water exposed to light. Larvae that have dived show a marked phototaxis invariably swimming towards the light, even when the water is illuminated from below or from the side, but eventually return to the surface (Ivanova, 1936b). At 17° to 19°C and in diffuse light 4th instar larvae of *Anopheles maculipennis messeae* remain at the surface almost the whole time but they swim and dive incessantly under the influence of strong light. Stimuli such as water ripples cause them to dive but this response becomes reduced when the light or temperature is decreased. The larvae show thigmokinesis since they stop moving after coming into contact with a solid object. However, when heavily shaded they remain motionless even when not in contact with solid objects (Ivanova,

1936a). The larvae of *Culex pipiens* are said to be positively phototactic when fed a mixed diet but to avoid light when fed a diet of ciliates which appears to be nutritionally inferior (Rudolfs and Lackey, 1929).

Diving is the only defence of surface-dwelling larvae against predators and larvae are found to dive in response to stimuli such as vibration, surface ripple, visible movement of objects and sudden change in light intensity (Holmes, 1911; Thomas, 1950; Mellanby 1958). Mellanby (1958) found that the alarm response of *Aedes aegypti* larvae, which had a specific gravity less than that of water, consisted of swimming to the bottom followed by continuous swimming activity until recovery from the alarm when the larvae floated passively to the surface. *Culex pipiens* and *Anopheles labranchiae atroparvus* larvae, on the other hand, were heavier than water and when alarmed released themselves from the surface and sank passively to the bottom. The *Culex* larvae made occasional movements on the bottom but the *Anopheles* larvae lay completely still; both species swam actively to regain the surface. (Species found by one author to be heavier than water are sometimes found by another author to be lighter, with a consequent difference in the nature of the avoiding response (cf. Bates, 1949; Mellanby, 1958; Christophers, 1960)). *Aedes communis* larvae dive when an object moves slowly over the surface of the pool whether it casts a shadow over them or not. Second and third instar larvae respond only if the angle subtended by the object at the head of the larva is greater than 21° but 4th instar larvae and pupae respond at angles down to about 10° (Hocking, 1953b). In the absence of alarming stimuli larvae and pupae of many species remain motionless at the surface for long periods, except, in the case of the larvae, for the movement of their mouthparts (Ivanova, 1936a; Hocking, 1953b). *Aedes aegypti* larvae differ from those of most species in showing considerable spontaneous activity (Jackson, 1953). The movements of the mouthparts are not only important in feeding but can move the larvae over considerable distances (Hocking, 1953b).

Whatever the nature and direction of the stimulus producing an alarm response, the direction taken by larvae is governed by light and gravity. Larvae of *Culex* sp. and *Aedes aegypti* in darkness still swim to the bottom in response to vibrations, apparently through geotaxis (Folger, 1946; Mellanby, 1958). Larvae of *Culex* sp. illuminated from the side by a moderately bright light aggregate near the light, but when stimulated by vibration swim away from the light (Folger, 1946). When illuminated from below and then stimulated with vibration, larvae of *Culex pipiens* and *Anopheles labranchiae atroparvus* sink to the bottom in the usual way but larvae of *Aedes aegypti* remain at the surface showing intense activity. Mellanby (1958) pointed out that *Aedes aegypti* is normally active for the duration of the alarm response and that when active it is negatively phototactic.

Rapid repetition of a stimulus leads to habituation within a few minutes so that the alarm response is no longer given. For example, larvae of *Aedes aegypti* alarmed by a single tap on the side of their container return to the surface after about 4 min, yet if the container is tapped repeatedly once per second the larvae return to the surface within the same period. However, if the period between stimuli is lengthened habituation is less rapid. Larvae which have habituated to vibration will respond immediately to a visual stimulus (Mellanby, 1958).

Haufe (1957) investigated the movements of *Aedes communis* larvae in 2 small pools in northern Canada in relation to the daily cycles of light and dark and of warming and cooling. Larvae in the sunlit region of a pool aggregated in a dense group during the morning but those in the region shaded by trees remained dispersed. Temperature measurements revealed that the larvae aggregated where the temperature most nearly approached 16°C and the aggregate moved round the pool in a clockwise direction as the region of preferred temperature moved with the sun. Any larvae which swam across the interface between the sunlit and shaded regions gave a diving response, and because of the low angle of incidence of light striking the water surface and of the refracted light all larvae diving at the interface entered or remained in the shaded zone. Larvae entering from the sunlit region eventually joined with larvae already in the shaded zone to form a second aggregation at the position in the shaded zone, where the water temperature approached most closely to the preferred temperature. The second aggregate also moved in a clockwise direction, maintaining a constant position relative to the first.

The larvae of *Anopheles minimus* live among vegetation at the sides of streams, and Muirhead-Thomson (1940b) has studied the responses to light and shade by which they avoid the strong current prevailing away from the edge. When placed in still water in a container with no shade the larvae are extremely active but eventually settle down at the edge, their thigmokinetic response (to touch) dominating their kinetic response to bright light. If a part of the container is shaded the larvae swim directly towards the shade, preferring a shaded zone in the middle of the container to the unshaded edge. When their swimming movements have carried them to the edge of the central shaded zone a strong avoiding reaction prevents them from re-entering the light. When placed in a channel of flowing water the larvae immediately swim towards any shade whether this is at the edge or in midstream. If there is shade but no anchorage in midstream the strong avoiding reaction to light prevents their return to the edge where they could safely anchor and they are finally swept away. If the larvae can anchor in midstream transfer of shade to the edge has no immediate effect although the larvae finally move to the shaded edge. The experiments show little evidence of avoidance of moving water. The various reactions to light — orthokinesis, negative phototaxis and possibly direct movement towards shade — which are intensified by water movement, would normally drive the larvae into the grassy edge of a stream where water movement is at a minimum. The stream-dwelling larvar of *Anopheles maculatus* show very similar responses but the larvae of *Anopheles hyrcanus,* which live in still water, behave differently. These larvae normally show no response to shade in still or flowing water and protect themselves against water movement by thigmokinesis. However, when the velocity of the current makes fixing at the edge difficult they show some attraction towards shade (Muirhead-Thomson, 1940b).

Analysis of the behaviour patterns of mosquito larvae has shown that they are composed of a number of taxes and kineses, particularly responses to light, gravity, temperature and contact. Bates (1949) has shown that behaviour varies greatly from one species to another, always being appropriate to the habitat. In more complex behaviour patterns these differences may result from different combinations of taxes and kineses but they can also result simply from selective elimination of responses. For example, larvae of *Anopheles darlingi* which live in small ponds are very sensitive to sudden changes in light intensity but larvae of *Anopheles nimbus* which breed in forest streams, and which might be swept away on diving, show no alarm response to light changes.

CHAPTER 13

CONTROL OF ADULT ACTIVITY

Circadian Rhythms

The regular variation in mosquito activity with time of day is very familiar, most species being active during a certain part of the day or night or at dusk and dawn. Until recently it was thought that the onset and cessation of activity were controlled entirely by climatic factors such as light intensity and relative humidity, but it is now known that circadian rhythms play an important part in the control of mosquito activity and all early observations must be reassessed. Endogenous circadian rhythms are maintained by a physiological clock within the organism; this must first be "set" by an external stimulus, such as a change from light to dark, but thereafter maintains the rhythm without further time cues (Harker, 1958, 1961).

Bates (1941b) appears to have been the first to show that the periodicity of mosquito behaviour can be independent of the environment. Adults of *Anopheles superpictus*, previously kept at approximately constant temperature and humidity and exposed to 12 hr bright light per day with 2 hr of dim light preceding and following the bright period, were kept in continuous dim light for 56 hr beginning at the end of a bright period. The mosquitoes became very active 2 hr after the change to dim light and the activity was renewed twice more at 24 hr intervals with no more than one hour's variation in time of onset. The females would bite during the active periods if given the opportunity and swarming of males was seen during the first 2 periods of activity. The rhythm appeared to have been set by the previous exposure to light and dark since a reversal of the normal activity rhythm which was obtained by exposing the mosquitoes to light at night and to darkness by day continued when the mosquitoes were transferred to constant dim light. The continuation of rhythmic activity under constant conditions suggests the presence of a circadian rhythm but only when a rhythm persists with a frequency deviating by a constant amount from 24 hr can it be certain that the rhythm is independent of all external stimuli (Aschoff, 1960). The observations on *Anopheles superpictus* suggest that biting and swarming may be controlled by circadian rhythms.

The control of oviposition in *Aedes aegypti* has been studied in considerable detail. Under the equatorial condition of 12 hr day and 12 hr night

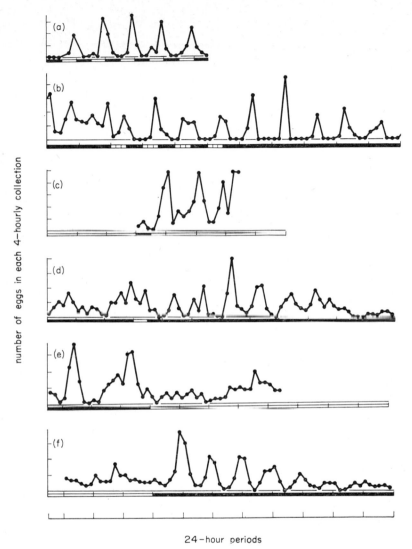

number of eggs in each 4–hourly collection

24–hour periods

FIG. 82a–f. Rhythmical oviposition in laboratory colonies of *Aedes aegypti*. (a) Pattern of oviposition under conditions of 12 hr light and 12 hr dark per day (from Haddow and Gillett, 1957); (b) induction of rhythmic oviposition in mosquitoes previously held in constant dark by transfer to 12 hr light and 12 hr dark per day, and persistence of the rhythm after return to constant dark; (c) effect of a single exposure to 12 hr darkness in an otherwise all-light regime (previous oviposition was irregular but not recorded); (d) effect of a single exposure to 12 hr light in an otherwise all-dark regime; (e) effect of change from constant dark to constant light; (f) effect of change from constant light to constant dark. (From Haddow, Gillett and Corbet, 1961).

populations of *Aedes aegypti* show a regular oviposition rhythm, most eggs being laid a few hours before sunset, and the same rhythm is obtained in the laboratory in response to 12 hr artificial light per day (Fig. 82a) (Haddow and Gillett, 1957). Mosquitoes which have been kept throughout life in constant dark lay irregularly but when transferred to a régime of 12 hr light and 12 hr dark per day they immediately start to lay rhythmically and the rhythm is maintained for at least 3 days after return to constant darkness, temperature and humidity, suggesting that it is circadian in nature (Fig. 82b) (Haddow, Gillett and Corbet, 1961). Rhythmical oviposition can be induced in mosquitoes kept in constant light or constant dark by a single period of exposure to dark or light (Figs. 82c, d). Exposure of mosquitoes held in the dark to a period of light is more effective in inducing rhythmical oviposition than exposure of mosquitoes held in the light to a period of dark. Mosquitoes laying irregularly in constant dark do not start laying rhythmically when transferred to constant light (Fig. 82e) but the opposite change — from constant light to constant dark — leads to rhythmical oviposition with the first peak appearing in the sixth 4 hr period of darkness and subsequent peaks following at 24 hr intervals for at least 5 days (Fig. 82f) (Gillett, Haddow and Corbet, 1959; Haddow, Gillett and Corbet, 1961). This indicates that the time cue which sets the clock is the change from light to darkness and that the change can be a sudden one. When mosquitoes reared in constant darkness were given a single exposure to light of 4, 8, 16 or 24 hr duration a regular oviposition rhythm developed in each case, not related to the time of onset of light but with the first peak in the sixth 4 hr period after the onset of darkness, confirming that it was the onset of darkness which was the light cue (Haddow, Gillett, and Corbet, 1961). Indeed, in mosquitoes reared in constant darkness exposure of the adult to light for 5 sec was sufficient to allow the return to darkness to be perceived and so to provide a time cue for a 24 hr rhythm which persisted for several days (Gillett, Corbet, and Haddow, 1959, 1961). Because the light cue occurs a number of hours before oviposition it is thought that the oviposition rhythm may be under hormonal control (Gillett, Haddow and Corbet, 1959) as the activity rhythm of cockroaches is known to be (Harker, 1958, 1961). The time lag of 21 to 24 hr between the light cue and first peak of oviposition activity indicates that it is the time of onset of dark on one day that determines the timing of oviposition activity on the next (Gillett, Corbet and Haddow, 1961).

Aedes aegypti can adopt an oviposition rhythm with a period different from 24 hr, e.g. 20 or 28 hr, if subjected to suitable régimes of light and dark. Such rhythms do not persist on transfer to constant light indicating that in the oviposition rhythm the endogenous element is weak and the exogenous element strong (Corbet, Haddow and Gillett, 1960).

Whether light conditions were normal during larval and pupal life or whether the early stages were subjected to constant light had no effect on the development of the 24-hr oviposition rhythm which appeared when the adults were placed in alternating light and dark and which failed to appear when they were placed in constant light (Haddow and Gillett, 1957). The circadian oviposition rhythm was shown to dominate any possible cycle caused by time of feeding in an experiment in which 3 groups of females kept under natural conditions of 12 hr light and 12 hr dark were fed blood at intervals of 8 hr. Oviposition began in the first group 77 hr after the blood meal during the hour noon to 1 p.m. and in the second group between 4 and 5 p.m. On a strict time basis oviposition would have been expected to start in the third group in the early hours of the night but in fact it was delayed and did not start until 11 a.m. to noon the following day, 19 hr after the second group (Haddow and Gillett, 1957). Thus females which complete their ovary development during darkness delay oviposition until the normal time for oviposition on the following day which is several hours after the onset of the following light period.

There is evidence that a circadian rhythm controls oviposition and the observations of Bates (1941) cited earlier suggest that biting and swarming may also have an endogenous element. Other activities of a rhythmic character are pupation (Sen, 1935; Nielsen and Haeger, 1954; Goma, 1959), erection of antennal fibrillae in the males of some species (Roth, 1948; Nielsen and Nielsen, 1958), the start of migration in *Aedes taeniorhynchus* (Nielsen, 1958; Provost, 1960), nectar feeding (Larsen, 1948; Haeger, 1955), feeding on sugar solution by captive males and females of *Aedes aegypti* (Gillett, 1961), and 'nonspecific' flight activity (Corbet, 1961b). All of these activities can be correlated with the natural cycle of light and darkness but it seems likely that some at least will be found to be influenced by endogenous rhythms. Although in any species each type of activity takes place at approximately the same time each day there is clear evidence that the different activities often occur at different times. The peak of oviposition activity precedes the peak of biting activity in *Aedes africanus* and *Aedes apicoargenteus* (Haddow, Corbet and Gillett, 1960). Males and females of *Aedes taeniorhynchus* feed on nectar for about 3 hr before and after the short periods of male swarming at dusk and dawn but nectar feeding ceases entirely during the periods of swarming (Haeger, 1955). The males of *Aedes caspius* erect their antennal fibrillae during the half hour before sunset or earlier but swarming does not start until after sunset (Nielsen and Nielsen, 1958). Periods of 'unspecific' flight activity, measured by captures in light traps, occur in many species at different times to swarming, biting

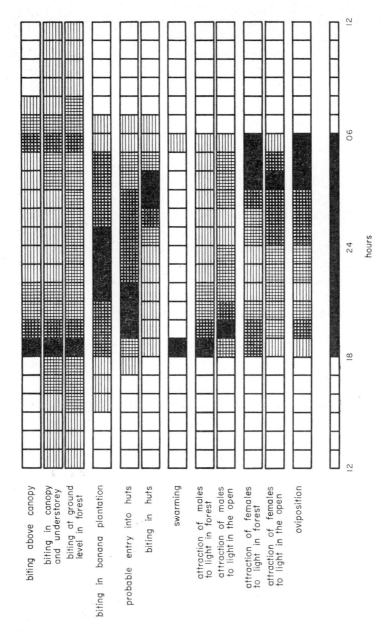

biting above canopy

biting in canopy
and understorey

biting at ground
level in forest

biting in banana plantation

probable entry into huts

biting in huts

swarming

attraction of males
to light in forest

attraction of males
to light in the open

attraction of females
to light in forest

attraction of females
to light in the open

oviposition

12   18   24   06   12

hours

Fig. 83. Changes in the extent to which various behaviour patterns are shown throughout 24 hr by *Mansonia fuscopennata* in the Entebbe area, East Africa, and their relation to light and dark. Five grades of activity are shown, from zero (white) to maximum (black). (From Haddow, 1961b).

and oviposition (Corbet, 1961b). Figure 83 summarizes such evidence for *Mansonia fuscopennata* and shows quite clearly that different activities often occur at different times. As Haddow (1961b) has pointed out, if these activities are controlled endogenously each species must have a number of circadian rhythms.

The shape of the graph of biting activity (Fig. 84) will be the result of 2 functions — the cycle of arrival in the vicinity of the bait through random flight and variations in timing of circadian rhythm between individuals (Colless, 1956b). Many species show 2 peaks of biting activity in each 24 hr (Fig. 84), one normally larger than the other, and Lumsden's

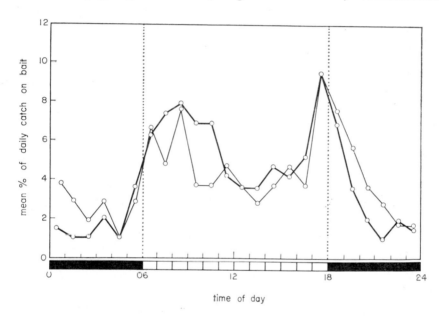

FIG. 84. The intensity of biting activity shown by females of the *Aedes tarsalis* group (thick line) and of the *Aedes abnormalis* group (thin line) at ground level in forest throughout 24 hr. (From Haddow, 1960).

(1952) suggestion that the 2 peaks are produced by mosquitoes of different ages has stimulated examination of the females comprising each peak. Gillett (1957b) found that the biting activity of young and old females of *Mansonia africana* followed the same pattern, Gillies (1957) found that the times of feeding of newly-emerged and older females of *Anopheles gambiae* were the same and Corbet (1961c) found no difference in the times of biting of parous and nulliparous females of *Mansonia fuscopennata,* although the proportion of parous and nulliparous females caught biting differed

R

at different heights in the forest. There is thus no evidence that the rhythm controlling biting is modified by the age or physiological condition of the female.

Certain observations suggest that the time of biting is affected by climatic factors as well as by the postulated circadian rhythm. For example, the peak of biting activity of *Mansonia fuscopennata* occurs at dusk at all levels in forest but in a banana plantation surrounded by forest it occurs several hours after dusk at a time when the microclimatic differences between forest and plantation have disappeared, and it occurs later still in

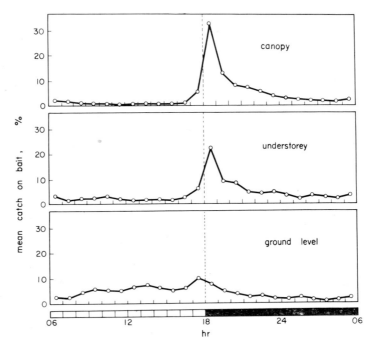

Fig. 85.   The biting rhythm of *Aedes africanus* at different heights in the forest. (From Haddow, 1961a).

huts (Fig. 83) (Haddow and Corbet, 1961a; Haddow, 1961b). In many species the biting rhythm varies at different heights in the forest, notably in *Aedes africanus;* this species shows a clearly-defined peak of biting activity during the hour after sunset in the forest canopy (about 57 ft), its preferred zone, but the peak is less marked in the understorey (about 35 ft), and at ground level the females bite mostly by day without any marked peak of activity (Fig. 85) (Haddow, 1961a). Certain species, including *Aedes africanus;* perform a cycle of vertical movement in the forest (Fig. 86); indeed, *Mansonia fuscopennata* can be seen rising through the forest just after sunset (Haddow, 1954, 1961b). Although this shows that the mosquitoes occurring at different heights are not distinct populations it does not account for the differences in biting rhythm at different heights.

The only experimental modification of a circadian rhythm by a climatic factor other than light is that by Bugher (1949). The flight activity of *Aedes africanus* placed in the dark at constant temperature and humidity was detected by a microphone and recorded, and it was found to resemble the pattern of biting activity in nature with high activity for about 2 hr after sunset, slight activity throughout the night and a slight increase in activity at dawn. Activity was depressed when the temperature was reduced from 30°C and it ceased entirely at 15°C. What is perhaps another

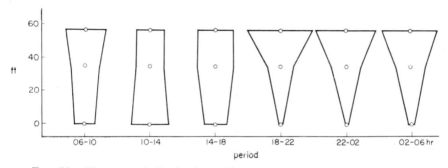

Fig. 86. The vertical distribution of biting females of *Aedes africanus* at different times of day and night in forest at Entebbe, East Africa. (Width indicates percentage of catch in each period. (From Haddow, 1961a).

example of modification of a circadian rhythm is the observation of Eyles and Bishop (1943) that egress of *Anopheles quadrimaculatus* from their resting places at sunset could be prevented by artificial illumination.

Certain sequences of physiological activity tend to be repeated regularly producing cyclical activity. In the tropics the gonotrophic cycles of *Anopheles minimus* and *Anopheles gambiae* last 48 hr and females which bite on 1 night lay and bite again 2 nights later (Muirhead-Thomson, 1951b). Such cyclic activity is not endogenous since it results from a repetitive series of events and its period is directly controlled by temperature. The behaviour of *Aedes taeniorhynchus* shows a 5-day periodicity; the females first bite about 4 days after emergence and again when 9 and 14 days old; they perform a peculiar flight when gravid when 7, 12 and 17 days old (Nielsen and Nielsen, 1953) and tend to be caught in light traps on the days on which they bite (Provost, 1952).

Remarkable long-term fluctuations in the intensity of the biting drive have been described in laboratory colonies of *Aedes aegypti* (see p. 269), and it appears that there may be an endogenous rhythm with a period of about 5 days affecting the intensity of the biting drive but distinct from the gonotrophic cycle.

Microclimate

The correlation between changes in light intensity and the start of biting, swarming, oviposition and other activities in many species led to the belief that these activities were controlled by light intensity, but now that circadian rhythms are known to be involved the evidence for most activities, and that is dealt with separately. This section is confined to merely serve as time cues or directly initiate activity. The evidence for the role of light in controlling swarming is more complete than for other activities, and that is dealt with separately. This section is confined to the modifying effects of micro-climate on activity, the many early observations on which remain valid today.

The peak of flight activity in *Aedes vexans*, when most were caught in light traps, was found to occur at different times on different nights, sometimes possibly correlated with relative humidity; the number of mosquitoes trapped on certain nights rose as relative humidity increased, to a maximum at 70 per cent R.H., but declined with further increase in humidity. No correlation was found with temperature (Platt *et al.*, 1958). The activity of *Culex pipiens* in the field, measured by the number caught, was also found to increase with humidity. Activity was greatest at 94–95 per cent R.H. but fell sharply near saturation (Rudolfs, 1925). The number of *Aedes sollicitans* and *Aedes cantator* alighting to feed increased with rising humidity to a maximum at 85 per cent R.H. and then declined (Rudolfs, 1923). Females of *Culex pipiens fatigans* in the laboratory refused to bite at 50 per cent R.H. and below but bit well about 70 per cent R.H. (Mayne, 1930).

The temperature must be above a certain level before mosquitoes will fly. Males of *Culex* sp. in nature would not fly when the temperature was below 15°C although the females were active at a slightly lower temperature (Wellington, 1945) but the arctic species *Aedes punctor* and *Aedes communis* would fly at 2·5°C (Gracheva and Shevkunova, 1959). The alighting of *Aedes sollicitans* and *Aedes cantator* to feed increased in the field with rising temperature between 15° and 32°C (Rudolfs, 1923) and in nature *Anopheles crucians* never bit at temperatures under 22°C (Mayne, 1926b). Females of *Anopheles quadrimaculatus* would not lay below 13°C

(Mayne, 1926a). It is well known that wind will diminish or prevent mosquito activity (Larsen, 1948; Lumsden, 1952; Haddow, 1954).

Catches of male and female mosquitoes in light traps have been used to measure mosquito activity during the night. Observations of Corbet (1961b) have shown that the flying mosquitoes which show a phototactic response to light traps are those which are not engaged in such specific activities as swarming, biting and oviposition. Their behaviour was interpreted as "nonspecific" flight activity. The numbers of mosquitoes caught in light traps on nights near full moon are only a small fraction of the numbers taken around new moon (Horsfall, 1943; Pratt, 1948; Onishi, 1959). The numbers of males and females attracted to a trap on any night are roughly proportional to the intensity of the light (Pratt, 1944; Barr *et al.*, 1960), and Provost (1959) considered that bright moonlight depressed the catches of light traps by reducing their apparent brightness since moonlight had no effect on the catches of suction traps nor, as Pratt (1948) had found, on the numbers of *Anopheles albimanus* caught in baited stable traps. Ribbands (1946) found that moonlight affected the time at which *Anopheles funestus* entered human habitations to feed. During moonless periods of the night the number entering huts was low but when the moon came out mosquitoes entered the huts in greater numbers. The proportion entering huts during twilight was 6 times greater on moonless nights than on nights after full moon, suggesting that many which had been unable to feed on a moonless night entered the huts during twilight on the following evening. This suggests that moonlight is necessary for upwind orientation to host odour (p. 265). The number of *Mansonia uniformis* attracted to hosts increases at full moon and the time of approach to hosts also varies in this species with change in phase of the moon (Antonipulle, David and Karunaratne, 1958).

At dawn the nocturnal species seek their daytime shelters and whether or not the increasing light intensity is responsible for the cessation of activity it appears to control the choice of resting place since indoor and outdoor humidities and temperatures are similar at that time (Shannon, 1935). The entry of *Anopheles quadrimaculatus* into daytime shelters was found to be gradual not concerted, and apparently occurred when direct sunlight struck the mosquitoes in the open (Eyles and Bishop, 1943). *Aedes cantans* rests in grass and bushes by day and as the shadows move across the grass in the course of the day the mosquitoes make short flights always ending up in a shady place (Nielsen and Greve, 1950). From the distribution of *Anopheles minimus* inside houses it was concluded that light was the most important factor in choice of resting place and the light intensity in the most frequented resting places was usually less than 0·01 ft-c (Muirhead Thomson, 1941b). *Anopheles sacharovi* and *Anopheles maculipennis* were found to prefer light intensities of 1–5 ft-c for their resting place, avoiding higher and lower intensities. Below 23°C a stronger light intensity was tolerated than at higher temperatures and very high temperatures caused the mosquitoes to seek darker quarters than usual (Shannon, 1935). Below 65 per cent R.H. the distribution of *Anopheles maculipennis* resting in a building was found to follow humidity, the higher the humidity in any part the more numerous the mosquitoes. When the relative humidity exceeded 65 per cent this response was abolished and distribution was influenced by light intensity and air movement. Avoidance of light was stronger at certain stages of the gonotrophic cycle (Simatchkova, 1936). The distribution of *Anopheles funestus* inside a small iron-roofed hut was found to vary with temperature. When the temperature was highest near the roof the mosquitoes were distributed on or near the floor and when the temperature was the same near the roof and near the floor the mosquitoes were found near the roof (De Meillon, 1934). In cases in which only temperature is measured it is possible that mosquito distribution is in fact controlled by relative humidity.

The avoiding response to light shown by resting mosquitoes becomes reversed at high temperatures. If mosquitoes are subjected to the heat of the sun while in the dark interior of a container they become positively phototactic when the temperature reaches a certain level, flying into bright sunlight. In *Anopheles sacharovi* and *Anopheles maculipennis* the change occurs when the temperature inside the container reaches 36°C (Shannon, 1935) and in *Anopheles minimus* at 38°C (Muirhead-Thomson, 1951b). Hibernating females of *Anopheles maculipennis messeae* are said to accumulate in dark places through photokinesis, the excitability of the mosquitoes increasing with greater light intensity. However, when the mosquitoes are disturbed they show a temporary positive phototaxis (Polyzhaev, 1936) such as is found in the escape behaviour of many species. A reversal of the response to light occurs at sunset in crepuscular and nocturnal species, the mosquitoes showing a strong positive phototaxis as they leave their daytime resting places. A similar response is shown at dawn by females of *Anopheles hyrcanus* which have entered a house and fed during the night, but females of *Anopheles maculipennis* and *Anopheles superpictus* do not show positive phototaxis at dawn and usually remain where they are (Detinova, 1962). Mosquitoes which are active during the day show varying responses to strong light; some such as *Eretmapodites silvestris conchobius* will bite in glaring sunshine (Hoogstraal and Knight, 1951) but many always remain in the shade.

In laboratory studies of the responses of adult mosquitoes to various environmental factors the choice-chamber technique has been widely used.

Mosquitoes are placed in a small chamber in which the factor to be studied differs in intensity at the 2 ends, all other factors being kept as constant as possible, and the number of individuals at each end is counted after a certain time. The study of responses to different temperatures is complicated by the variation in relative humidity which accompanies any difference in temperature. Muirhead-Thomson (1938) solved this problem by working in a range of relative humidity over which the mosquitoes showed no preference for a particular humidity and this is probably more satisfactory than working at a constant saturation deficit (Dakshinamurty and Sharma, 1951b) when there will still be a variation in relative humidity, to which rather than saturation deficit the mosquitoes apparently respond (p. 255). The choice-chamber technique suffers from the many drawbacks of investigating behaviour in the laboratory and there is little reason to consider that the mosquitoes' responses resemble anything happening in nature, but they do give some measure of the sensitivity of mosquitoes to humidity and temperature. One failing of the method was described by Haufe (1958) who found that when mosquitoes in a gradient were disturbed they tended to come to rest at the end of the gradient opposite to their previous positions.

Females of *Culex pipiens fatigans* were offered alternative temperatures in the dark within a humidity range to which they appeared unresponsive. Most newly-emerged females avoided the higher temperature when one or both were over 25°C but showed little choice below that temperature. Gorged and gravid females avoided the higher temperature above 20°C and hungry females still showed some avoidance of the higher temperature between 10° and 15°C. Between 23° and 29°C females were sensitive to a difference of 1°C across the chamber, a gradient of 0·05°C per cm (Muirhead Thomson, 1938). Adults of *Anopheles quadrimaculatus* avoided high temperatures under experimental conditions at 70–80 per cent R.H. At 30°C the mosquitoes clustered at the cooler end of a gradient of 2°C in 137 cm and above 35°C they could distinguish differences of 1°C (Platt *et al.*, 1957). Freshly-gorged females of *Anopheles minimus* given a choice of temperature, in a humidity range in which they showed no preference of humidity, avoided the higher temperature above 30°C but below 30°C showed no preference. Hungry females avoided the higher temperature above 25°C (Muirhead-Thomson, 1941b). Females of *Anopheles stephensi* apparently preferred 25°C to 20°C at a constant saturation deficit of 7 mm Hg (Dakshinamurty and Sharma, 1951a) but they might have been responding to the higher relative humidity. Hundertmark (1941) found that hibernating females of *Anopheles maculipennis messeae* and *Anopheles labranchiae atroparvus* preferred 15°C to higher temperatures except when this took them into saturated air and Martini and Teubner (1933) found that hibernating *Anopheles maculipennis messeae* preferred a temperature of 6°–8°C and *Anopheles labranchiae atroparvus* 10°–13°C.

When placed in a choice chamber in the dark at 25°C females of *Culex pipiens fatigans* chose the higher of two humidities when the difference was very great, as between 10 per cent and 60 per cent R.H., but over the range of 30–85 per cent. R.H. the females were not affected by differences of 30 per cent (Muirhead-Thomson, 1938). (In experiments with the same species, but checking the responses only after 24 hr, Hundertmark (1941) found greater sensitivity, females at 23°C preferring 73 per cent over 65 per cent R.H. and 95 per cent over 84 per cent R.H.). The females showed a strong avoidance of humidities over 95 per cent R.H., the response being strongest in gorged and gravid females and less strong in newly-emerged and hungry females. Near saturation all except the hungry females responded to a difference of 1 per cent R.H. across the chamber, a gradient of 0·05 per cent R.H./cm; hungry females at this humidity did not respond to differences of less than 3 per cent R.H. Males showed a similar avoidance of high humidities but any slight avoidance of low humidities was masked by their activity. When the experiments were repeated in the light at 25°C the results were much less strongly marked and they disappeared entirely at dusk (Muirhead-Thomson, 1938). In the hands of Dakshinamurty and Sharma (1951a) females of *Culex pipiens fatigans* in the light showed no response to differences of humidity at temperatures below 30°C; above 30°C they preferred the higher humidity when given the choice of 40 per cent and 60 per cent R.H. or 60 per cent and 80 per cent R.H. but preferred 80 to 100 per cent R.H.

Males and females of *Anopheles quadrimaculatus* preferred the higher of 2 humidities up to 70 per cent R.H. when they differed by 5 per cent or 10 per cent. There was little difference in response to 70 per cent and 80 per cent R.H., but above 80 per cent the lower humidities were preferred. The responses to relative humidity were the same at all constant temperatures in the range 15°–32°C and in light intensities from darkness to 500 ft-c (Platt *et al.*, 1957). Sensitivity to differences of 1 per cent R.H. at high humidities has been claimed for *Anopheles maculipennis messeae*, *Anopheles maculipennis maculipennis* and *Anopheles labranchiae atroparvus* (Hundertmark, 1938). In various species of *Anopheles* as in *Culex pipiens fatigans* the humidity preference varies under different physiological conditions. Young unfed females of *Anopheles labranchiae labranchiae* preferred 94–95 per cent R.H. over higher and lower humidities after 1 day in the choice chamber but preferred 97 per cent. R.H. after 2 days. *Anopheles superpictus* preferred 81 per cent R.H. at first but showed an increasing preference for higher humidities until it preferred 89–94 per cent R.H. on the fourth day. *Anopheles labranchiae atroparvus* preferred

89 per cent R.H. on the first day after a blood meal but preferred 94–95 per cent R.H. after 3 days when digestion was complete (Hundertmark, 1941). Females of *Anopheles minimus*, in all physiological conditions, showed no marked humidity preference between 50 per cent and 100 per cent R.H. (Muirhead-Thomson, 1941b).

Certain results suggest that mosquitoes respond to relative humidity rather than to saturation deficit. The proportion of females of *Culex pipiens fatigans* preferring 78 per cent over 98 per cent R.H. was similar at 20°, 30° and 35°C although the saturation deficit varied greatly at these temperatures (Muirhead-Thomson, 1938) and females of *Anopheles quadrimaculatus* preferred 70 per cent R.H. over 50 per cent and 90 per cent R.H. at both 15° and 32°C, a result which would not have been obtained if the mosquitoes had been selecting a particular saturation deficit (Platt et al., 1957).

Little is known of the reaction of mosquitoes to light under experimental conditions. Females of *Anopheles quadrimaculatus* were repelled by bright daylight but showed no response to differences of light intensity up to 500 ft-c, whereas females in a choice chamber at a light intensity of 2–3 ft-c showed no significant preference for a background of any colour (Platt *et al.*, 1957). In a choice chamber in daylight at constant temperature and humidity, unfed females of *Anopheles labranchiae atroparvus* preferred to settle on a black background to a grey one but preferred white to black. Freshly-gorged females showed no preference by day but at night more preferrred light backgrounds to dark ones. When offered combinations of humidity and colour the favoured humidity determined the resting place (Hundertmark and Martini, 1938). *Aedes aegypti* preferred to settle on the darker shades of any colour but *Aedes taeniorhynchus* preferred the brighter shades and *Aedes sollicitans* preferred the darker shades of the brighter colours and the lighter shades of colours containing blue (Gilbert and Gouck, 1957).

Haufe (1954) has examined the effects of constant and varying pressures on the flight activity of females of *Aedes aegypti* under laboratory conditions. When the mosquitoes had been acclimatized to the prevailing pressure their activity, calculated from the number flying, was approximately the same at all levels of static pressure between 550 mm and 800 mm Hg. However, a rise or fall of 7 mm Hg or more greatly increased the flight activity of acclimatized mosquitoes. After acclimatization to pressures over 735 mm Hg the activity following a decrease in pressure of 15 or 30 mm Hg was 1·5–2·4 times greater than that following a similar increase. When the pressure levels were less than 735 mm Hg the activity following a decrease in pressure was less than that following an increase. The mean atmospheric pressure at the time of these experiments was

735 mm Hg, and observations over some months suggested that the effect of atmospheric pressure on the flight activity of mosquitoes may depend upon physical characteristics of the individual acquired at the time of emergence. Between 3 and 6 hr at a constant pressure were needed for complete acclimatization and it was found that the activity of an incompletely acclimatized mosquito was unpredictable. Haufe (1954) has suggested that irregular patterns of insect behaviour in the field under apparently similar pressure conditions may be due to incomplete acclimatization of the insects to one natural barometric condition before exposure to a pressure change, but temperature or humidity changes could also be the cause of this.

The Control of Swarming

The dancing of male mosquitoes in swarms is an activity of a strongly rhythmic character, being limited in practically all species in which it is found to periods of twilight, either dusk alone or dusk and dawn. A circadian rhythm possibly plays some part in controlling the onset of swarming in *Anopheles superpictus* (p. 242). Other species have not been investigated sufficiently to show whether endogenous rhythms affect the time at which they swarm but there is much evidence to show that light intensity is an important factor.

Detailed laboratory experiments have been performed on the effects of light intensity on swarming in *Culex pipiens fatigans* by Nielsen and Nielsen (1962). The mosquitoes were contained in a cage of approximately $1\frac{1}{2}$ m³ and they swarmed around a stand bearing thermocouples (stand swarms) and over a black spot on the floor (marker swarms). At intervals of 12 hr the light was alternately faded gradually to darkness to simulate dusk and increased gradually from darkness to the intensity of daylight to simulate dawn.

Under 'dawn' conditions the males would start to swarm as darkness gave way to dim light and the swarms disappeared when the light intensity reached about 2 log lux. If the light was switched on to give full intensity at once no swarming occurred. If the light intensity was increased steadily over 5–15 sec stand and marker swarms appeared after a delay of a few minutes; for example, a delay of 3–4 min was recorded after the light intensity had been raised to 3·0 log lux. Nielsen and Nielsen concluded that the urge to swarm was present before light appeared and that swarming was normally released by a particular light intensity, but that when the light intensity was gradually but rapidly raised to what was normally an inhibitory level before swarming had begun the accumulated drive led to swarming after a delay.

Under 'dawn' conditions the start of the marker swarms was delayed to progressively higher light intensities as the temperature rose between 15° and 31°C, i.e., the threshold rose, but the light intensity which brought swarming to an end was higher at intermediate temperatures, 20°–23°C, than at lower or higher temperatures. There was no clear effect of temperature on the light intensity at which the stand swarms appeared at 'dawn' but the light intensity at which these swarms disappeared was higher at intermediate temperatures than at lower or higher temperatures.

Under conditions of decreasing light intensity, resembling dusk, marker swarms appeared only when the temperature was above 25°C although stand swarms appeared over a wide range of temperatures. A gradual fall in light intensity was essential for swarming and light changes lasting less than 1 min produced few swarming mosquitoes. In experiments performed at moderate temperatures the light intensity at which stand swarms first appeared at dusk was close to that at which stand swarms disappeared at dawn, i.e., about 1·6 log lux. From a few experiments performed at higher temperatures it appeared that the start of stand swarms at dusk was delayed by high temperatures until lower light intensities than usual. Normally, the dusk swarms ended and the dawn swarms began at very low light intensities.

In 4 'dusk' experiments performed at 21°–23°C the light was held all night at a particular intensity. At 1·68 log lux, which is just above the normal threshold for the start of swarming, only a few swarm-like movements were seen. At intensities of 1·38, 1·08 and 0·78 log lux swarming continued until the light intensity was increased for 'dawn' observations 12 hr later. It was observed that the higher the light intensity during the night the higher the threshold for the cessation of swarming. In these lengthy swarms only a few individuals took part at any one time.

When the cycle of 12 hr light and 12 hr dark was changed to one with periods of 5 hr or less there was a considerable reduction in swarming. On a day with 8 changes of light between 08 00 and 19 00 hr it was found that 30–50 mosquitoes danced in stand swarms at the first dawn and last dusk but that the other dawns had only 15, 2 and 1 participants and the other dusks 4, 4 and 2 participants. Marker swarms were very greatly reduced after the intervals between light changes had been shortened. A possible interpretation of these experiments is that changing light intensity alone is sufficient to stimulate swarming in a few individuals throughout the day but that an endogenous rhythm is present which renders the mosquitoes more sensitive to the light stimulus at the accustomed times of dawn and dusk.

The close correlation observed in the laboratory between the swarming of *Culex pipiens fatigans* and low light intensities resembles the restriction of swarming of mosquitoes in nature to dusk and dawn. There are other resemblances also. High temperature was found to delay the start of swarming of *fatigans* at 'dusk' in the laboratory to a lower light intensity than normal, and it has been observed in the field that whereas *Anopheles labranchiae atroparvus* starts to swarm at 35–40 ft-c at a temperature of 25°C, swarming is delayed until the light intensity has fallen to 10 ft-c when the temperature is 30°C (Cambournac and Hill, 1940). *Culex pipiens* var. *pallens* in Japan would start to swarm at 10–15 lux in July, about 20 min after sunset, at 1200 lux in late October, 15 min before sunset, and at 1700 lux in late November, 30 min before sunset; in each case swarming stopped at dark (Omori, 1954). When the low light intensity of dusk was maintained all night in the laboratory *fatigans* continued swarming throughout the night, and in the field *Psorophora confinnis* was seen by Provost (1958) to continue swarming over an hour longer than usual when bright moonlight caused the light intensity to remain over the level at which swarming normally ceased. In *Aedes cantans* the duration of swarming increases as the duration of twilight increases towards the summer solstice (Nielsen and Greve, 1950). A fall in light intensity during the day led to swarming by a few individuals of *fatigans* in the laboratory, and *Aedes cantans* was once seen to swarm at 14 00 hr in the field, apparently in response to a fall in light intensity associated with approaching rain (Nielsen and Greve, 1950). In contrast, a reduction of light intensity during the day to the level at which swarming normally occurred failed to stimulate wild *Anopheles labranchiae atroparvus* to swarm, even as late as an hour before swarming normally started (Cambournac and Hill, 1940).

The corroboration provided by these observations of natural swarms suggests that the males of *Culex pipiens fatigans* studied by Nielsen and Nielsen (1962) reacted to changes of light intensity as they would have done in nature so that some reliance may be placed upon the conclusions suggested by these experiments. These are that swarming is released at dusk by light intensity falling to a particular level and continues until light intensity has fallen below a certain level, that swarming begins at dawn at a certain low light intensity, later being inhibited when light intensity has reached approximately the level at which swarming started at dusk, and that the various thresholds of light intensity vary according to the temperature.

Only suitably-designed experiments can show whether circadian rhythms underlie behaviour. Bates (1941b) showed that males of *Anopheles superpictus* would continue to swarm at the usual times when subjected to continuous dim light for 56 hr but no other suitable experiments have been performed with swarming mosquitoes. There are a few observations, however, which suggest the presence of a circadian rhythm underlying swarming: neither *Anopheles superpictus* (Bates, 1941b) nor *Anopheles labranchiae atroparvus* (Cambournac and Hill, 1940) could be caused to swarm by reproducing evening light conditions during the day although a light change in the evening would stimulate swarming, and more *Culex pipiens fatigans* swarmed in the laboratory at the hours of 'dusk' and 'dawn' to which they had been conditioned than at additional periods of dim light introduced during the day (Nielsen and Nielsen, 1962). We may conclude that an endogenous rhythm probably underlies the swarming of some, possibly all, swarming species, causing the males to swarm in response to low light intensities in the evening, and in some species also at dawn.

Conclusions

We have evidence that swarming, biting and oviposition are controlled by circadian rhythms and several other activities which show a 24 hr periodicity may be controlled by circadian rhythms also. The various activities are normally performed at slightly different times of day but this is not sufficient evidence to prove that each has an entirely separate endogenous mechanism; all may be controlled by one internal clock.

It has been shown that low temperature, light and wind can inhibit activities normally controlled by circadian rhythms but very little else is known about the interaction of climatic factors and endogenous rhythms in determining the proportion of a population active at any time. Studies on swarming, which appears to have an endogenous element, have shown that it starts when the light intensity falls or rises to a certain level and may continue until light conditions become inhibiting. It seems possible that the endogenous mechanism builds up an internal drive and that swarming is released by certain light intensities. Temperature has been shown to affect light intensity thresholds. The fact that exodus from resting places (Eyles and Bishop, 1943), swarming (Nielsen and Greve, 1950) and migration (Haeger, 1960) may start earlier than usual when the sky is overcast shows that the time of onset of these activities is not rigidly predetermined.

There is at present no conclusive evidence showing the selective value of the various activity rhythms of any species. Pittendrigh (1950) has drawn attention to the close correlation between fluctuations in humidity and biting activity in *Anopheles bellator* and *Anopheles homunculus* in Trinidad forests, and Galindo (1958) has described how *Sabethes chloropterus* in neotropical forests bites principally from 14 00–15 00 hr which is the midday rest period of the arboreal mammals which are its hosts. The number of *Aedes africanus* biting at different times of day and night shows a very close correlation with the fluctuations in relative humidity of their forest environment (Haddow, 1945), but the time of maximum biting activity, 18 00–19 00 hr (Haddow, Gillett and Highton, 1947), also corresponds to the time at which monkeys, which are probably the principal hosts of this species (Haddow and Dick, 1948), are first settled in their sleeping places (Lumsden, 1951; Buxton, 1952). Haddow (1961a) found that the only East African mosquitoes which show precisely-timed peaks of biting activity are those which bite mainly in the crepuscular periods so the exact time of biting may be of little importance for many species. Clearly the adaptive value of activity rhythms will have to be investigated in the field for each species separately.

It appears that the activity of a mosquito at any moment will be determined by its physiological condition, e.g., whether gravid or non-gravid, by one or more circadian rhythms which will be set by the daily cycle of light and darkness, and by climatic conditions which may modify the timing of the circadian rhythms and which if adverse will reduce the proportions of a population responding.

CHAPTER 14

FLIGHT BEHAVIOUR

KENNEDY (1939) has made a detailed investigation in the laboratory of the responses of females of *Aedes aegypti* during flight to certain visual stimuli and to wind, and his analysis of these responses gives us considerable insight into the mechanism of orientation of flying mosquitoes.

In one set of experiments mosquitoes in a small cage were stimulated to fly by the breath of an observer and the subsequent orientation of the mosquitoes was recorded. In the absence of wind the mosquitoes were orientated at random. In 2 experiments when wind was provided 82 and 85 per cent of the active individuals flew against the wind, but when the experiment was performed twice in complete darkness only 55 and 63 per cent flew against the wind, the slight preponderance of individuals flying upwind in darkness being ascribed to a minority which touched the roof with their forelegs. It was concluded that free upwind orientation was not an orientation to the wind itself, since it was effectively eliminated in darkness, but that it was related to the apparent movement of the background. Kalmus and Hocking (1960) repeated this experiment with *Aedes aegypti* and came to the same conclusion. Other experiments by Kennedy (1939) confirmed the importance of the background in orientation. When caged mosquitoes were stimulated to fly in still air over a moving, striped substrate, 80 per cent flew in the direction of movement of the substrate but faster than the substrate although their orientation was random when the substrate was stationary. In these experiments the few mosquitoes which flew downwind or against a moving substrate appeared to be unstable whereas those flying upwind or with the substrate were perfectly stable.

The average ground speed of the caged mosquitoes in still air was 17 cm/sec whereas in a 33 cm/sec wind the average ground speed was 16 cm/sec and the average air speed 49 cm/sec. The mosquitoes thus appeared to fly at speeds which kept the apparent rate of movement of the background constant, so that the tendency of opposing winds to reduce this rate was counteracted by higher air speeds. Bässler (1958) repeated this experiment, also using females of *Aedes aegypti,* and confirmed that their air speed increased steadily as the wind speed rose to 150 cm/sec, so that the mosquitoes always advanced over the substrate although there

261

was a regular slight reduction in ground speed with increasing wind speed (Fig. 87).

Kennedy (1939) found that when the striped substrate was moved most mosquitoes flying in still air would face the direction of stripe movement, often flying faster but never more slowly than the stripes; the few individuals which flew against the direction of stripe movement reversed their orientation when the speed of stripe movement reached 13–17 cm/ sec. When wind passed in the same direction as the substrate the mosquitoes flew facing the wind and against the stripe movement, but staying in

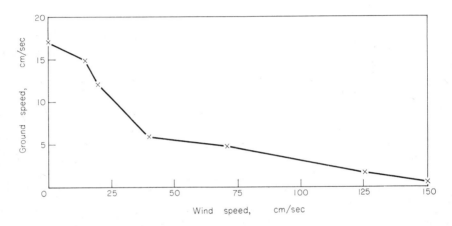

FIG. 87. Relationship between ground speed of flying *Aedes aegypti* and wind speed. (From Bässler, 1958).

a constant position, probably orientated to the observer's head above them. When the speed of oncoming stripe movement reached 13–17 cm/ sec the mosquitoes were carried backwards by the wind from their former constant positions. Kennedy concluded that the maximum speed of image movement from before, backwards over the eyes, which the insects would tolerate without compensation was about the same as the average retinal velocity which they experienced in forward flight in still air over a stationary background. This was also the same as the average speed of image movement which they experienced when flying at a considerably image movement from before, backwards over the eyes, which the insects speed which occurred in the experiments was probably due to the closeness of the mosquitoes to the substrate for the cage was only 10 cm high. This would have caused a high rate of image movement but mosquitoes free to fly higher over the substrate could clearly reach much greater ground speeds for the same rate of image movement. Mosquitoes flying over moving stripes in still air presumably faced in the direction of stripe movement because the alternative would have produced too rapid a rate of image movement from before backwards over the eyes whereas flying in the same direction as the moving stripes, but slightly faster, the mosquitoes were able to produce a satisfactory rate of image movement. Presumably the mosquitoes did not fly downwind under cage conditions because the rate of image movement would again have been too high.

Mosquitoes flying in the cage alighted as the wind velocity was increased, and those still flying in a wind of 100 cm/sec or more maintained their positions until they suddenly alighted on the floor without having been carried backwards in a single case. They were thus able to fly at a maximum air speed of about 150 cm/sec (3·3 m.p.h.). The mosquitoes were apparently unable to tolerate any image movement from behind forwards over the eyes for they never allowed themselves to be carried backwards, alighting when their exertions became inadequate to prevent this. Kennedy noticed that a decrease in wind speed stimulated mosquitoes to take off so that the number taking off when wind speed had dropped to a certain level was far greater than the number which had been taking off while the wind speed was constant at that low level. Hocking (1953a) obtained maximum speeds of flight on a flight mill of 222 cm/sec (5·0 m.p.h.) for females of *Aedes impiger* and 252 cm/sec (5·6 m.p.h.) for females of *Aedes flavescens;* according to Nielsen and Nielsen (1953) males of *Aedes cantans* swarming above tree tops could maintain their positions in winds of up to 8 m/sec (18 m.p.h.).

Kennedy (1939) studied the responses of flying mosquitoes, suspended from threads but able to rotate freely through 360°, to the horizontal movement of vertical surfaces bearing vertical stripes. He found that conspicuous movement on 1 side stimulated an ipsilateral rotation of the mosquito towards the movement but that once the image of the moving object had been brought to the front of the eyes any further movements of the object were compensated for by rotation of the mosquito. The way in which suspended mosquitoes always compensated for rotation of their background suggested that they could not tolerate lateral movement of the image of the background across their eyes. If this was the case mosquitoes would not fly across the wind when close to the ground but would compensate for the lateral movement of the background which this would cause by turning into the wind. A field observation which can be interpreted in this way was made by Le Prince and Orenstein (1916) in Panama; large numbers of *Anopheles albimanus* were seen flying 30–40 ft above the ground at right angles to a strong breeze, but during occasional stronger puffs the mosquitoes headed directly into the wind. The visual orientation of mosquitoes to a moving host possibly involves a similar response to that found by Kennedy in which the image is brought to the front of the eyes and kept there by compensatory movements.

The following conclusions can be drawn from Kennedy's experiments:

(1) Upwind orientation is not an orientation to the wind itself, since it is abolished in complete darkness, but results from compensatory movements made in response to visual stimuli.

(2) Flying mosquitoes adjust their speed so that the image of the background passes over their eyes at a constant rate. The ground speed of a mosquito is therefore affected by the height at which it flies and by wind speed.

(3) Flying mosquitoes do not tolerate images passing over their eyes from behind forwards, nor do they tolerate lateral movement of images across their eyes.

(4) Any circumstances tending to upset these conditions will result in compensatory movements by the flying mosquito. If the mosquito is near the ground these movements will normally lead to upwind orientation, for flight downwind would cause too high a rate of image movement and flight across the wind would cause lateral movement of images over the eyes.

Bässler (1958) studied the responses given to certain stimuli by females of *Aedes aegypti,* held rigidly at the thorax, during stationary flight. When the mosquitoes were subjected to increasing wind speed the amplitude of the wing beat progressively decreased, but if the antennal flagella were first removed this decrease was replaced by a very slight increase. At constant wind speed the amplitude of the wing beat was found to decrease in proportion to the rate of movement from before backwards of the substrate, and the effect of wind and substrate movement would add to give a maximum reduction in amplitude.

Measurement of the strength of the air streams from the 2 wings when a mosquito had been rotated 30° on its longitudinal axis showed that the wing on the side which was lower beat more strongly than the opposite wing, an action which would normally compensate for such a rotation giving stability in roll. Amputation of both antennal flagella practically eliminated the increased wing beat on the lower side. When equal portions were removed from the two flagella the insects showed a reduced response to such rotation, the response becoming progressively smaller as more of the flagella was removed. Unilateral operation had a much stronger effect. The response to rotation was very greatly reduced after unilateral removal of one flagellar segment and was abolished after removal of 2 segments; however, these insects were not unstable in free flight.

When a fine jet of air was directed at an antennal flagellum, bending it back at the flagellum-pedicel joint, the insect responded by moving the antenna inwards at the pedicel-scape joint. Such unilateral stimulation also produced a stronger wing beat on the unstimulated side although, as Bässler pointed out, unilateral stimulation of this sort would not normally occur. Although the mosquitoes could fly more or less normally after amputation of both flagella these different experiments of Bässler (1958) suggest that the antennae may be important for maintaining equilibrium during flight, functioning through the effect on Johnston's organ of flagellar displacement.

Kennedy (1939) and Fraenkel and Gunn (1940) have pointed out that an animal cannot orientate itself by the mechanical effects of a uniform current on which it is borne and that the orientation of animals into currents of air or water, which is often observed, must be by means of visual stimuli. Tactile stimuli can be used for orientation when the animal is touching a substrate and only then can such terms as rheotaxis and anemotaxis be employed. Kennedy suggested that mosquitoes downwind from their hosts were activated by scent and that subsequent flight into the wind by visual orientation would bring the mosquitoes to the hosts. Such orientation into the wind would necessitate flight near the ground since it is controlled by the rate of image movement over the eyes, and it is of great interest that when Laarman (1959) investigated this problem by sampling the mosquitoes flying at different heights by means of rotating nets he found that as a rule anophelines apparently searching for food at night did not fly more than 60 cm above the ground. Kalmus and Hocking (1960) reported *Aedes* females approaching human hosts from downwind and at ankle height. The observation that mosquitoes enter human habitations in greater numbers during moonlit periods of the night (Chapter 13) is also relevant. Wright (1958) considers that a wind-borne scent is not evenly dispersed in the air but that it is distributed in many separate filaments or trails, and he suggests that insects are able to find the source of a scent by klinokinesis, i.e., by flying straight when scent trails are encountered at a high rate and by tending to turn when the interval between trails is high.

Mosquitoes are known to disperse considerable distances from their larval habitats, in some cases many miles. *Anopheles pharoensis* has been taken in the Eastern Desert of Egypt, 35 miles from the Nile Valley and 45 miles from the nearest larval habitat to the north-west in the direction of the prevailing wind (Kirkpatrick, 1925). *Aedes sollicitans* were once caught in large numbers aboard a ship which passed no nearer than 110 miles to the Atlantic coast of the U.S.A., the flight from N. Carolina being assisted by a south-west wind (Curry, 1939). Flights of several miles are commonly made by females of *Anopheles sacharovi* before hibernation and these flights can be classified as migrations since they are not arrested by the first blood meal and shelter that the mosquitoes find, as are those of earlier generations (Kligler, 1928; Kligler and Mer, 1930; Kennedy, 1961). Similar flights apparently occur before and after hibernation in *Anopheles occidentalis* (Freeborn, 1921, 1932). The adults of *Aedes taeniorhynchus* start on a regular post-emergence migration when they are 6–13 hr old, continuing for about 4 days, the females travelling up to 20 miles, the males not more than 3 (Provost, 1952; 1957; Nielsen, 1958). Similar migrations are made by *Aedes sollicitans* and *Aedes cantator,* also salt-marsh mosquitoes (Smith, 1904).

By extrapolation from flight-mill data Hocking (1953a) estimated the average range of flight in still air of females, of a number of species, which had fed once on nectar. The distances were: *Aedes communis* 22 km, *Aedes punctor* 46 km, *Aedes impiger* 48 km and *Aedes campestris* 53 km. Few direct observations have been made of mosquitoes on long flights but there is some evidence that their orientation is determined by the wind; for example, during the dispersal flight of *Aedes taeniorhynchus* the mosquitoes fly into the wind if it is very light but with the wind if it is stronger (Haeger, 1960), the mosquitoes flying at least 15–20 ft above the ground. In a number of cases long flights by mosquitoes have been shown to take place downwind (Curry, 1939; Garrett-Jones, 1950; Provost, 1957; Harden and Chubb, 1960) so it is to be expected that mosquitoes able to feed and to fly downwind could travel very great distances. Although in the laboratory mosquitoes normally fly into the wind, no doubt in nature mosquitoes can fly downwind by flying high enough above the ground for the rate of image movement over the eyes to be within the limits tolerated.

CHAPTER 15

HOST-SEEKING BEHAVIOUR

The Biting Drive

It is well known that in the field most species of mosquitoes bite for a restricted period during each 24 hr (Fig. 83), and those species which will bite throughout the 24 hr bite most readily during 1 or 2 limited periods (Fig. 84). Similar results are obtained in the laboratory with many species, and Laarman (1955, 1958) has used the term 'feeding drive' to describe the condition of the mosquito in which it responds to host stimuli by orientating to and attacking the host. The term 'biting drive' will be used here in describing this condition, for it is independent of nectar feeding and is not known to be caused by hunger.

Experimental evidence is described in Chapter 13 for the influence of a circadian rhythm on biting activity and it is likely that the rhythmical nature of host-seeking activity is due to some endogenous mechanism. Since mosquitoes may bite at almost any hour if disturbed in their resting places (Haddow, 1945) it is necessary to distinguish the reactions of disturbed mosquitoes to the immediate presence of a host from the rhythmical activity which is controlled endogenously, although almost nothing is known of the behaviour of wild mosquitoes in the absence of hosts during periods of host-seeking activity.

The view that biting activity is induced by a favourable microclimate (Haddow, 1945) has given way to the idea that it is controlled endogenously (Haddow, 1961b), but climatic factors still influence the expression of the circadian rhythm. For example, the numbers of *Aedes sollicitans* and *Aedes cantator* alighting to feed on man in the field were found to increase with rising humidity reaching a maximum at 85 per cent R.H. and to increase with rising temperature between 15° and 32°C (Rudolfs, 1923), and *Anopheles crucians* would not bite in the field at temperatures below 22°C (Mayne, 1926b). It is probably true to say that mosquitoes will respond to host stimuli over a fairly wide range of climatic conditions but that any condition which depresses or inhibits mosquito activity in general will have the same effect on biting activity.

Similar observations have been made in the laboratory. A high rate of biting was obtained with *Aedes aegypti* between 25° and 35°C but very few bit at 15°C (Lumsden, 1947). Kingscote and Francis (1954) found no differences in the intensity of biting activity between 48 and 74 per cent R.H. and Lumsden (1947) found that relative humidity had no effect on biting activity over the range 5–98 per cent. However, Lewis (1933) found that at 25° and 30°C *Aedes aegypti* would bite much less readily at 60–70 per cent R.H. than at 95 per cent R.H., and Gill (1921) found that *Culex pipiens fatigans* would not feed below 40 per cent R.H. Kingscote and Francis (1954) obtained significantly higher biting rates with *Aedes aegypti* when atmospheric pressure was high, and a similar tendency was noted in the same species by Rahm (1958a). It must be remembered, however, that in the laboratory mosquitoes are under highly unnatural conditions, so that it is doubtful whether the effect of climatic conditions on the behaviour of a laboratory colony can be taken as a guide to the responses of mosquitoes in nature. It is interesting in this connection that *Aedes aegypti* bites principally by day in the field (McClelland, 1959, 1960a) but will bite more readily in darkness than at a light intensity of 0·5 m-c in the laboratory (Seaton and Lumsden, 1941).

In a newly-emerged laboratory population of *Anopheles labranchiae atroparvus* the biting drive builds up slowly; very few bite sooner than 18 hr after emergence but the number ready to bite increases steadily after that time until by 48–60 hr after emergence 90 per cent have usually engorged (Laarman, 1955). A similar development of the biting drive has been described in *Anopheles quadrimaculatus* (Burgess and Young, 1944) and *Aedes aegypti* (Macdonald, 1956). The sequence in which activities such as biting and mating are first performed varies between species. Biting was found to precede mating in the great majority of *Aedes aegypti* females in the field in Kenya (Teesdale, 1955) whereas in wild *Psorophora confinnis* mating normally occurs before the females start to bite (Provost, 1958). No difference in avidity for blood feeding was found between virgin and mated females of *Aedes aegypti* offered blood within a few days of emergence (Seaton and Lumsden, 1941; Lang, 1956) although among older females biting activity was less intense in virgins than in mated individuals (Burgess, 1959). Five-day-old virgin females of *Anopheles quadrimaculatus* bit very poorly although females of that age kept with males would bite, there being a significant correlation between biting rate and percentage of males in the group (Terzian and Stahler, 1949).

A curious interruption of the sequence of host finding and biting is found in nature in several species which approach within a short distance of a host and then rest for a time before attacking. There is a delay of about 4 hr between the appearance of *Anopheles gambiae* on the walls of animal enclosures and biting (Smith, 1958) and *Mansonia fuscopennata* appears to enter huts several hours before biting (Haddow, 1961b). Similar observations have been made on *Anopheles funestus* (Ribbands,

1946), *Anopheles aquasalis* (Senior-White, 1953) and *Anopheles leucosphyrus* (Colless, 1956b).

Responses to the host appear to be inhibited in most species during the gonotrophic cycle but a small proportion of anopheline females biting in nature are found to contain partly- or fully-developed eggs (Senior-White, 1953; van den Assem, 1959) and in *Aedes aegypti* a third of the wild females caught biting may be gravid (Macdonald, 1956). Examination of the reproductive organs of females caught biting in nature revealed that most parous females of *Anopheles gambiae* and *A. funestus* had oviposited the same night whereas more than half the parous females of *A. nili* and *A. coustani* caught biting had laid on a previous night (Hamon *et al.*, 1961). Biting is inhibited in hibernating females of *Culex pipiens pipiens* (Tate and Vincent, 1936) and *Anopheles maculipennis messeae* (de Buck and Swellengrebel, 1934) but females of *Anopheles labranchiae atroparvus* take occasional blood meals throughout the winter (Swellengrebel, 1929). A temporary inhibition of the biting drive has been shown to develop gradually after virgin females of *Aedes aegypti,* containing mature oocytes, are mated; the inhibition is complete 2 hr after mating but biting again reaches a high level 4–5 hr after mating (Lavoipierre, 1958b). It is not known whether mating also temporarily inhibits biting in non-gravid females.

Under natural conditions the gonotrophic cycle in *Aedes taeniorhynchus* lasts 5 days and females of a single brood bite at intervals of 5 days, developing and laying their eggs in the intervening periods (Nielsen and Nielsen, 1953). When a laboratory colony of *Aedes aegypti* was offered a meal on the same host for 5 min each day it was found that biting activity in inseminated females declined late in each gonotrophic cycle to rise again after oviposition. Biting fell off sharply after the oocytes had reached stage III, the few mosquitoes which still fed taking only small blood meals. Biting was inhibited much less by the presence of mature eggs in the ovary in virgin females of *Aedes aegypti* than it was in inseminated females. Although the virgin females did not lay more than a very small fraction of the eggs they developed, biting still showed a cyclic character with a period of 5 days, similar to that of inseminated females which laid their eggs (Lavoipierre, 1958a). A somewhat similar cycle of activity has been found in both virgin and inseminated females of *Aedes aegypti* fed sugar but not blood; these females probed in response to a current of warm, moist air after activation with carbon dioxide, and the percentage which probed followed a cyclic pattern with a period of 4–6 days (Fig. 88). Probing activity over a human arm did not follow any clearly-defined pattern, so the cyclical nature of the response in nulliparous females may only have been manifested under conditions of suboptimal stimulation (Burgess, 1959). There is thus slight evidence that an endogenous rhythm with a period of several days exists, distinct from the gonotrophic cycle, affecting the intensity of biting in the population.

Little is known about the control of biting activity in mosquitoes but there is some evidence that a circadian rhythm is involved and it seems likely that the normal pattern of biting with one or more peaks of activity every 24 hr is controlled endogenously. Microclimate influences the

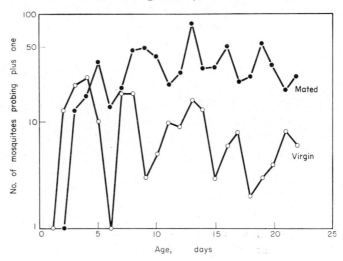

FIG. 88. The cyclical nature of the probing response given by sugar-fed females of *Aedes aegypti* to a current of warm moist air after activation by carbon dioxide. (From Burgess, 1959).

biting rhythm to the extent that unfavourable conditions reduce the number of mosquitoes biting or inhibits biting altogether. The biting drive is generally inhibited during ovary development although this inhibition is reduced in virgin females of *Aedes aegypti*; biting may also be inhibited during hibernation. Certain evidence suggests that a rhythm with a period of several days may influence the intensity of the biting drive.

Responses to Individual Factors

Experimental Procedure

The factors which have been implicated in the location and recognition of the host by mosquitoes are heat, moisture, carbon dioxide, odour and various visual factors. The responses of mosquitoes to a host can be divided into three components — activation (i.e., some change which makes mosquitoes respond more strongly to orientating stimuli), orientation and alighting. The investigation of host-seeking behaviour therefore normally involves stimulating mosquitoes with one factor at a time and observing which components of the behaviour pattern the mosquitoes show. Unfortunately, relative humidity is so strongly affected by changes of temperature that the responses of mosquitoes to heat and moisture cannot easily be investigated in complete isolation from one another, especially as dry air is repellent to mosquitoes.

Laboratory experiments are frequently performed with olfactometers in which a current of air carries the factor under investigation into a cage containing mosquitoes and the responses of the mosquitoes to the test air stream and to a control air stream are compared (Fig. 89). As Laarman

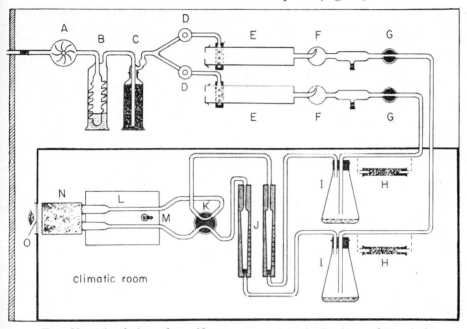

Fig. 89. The design of an olfactometer used in the Institute of Tropical Medicine, Leiden. In this model 2 air streams enter a small cage containing mosquitoes and the responses of the mosquitoes to the air streams are recorded by an observer isolated in a separate room. (After Brouwer, 1960b).

A = pump sucking in air through filter.
B = washing bottle containing water.
C = drying bottle containing silica gel.
D = stopcock to regulate rate of flow.
E = cylinder into which a human arm can be inserted to provide a source of odour.
F = splash head.
G = stopcock.
H = tube of sodasorb to absorb CO_2; can be disconnected.

I = 2 l. flask containing water.
J = air-flow meter.
K = 4-way stopcock.
L = water bath to heat air currents.
M = lamp to illuminate outflow apertures.
N = cage containing 50 mosquitoes.
O = glass window for observation of mosquitoes.

(1955) has shown, the production of 2 air streams which differ only in the experimental factor is an extremely difficult process. The size of cage used with the olfactometers may range from less than 1 ft³ (Laarman, 1955) to 360 ft³ (Brown *et al.*, 1951). Other laboratory methods of studying the responses of mosquitoes are to place sources of stimuli within the cage (Peterson and Brown, 1951) or to allow convection currents to rise through the perforated floor of a cage (Rahm, 1956).

It is particularly important in experiments on host-seeking behaviour that the observer should be isolated from the mosquitoes, preferably in another room, for carbon dioxide from an observer has been shown to stimulate *Aedes aegypti* to respond to convection currents of warm, moist air which otherwise produced no response (Burgess, 1959). It is also important to know the state of activity of the mosquitoes during the experiment since in most species the intensity of the biting drive varies according to the time of day. These refinements of experimental method have not always been used, even in recent years, so the interpretation of published results is often difficult, while the use of different responses for measuring attraction, e.g., approach to the stimulus or alighting, also makes it difficult to compare the results of different workers.

In nature host-seeking behaviour probably consists of a chain of reactions involving successive responses to different stimuli so it is important to remember in interpreting laboratory experiments, where the responses to a single stimulus are studied, that the responses observed may be only a small part of normal host-seeking behaviour.

Responses to Heat

The manner in which mosquitoes are attracted to objects heated above air temperature in laboratory and field experiments leaves no doubt that body temperature is an important factor in host finding (Howlett, 1910; Brown, 1951; Peterson and Brown, 1951).

Howlett (1910) showed that convection currents were responsible for this attraction, not radiation, for females of several species would respond by orientation and probing when they were held in a cage over a warm object, but their response was slight when the warm air from its surface passed clear of them. The ineffectiveness of radiant heat was confirmed by Peterson and Brown (1951) who showed that the interposition between mosquitoes and a heat source of a window of thallium bromoiodide, which was transparent to infra-red radiation but which eliminated convection currents, stopped the response of the mosquitoes to the heat source. They further showed that equal numbers of *Aedes aegypti* approached the surfaces of a warm cube which were of the same temperature but of different emissivities. The vertical distance over which convection currents rising from an animal are effective is not known but *Aedes aegypti* contained in a cage held 30 cm above the head of a man responded to the convection current containing body odours which rose from the man (Mer, Birnbaum and Aioub, 1947).

To find whether mosquitoes respond to high temperature as such or to temperature gradients, Laarman (1955) passed 2 streams of dry air into a cage containing *Anopheles labranchiae atroparvus* which had been activated by carbon dioxide; one air stream was at room temperature, the other was cooled by 1°–2°C. The mosquitoes showed a clear preference for the cooler air, hovering in front of the airport but rarely alighting, leading Laarman to conclude that mosquitoes which orientate to heat sources are reacting to temperature gradients. However, rats cooled below room temperature to varying extents proved less attractive to *Aedes aegypti* than rats at or above room temperature (Kingscote and Francis, 1954).

In the laboratory mosquitoes apparently show a complete response to a heat source culminating in alighting and probing; for example, *Anopheles labranchiae atroparvus* which fly over a warm object during their period of activity in the evening will alight on it and probe (van Thiel, 1937). However, there is little evidence that clearly demonstrates the effect of heat alone on activation, orientation or alighting because few experiments have been performed in dry air and in isolation from the observer. There is some evidence that heat does not activate mosquitoes; thus *Aedes aegypti* stopped responding to convection currents when carbon dioxide was no longer admitted to the cage (Burgess, 1959), and in an olfactometer, in the absence of carbon dioxide, *Anopheles labranchiae atroparvus* would orientate to the same extent to an air stream at room temperature and to one 1°–2°C warmer or would avoid the warmer, although the warmer air stream was preferred in the presence of carbon dioxide (Laarman, 1955). There is no reason to doubt that convection currents enable mosquitoes to orientate to the host very effectively over short distances. Heat probably also stimulates alighting since after activation with carbon dioxide *Anopheles labranchiae atroparvus* would alight in response to a dry air current 2·5°C above room temperature (Laarman, 1955), and the same species would show proportionately less alighting activity and more hovering activity in an olfactometer when the temperature of a warm, moist air stream bearing body odour was reduced from 34° to 26°C (Ismail, 1962).

Temperature may play a part in the selection of an individual host from others in close proximity to it for when the hands of 2 individuals, differing only in skin temperature, were offered to *Aedes aegypti* more females landed on the warmer hand, and when a hand was cooled and then offered with the other hand of the same individual the mosquitoes again preferred the warmer hand (Smart and Brown, 1956).

Responses to Moisture

Water vapour clearly affects the behaviour of mosquitoes. In a large-cage olfactometer many more *Aedes aegypti* approached a stream of warm air of 80–90 per cent R.H. than one of 15–20 per cent R.H. (Brown, Sarkaria and Thompson, 1951). In a small-cage olfactometer, few *Anopheles labranchiae atroparvus* responded to unchanged streams of outdoor air although when the air was moistened the mosquitoes immediately alighted in large numbers around the port, and mosquitoes of the same species responded strongly to a current of air which had passed over a rabbit but showed very little response when the same air stream had been dried, although an inhibiting effect of abnormally dry air cannot be discounted here (Laarman, 1955).

However, water vapour is not always attractive. Whereas at air temperatures of 17°–18°C many more *Aedes* would land on a moistened, warm dummy in the field than on a dry one, at air temperatures of 8°–13°C the moistened dummy was much less attractive than the dry one even though its surface temperature was slightly higher (Brown, 1951). Laarman (1955), working with a small-cage olfactometer, found that the response of *Anopheles labranchiae atroparvus* to rabbit odour was greatly reduced after the relative humidity was raised to 90 per cent. Smart and Brown (1956) found that when offered 2 hands, of different individuals, of similar surface temperature but differing in transpiration rate, in air of 30–65 per cent R.H. and at 26°–32°C, *Aedes aegypti* showed a highly significant preference for landing on the hand which transpired less water. When a hand was held in hot dry air and made to transpire rapidly and was shortly afterwards offered with the other hand of the same individual and at the same skin temperature, more mosquitoes alighted on the untreated hand with the lower moisture output, and the greater the moisture output of the treated hand the greater was the relative attractiveness of the normal hand, the correlation coefficient being highly significant. A similar result was obtained by Gouck and Bowman (1959) who found that the number of *Aedes aegypti* biting the forearms of 3 individuals was inversely proportional to the transpiration rate.

Currents of moist, unheated air can lead to orientation by the mosquito in olfactometers, as in the experiments with *Anopheles labranchiae atroparvus* described above, but there is no evidence to show the importance of moisture gradients in orientation to a host in the field. The most pronounced effect of water vapour is on alighting. For example, *Aedes aegypti* would alight and probe on an olfactometer port emitting warm, moist air, whereas with warm, dry air they would seldom alight and then only momentarily (Brown, *et al.,* 1951). If unheated air containing host odours was dried before being passed into an olfactometer this reduced the proportion of responding *Anopheles labranchiae atroparvus* which alighted and increased the proportion which hovered in front of the port; restoration of water vapour led to a reduction in the proportion hovering and an increase in the proportion alighting (Laarman, 1955).

We may conclude that mosquitoes orientate towards currents of moist air and show a strong tendency to alight at the source provided the humidity is not raised to near saturation, so that moisture is probably an important part of the emanations of a host, acting over a short distance.

Responses to Carbon Dioxide

The emission of 10 per cent carbon dioxide in air from the head of a heated dummy in the field, at a rate corresponding to the normal human exhalation rate of 200 ml carbon dioxide per minute, led to a landing rate of various *Aedes* species 30–60 per cent greater than on a control from which no gas was emitted (Brown, 1951). In experiments with large-cage olfactometers the addition of 10 per cent carbon dioxide to warm, dry air doubled the number of *Aedes aegypti* approaching within half an inch of the experimental port (Brown, *et al.,* 1951) and the addition of 10 per cent carbon dioxide to unheated air of 0 per cent or 50 per cent R.H. increased several-fold the number of *Aedes aegypti* alighting around the experimental port (Willis and Roth, 1952). It was found by Brown *et al.* (1951), however, that addition of 10 per cent carbon dioxide did not increase the number of *Aedes aegypti* responding to moist, warm air of 80 per cent R.H. Using a small-cage olfactometer Willis and Roth (1952) found that carbon dioxide repelled *Aedes aegypti* at all concentrations but this was probably due to the design of the olfactometer since *Aedes aegypti* were attracted by carbon dioxide in a large-cage olfactometer used by the same authors and *Anopheles labranchiae atroparvus* were attracted by carbon dioxide in the small-cage models used by van Thiel (1947) and Laarman (1955).

Carbon dioxide is excreted both from the lungs and through the skin. Brouwer (1960a) showed that the carbon dioxide excreted from the surface of the human forearm did not account for the attractiveness to *Anopheles stephensi* of air which had passed over the forearm. However, carbon dioxide appears to be an important component of human breath in the stimulation of mosquitoes for the superior attractiveness to *Anopheles labranchiae atroparvus* of human breath over the control air stream in an olfactometer disappeared when carbon dioxide was added to the control (Laarman, 1955).

From general observations carbon dioxide has been said to activate mosquitoes rather than to lead to orientation or alighting (Rudolfs, 1922; Willis, 1947), and Laarman (1955), using *Anopheles labranchiae atroparvus* in a small-cage olfactometer, attempted to find whether this was true. In the absence of stimulation the mosquitoes were always relatively inactive by day but when carbon dioxide flowed down through the top of the cage in a slow current, giving a concentration of about 4 per cent, the mosquitoes immediately started to fly about and accumulated on the gauze under the orifice discharging carbon dioxide where they displayed incessant searching and probing movements. In similar daytime experiments in which 2 streams of outdoor air, one of them 1°–3°C above room temperature, were blown into the cage few mosquitoes would respond in the absence of carbon dioxide but when carbon dioxide simultaneously flowed down through the top of the cage many mosquitoes would make for the two air ports, particularly the warmer, while the carbon dioxide stream itself hardly attracted them. The activating effect of carbon dioxide has been confirmed by Burgess (1959) who showed that only after the introduction of a few millilitres of carbon dioxide into the cage, or in the presence of an observer, would *Aedes aegypti* respond to a convection current of warm, moist air. It appears that an air current containing carbon dioxide is sufficient to cause activation, orientation and alighting, but in the presence of a second factor, e.g., heat, the activated mosquitoes orientate to that factor.

The orientating effect of carbon dioxide was shown in field experiments when large numbers of *Culex tarsalis* were caught in a trap of the stable type from which 26 ml. of carbon dioxide were released per minute, equivalent to the output of a chicken; an increase in the discharge of carbon dioxide led to an increase in the number of mosquitoes caught. This experiment also illustrated the activating effect of carbon dioxide for observers entering the trap were quickly attacked although *Culex tarsalis* does not normally bite by day (Reeves, 1953).

It remains to be determined whether under natural conditions carbon dioxide is important as an activator at large or small distances from the host and whether it is used by the mosquito in orientation to the host.

Responses to Odours

The response of mosquitoes to odours from the host was clearly demonstrated in olfactometer experiments by Laarman (1955, 1958). Air which had passed over a rabbit and which had been freed of carbon dioxide and moisture and then moistened again before being discharged into the cage at room temperature was compared with a control stream of moistened air also at room temperature; over 80 per cent of *Anopheles labranchiae atroparvus* which responded to the air streams, by alighting or hovering in front of the ports, responded to the experimental air stream although heat, moisture and carbon dioxide had been eliminated as differential stimuli. Similar results have been obtained with *Anopheles quadrimaculatus* (Willis, 1947), *Anopheles stephensi* (Brouwer, 1960a) and *Aedes aegypti* (Rahm, 1957b), all of which showed stronger responses to air which had passed over a human arm than to control air streams of similar temperature and humidity.

Laarman (1955) argued that the principal effect of smell was as an activator. *Anopheles labranchiae atroparvus* stimulated by an air stream which had passed over a host would continue their searching activity for some minutes after the air stream stopped although their responses to streams of warm air or carbon dioxide would cease as soon as the stimuli disappeared. Furthermore, this species preferred an air stream containing human expired air over a control air stream when the temperatures of the two were similar but when the control air stream was $1°$–$4°C$ warmer than the experimental containing human breath the mosquitoes showed a marked preference for the warmer air stream. Laarman considered that smell was principally an activator, raising the sensitivity of the mosquito to temperature gradients and also releasing a search response the chief feature of which was flight into the wind, the wind providing a directive component which orientated the mosquitoes to the host.

Sweat, blood, and urine have been investigated as likely sources of odour. Some workers have obtained negative results with sweat (Howlett, 1910; Rudolfs, 1922; Reuter, 1936) but others have obtained clear responses to it. Parker (1948) found that *Aedes aegypti* accumulated on the side of the cage and probed when human armpit sweat was held a short distance away in still air, responding slightly but significantly more than to moisture alone. Brown *et al.* (1951) found that air blown through a solution of armpit sweat, diluted so that the product of one armpit was contained in 60 ml. of water, caused a significantly larger number of *Aedes aegypti* to approach the experimental port in an olfactometer than approached the control port; when 10 times more concentrated the sweat was slightly repellent. Forehead sweat tested in the same manner and in similar concentrations produced no significant effect (Thompson and Brown, 1955). Odours from sweat obtained from the human hand when combined with a current of warm moist air caused more *Aedes aegypti* to approach a separating gauze and to probe than did a current of warm moist air alone, although the air containing sweat odours was less attractive than a current of air which had passed over a human hand. The carbon dioxide produced by the skin appeared to be too slight to account for the difference (Rahm, 1956, 1957b). Dummies whose clothing was soaked with human sweat from the armpits and general body surface were significantly more attractive to *Aedes* in the field than controls with equally moist clothing (Brown, 1951, 1958).

These results indicate that mosquitoes are attracted by both human eccrine and apocrine sweat. The eccrine sweat glands are distributed over the general body surface of man but are most concentrated on the palms and soles and their secretion contains sodium chloride, lactic acid, amino acids, urea and ammonia; the apocrine sweat glands are largely restricted to the axillary, perigenital and perianal regions and their secretion contains protein, carbohydrate and ammonia. The protein of apocrine sweat makes it a good medium for bacteria and the decomposition products of this sweat give rise to the characteristic smell of the human adult. Individual variations in odour may reflect chemical differences in apocrine sweat or differences in the bacterial flora or both. Eccrine sweat is apparently always odourless but a mild odour may develop from bacterial action on skin debris (Shelley *et al.,* 1953; Weiner and Hellman, 1960). Sebum, the product of the sebaceous glands, is a mixture of lipids and is produced most abundantly on the forehead and in smaller amounts elsewhere; there is little indication whether or not it is attractive to mosquitoes. The volatile acids in the sebaceous portion of armpit secretions, released from ester linkages by addition of acid, were found to have a slight repellent effect in a large-cage olfactometer; the volatile bases released from armpit secretions by addition of alkali had no attractive or repellent effect (Thompson and Brown, 1955). However, cholesterol, which is a constituent of human sebum (MacKenna *et al.,* 1950), was found by Rudolfs (1922) to be attractive to mosquitoes.

van Thiel and Weurman (1947) clearly demonstrated that free blood attracts mosquitoes when they showed that traps containing heated, defibrinated pig's blood caught 7–9 times more *Anopheles labranchiae atroparvus* released into a very large cage surrounding the traps in the open air than did traps producing warmth and moisture alone. Burgess and Brown (1957) found that *Aedes aegypti* approached whole bovine blood exposed in a fairly-large cage more often than they approached distilled water; whole blood also provoked more responses than did a suspension of corpuscles which resembled it in colour, while the plasma was 4–5 times more stimulating than water. Removal of carbon dioxide reduced the stimulating power of the blood by about one-half. In olfactometer experiments, Laarman (1955, 1958) found that air which had been bubbled through citrated rabbit's blood provoked a strong response in *Anopheles labranchiae atroparvus* although cow's blood had no effect. Schaerffenberg and Kupka (1951) isolated from blood a colourless substance with a smell somewhat like that of fresh blood. Under cage conditions *Culex pipiens* approached a 1 per cent solution of this substance, which was not identified, more frequently than they approached sugar solution or distilled water. Human urine in certain dilutions was shown by Roessler (1961) to attract females of *Aedes aegypti*.

Rudolfs (1922) investigated the responses of females of *Aedes sollicitans* and *Aedes cantator* to a number of pure compounds and found that different compounds had attractive, repellent or activating effects. This work was overlooked or neglected for many years but the problem has recently been reinvestigated and the results obtained up to the present time are summarized in Table 20.

In an investigation into the attractiveness of amino acids Brown and Carmichael (1961a, b) tested a number of protein hydrolysates by warming them to 37°C and exposing them on filter paper in a cage. Of 16 different hydrolysates 11 were significantly more attractive to *Aedes aegypti* than heated distilled-water controls and 8 were more attractive than bovine plasma, which was itself significantly attractive. Lactalbumin hydrolysate was one of the attractive hydrolysates, and when 17 amino acids were exposed separately in the concentrations at which they occur in 10 per cent lactalbumin solution only 3 were found to be significantly attractive. These were L-alanine ($p=0\cdot01$), L-proline ($p = 0\cdot01$) and L-arginine (p very slightly greater than $0\cdot05$). When deprotenized bovine plasma was passed through a resin column the most attractive eluate was found to contain lysine, and the 2 most attractive eluates from deproteinized human plasma contained alanine and lysine. The addition of lysine to the 16 other amino acids of lactalbumin, when exposed at pH 7·4, raised the ratio of attractiveness compared with distilled water from 1·12 to 6·13. The exposure of lysine in a cage stimulated the resting mosquitoes to take to the wing and repeatedly approach the sample, occasionally alighting on it, the responses closely resembling those made to a guinea pig or a human hand introduced into the cage. The potency of lysine was such that a 0·0001 per cent solution of pH 10 had an attractiveness ratio over the control of 2·86. Lysine was also attractive to *Aedes stimulans* and *Culex pipiens*. Alanine produced similar responses to lysine in *Aedes aegypti* although not so strongly.

Roessler (1960, 1961) investigated the attractiveness of pure compounds by evaporating them in a current of air which passed to a cage containing *Aedes aegypti*, the response of the mosquitoes to the odour-bearing air stream being compared with that to a control air stream. The mosquitoes showed a highly-significant degree of attraction to $24 \times 10^{-2} \mu g$ tyrosine and also to mixtures of aspartic and glutamic acids, of serine and threonine, and of proline and histidine. A mixture of lysine and arginine was attractive at the 5 per cent probability level.

TABLE 20.   THE EFFECTS OF THE VAPOURS OF CERTAIN COMPOUNDS ON
FEMALE *Aedes* IN THE LABORATORY. (THE EXPERIMENTS OF RUDOLFS (1922)
WERE NOT FULLY CONTROLLED AND SOME OF HIS RESULTS ARE DIFFICULT
TO EVALUATE).

Compound	Amount	Effect	Reference
alanine	—	attractive	Rudolfs (1922)
alanine	0·025 g	attractive ($p=0·01$)	Brown and Carmichael (1961b)
arginine	0·015 g	attractive ($p=>0·05$)	Brown and Carmichael (1961b)
aspartic acid	—	attractive	Rudolfs (1922)
lysine	5 μg	attractive ($p=0·01$)	Brown and Carmichael (1961b)
phenylalanine	—	attractive	Rudolfs (1922)
tyrosine	$24\times10^{-2}\mu$g	attractive ($p=0·01$)	Roessler (1961)
benzoic acid	—	attractive	Rudolfs (1922)
hydroquinone	10 μg	attractive ($p=0·02$)	Roessler (1961)
catechol	1·3 μg	attractive ($p=0·01$)	Roessler (1961)
resorcinol	$2·5\times10^{-2}\mu$g	attractive ($p=0·01$)	Roessler (1961)
oestrone	$1·15\times10^{-2}\mu$g	attractive ($p=0·01$)	Roessler (1961)
oestradiol-17 β	$1·4\times10^{-5}\mu$g	attractive ($p=0·01$)	Roessler (1961)
oestriol	$8·7\times10^{-9}\mu$g	attractive ($p=0·01$)	Roessler (1961)
equilenin	$9·2\times10^{-5}\mu$g	attractive ($p=0·01$)	Roessler (1961)
androstane-3,17-dione	$2·6\times10^{-5}\mu$g	attractive ($p=0·001$)	Roessler (1961)
haemoglobin	—	attractive	Rudolfs (1922)
cholesterol	—	attractive	Rudolfs (1922)
lactic acid	—	repellent	Rudolfs (1922)
lactic acid	0·8%	repellent ($p=0·001$)	Brown et al. (1951)
carbon dioxide	—	activating	Rudolfs (1922)
ammonia	0·5%	activating	Rudolfs (1922)
ammonia	0·2%	repellent	Brown et al. (1951)
urea	—	no effect	Rudolfs (1922)
indole	0·1%	repellent	Rudolfs (1922)
skatole	0·1%	repellent	Rudolfs (1922)

Roessler (1960, 1961) found that phenol was strongly repellent to *Aedes aegypti* but that the position isomers of diphenol showed varying degrees of attractiveness. The mosquitoes showed attraction significant at the 2 per cent probability level to an air stream which had passed over 10μg hydroquinone (para-diphenol) but no clear response was given when other amounts of hydroquinone were used. The mosquitoes showed a highly-significant attraction to 0.025μg resorcinol (meta-diphenol) and to 1.3μg catechol (ortho-diphenol) as well as to certain larger amounts of these substances. Five steroids were also found to have a significant attractive effect — oestrone, oestradiol-17β, oestriol, equilenin and androstane-3,17-dione. All were active at extremely low concentrations, indeed the mosquitoes showed a positive response, significant at the 2 per cent probability level, to $1.4 \times 10^{-9}\mu$g oestradiol-17β which gave an estimated vapour concentration of approximately 41 molecules/cm^3.

Human beings differ markedly from one another in their attractiveness to mosquitoes. When *Aedes aegypti* were able to choose between streams of warm, moist air which had passed over the hands or over the armpits of two individuals they would frequently show a strong selection of those from one individual. In tests with 4 men and 3 women, examined in pairs, it was found that individual attractiveness varied from one experiment to another and that individuals of one sex might or might not differ significantly from one another in their attractiveness, but the men were almost invariably much more attractive than the women (Rahm, 1958a). When *Anopheles stephensi* were offered 2 air streams which had passed over the skin of different individuals and which differed only in odour they also made a significantly stronger response to one air stream (Brouwer, 1960b).

Laarman (1955, 1958) found that a laboratory colony of *Anopheles labranchiae atroparvus* reacted to odours from rabbit blood but not to odours from bovine blood, and that after carbon dioxide had been removed from the air streams the cultured mosquitoes showed a much stronger response to rabbit odour than did wild mosquitoes of the same species. As the laboratory colony had been fed on rabbits for at least 20 generations Laarman concluded that the mosquitoes had become adapted to the odours of the rabbit. A similar result was obtained by Brouwer (1960b) who found that a colony of *Anopheles stephensi* maintained on human blood showed a stronger response to human odour than did a colony normally fed on guinea pigs. McClelland (1960b) has reported differences of host preference between strains of *Aedes aegypti*.

Host odour is clearly of very great importance in activating and attracting mosquitoes, and amino acids, diphenols and steroids have been implicated so far as possible attractive compounds. Possible sources of host odour are sweat, the skin itself, and blood circulating through the capillaries of skin and lungs (Thompson and Brown, 1955: Rahm, 1957a; Schaerffenberg and Kupka, 1959). Although sweat has been clearly implicated in the attraction of mosquitoes it is difficult to assess its importance. Rahm (1957a, b) found that warm, moist air which had passed over the human hand was considerably more attractive to *Aedes aegypti* than warm, moist air containing odours of hand sweat, and he suggested that attractive substances evaporated from the hand in addition to those contained in sweat. Steroids pass readily across the skin and mucuous membranes (Speert, 1948), so sweat is obviously not the only, or even necessarily the major, source of volatile compounds. Schaerffenberg and Kupka (1959) considered that host odours originated in the blood and passed through the skin, and it is interesting that lysine and alanine, shown by Brown and Carmichael (1961b) to be strongly attractive to *Aedes aegypti*, are 2 of the 4 most abundant free amino acids in human blood (Stein and Moore, 1954). Brown and Carmichael (1961b) have suggested that odour is the principal factor in host finding and that the preferential selection of a particular host species may be due to the nature of its amino acid emanations. Roessler (1960, 1961) considered the different attractiveness of different human individuals to be due to varying quantities of steroids circulating in their blood.

Wright (1958) has used micrometeorological theory and data to show that if an odorous substance with a molecular weight of 100 volatilized at the rate of $1\mu g$ per second, with a wind speed of 2 m.p.h. or less and with otherwise average conditions the concentration one mile downwind at ground level would be over 60 molecules per mm^3 of air. Since oestradiol-17β is said to be attractive to *Aedes aegypti* at a concentration of 41 molecules per cm^3 of air (p. 281) it seems probable that windborne host odours will sometimes be produced in sufficient amounts to activate mosquitoes at distances of 1 mile or more. This is not unlikely since the sex attractants of certain insects are active at distances of several miles from their source (Dethier, 1947).

Responses to Visual Factors

The importance of vision was demonstrated by an experiment in which *Aedes aegypti* approached a transparent, air-tight box containing an anaesthetized deer mouse in greater numbers than they approached an empty box. Nearly twice as many mosquitoes approached an air-tight box containing an active deer mouse as one containing an anaesthetized mouse. Airborne factors could be added to the visual factors by perforating the boxes, and with both still and moving mice this led to an increase in the number of approaches. When the mice were anaesthetized a perforated, opaque container attracted more mosquitoes than one which was air-tight and transparent but with moving mice the air-tight, transparent container was the more attractive. Under these conditions, therefore, when the host is stationary airborne factors are more important than visual factors, but when the host moves visual factors are the more powerful (Sippell and Brown, 1953).

Experiments with inanimate objects have also illustrated the way in which host-seeking mosquitoes respond to visual factors. The stimulating effect of movement was shown when more *Aedes aegypti* approached a moving, black canister emitting moist air than a stationary one (Sippell and Brown, 1953), and observation of Canadian *Aedes* in the field revealed that they would abruptly orientate to a revolving cylinder bearing black and white stripes when they were approximately 32 in. away (Haufe and Burgess, 1960). More *Aedes aegypti* approached a black cube than one painted with black and white squares but the attractiveness of the checkered cube could be raised by reducing the size of the squares. It was found that the number approaching different checkered cubes was directly proportional to the length of the black-white interface suggesting that, as with many other insects, objects with greater contour are preferred (Sippell and Brown, 1953).

Mosquitoes show a distinct preference for human hosts wearing certain colours. Brown (1954) recorded the rate at which certain Canadian *Aedes* alighted on men or heated dummies clothed in materials of different texture and colour. The total brightness of each cloth was found by summing its reflectivities at different wavelengths after correcting each reflectivity measurement for the energy of diffuse daylight at that wavelength. It was found that, in general, the attractiveness of a cloth as a landing surface was inversely proportional to its brightness as measured by the amount of light reflected in the range 4750–6250 Å (blue to orange), although the correlation was poor when the reflection of all visible and ultraviolet light, 3000–7000 Å, was considered. When the attractiveness of 3 types of fabric was correlated with the amount of light reflected at particular wavelengths, the highest correlations were obtained with wavelengths of 5000, 5500 and 6000 Å but there was no correlation below 4500 Å, from the violet into the ultraviolet, and correlation was poor at 6500 Å (red) and absent at 7000 Å.

Brett (1938) placed gloved hands in cages of *Aedes aegypti* and recorded the numbers alighting on gloves of different colours. The mosquitoes showed a preference for alighting on surfaces of low reflectivity although red was more attractive than several colours of a lower reflection coefficient and blue was more repellent than several colours with a higher reflection coefficient. Gjullin (1947) measured landing rates on different coloured shirts worn successively by one man in the field. The number of *Aedes dorsalis* alighting was inversely proportional to the specular reflection coefficients of the test colours within the range 4000–7500 Å, whereas the number of *Aedes geniculatus* alighting showed a similar relationship over the 2540–7500 Å range.

These results are difficult to interpret satisfactorily without a better knowledge of colour vision in mosquitoes. Dark shades are clearly attractive and it is likely that bright shades are actively repellent since even in very dim light in the field a black dummy was more attractive to *Aedes* than a white one (Brown, 1951). The fact that red is more attractive than would be predicted from its brightness suggests that it does not fall within the visible spectrum of mosquitoes and so is perceived as black. Brown (1954) explained the attractiveness of red dummies in the field as due to their contrast against the foliage, and the unexpectedly low attractiveness of green dummies he ascribed to their lack of contrast.

Skin colour affects the responses of mosquitoes, for when *Aedes aegypti* were offered 2 hands of similar skin temperature but differing slightly or greatly in degree of pigmentation they alighted in significantly greater numbers on the darker hand (Smart and Brown 1956).

Certain observations suggest that the presence of mosquitoes on the skin of a host may make it more attractive to other mosquitoes. Sippell and Brown (1953) found that when 20 mosquitoes were pinned to the grey surface of a heated cube the number of *Aedes aegypti* approaching the surface rose by 47 per cent; small, black squares pinned to the surface, or the pins alone, also significantly increased the attractiveness of the surface. In experiments with heated cubes, surfaces covered with black enamel or with a mirror were very much more attractive to *Aedes aegypti* than a dull black surface suggesting that the mosquitoes were attracted by their own reflections (Peterson and Brown, 1951; Sippell and Brown, 1953). The attractiveness may in fact have been due to a flicker effect, produced by the mosquitoes own image or by its movement relative to the pinned mosquitoes, but the possibility of a direct response to mosquitoes already on the skin of the host is worth investigating.

Location of Sensilla Used in Host Finding and Probing

Apart from sight of the host, all factors involved in its location, including heat, are airborne. Sight is doubtless of great importance for host finding in day-flying mosquitoes, although its importance is difficult to measure, but even *Aedes aegypti* which flies and bites principally by day is able to locate a hand in a small cage of about 1 ft³ after being blinded (Roth, 1951).

The importance of the antennae in the perception of airborne factors has been demonstrated by the amputation of all other appendages from the head and by amputation of the antennae themselves. Removal of the proboscis and palps from females of *Anopheles quadrimaculatus* and *Aedes aegypti* did not prevent their flying to a hand in a small cage and attempting to probe (Roth, 1951) nor did amputation of all the tarsi from *Aedes aegypti* prevent their locating a hand under similar circumstances (Rahm, 1958b). Amputation of both antennal flagella left *Aedes aegypti* rather quiescent although *Anopheles quadrimaculatus* could still be disturbed easily, but neither species showed any directional response to a hand placed in the small cage. Amputation of a single flagellum in *Aedes aegypti* only slightly reduced the number which located and attacked a human hand, although less than one-third located the hand when it was partly surrounded by a celluloid cylinder (Roth, 1951). Although the use of the eyes was not prevented in these experiments the results suggest that the antennae are of great importance in location of the host.

A number of attempts have been made to investigate the sensitivity of the antennae to individual factors such as carbon dioxide or moisture by studying the responses of mosquitoes to these factors after the progressive amputation of segments of the antennal flagella. Females of *Aedes aegypti* with only 9 flagellar segments on each antenna responded as strongly to the human hand as controls with 13 segments; with 6 or fewer segments the response diminished in proportion to the extent of the amputation until with no flagellar segments left it was very slight (Rahm, 1958b). The preference shown by females of *Aedes aegypti* in a small-cage olfactometer for the drier of 2 air streams was more and more reduced by the progressive amputation of flagellar segments and although a marked response was given when only 1 segment was present this disappeared on complete amputation of the flagella (Roth and Willis, 1952). Females of *Aedes aegypti* with only 9 flagellar segments responded to a heat source as strongly as normal females but progressively fewer females responded when the number of segments was reduced to 6 or 3 and the response was abolished by complete amputation (Roth, 1951). Progressive amputation of flagellar segments in females of *Aedes aegypti* reduced their response to carbon dioxide and the slight response which was shown when only one flagellar segment was present was abolished on elimination of this segment (Willis and Roth, 1952). The preference shown by females of *Aedes aegypti* for the odours of certain individuals over those from others was reduced and finally eliminated by progressive amputation of flagellar segments (Rahm, 1958b). In an experiment performed by Bässler (1958), *Aedes aegypti* females were offered a choice of air rising from a hand and from a source of moisture and warmth. Normal females strongly preferred air from the hand but this preference was progressively reduced as more and more segments of the flagella were amputated until females which retained only 3 or fewer segments on each flagellum preferred the warm, moist air to the hand air. It was considered that odour perception was more effectively reduced by amputation of the distal segments of the antenna than was perception of moisture and warmth. Bar-Zeev (1960b) studied the rate at which females of *Aedes aegypti* settled in 2 positions differing in relative humidity and found that the preference for one position over the other could be abolished by covering the antennae with grease.

All segments of the flagella of female *Aedes aegypti* bear thin-walled hairs of the chemosensory type and peg organs (p. 199), and the amputation experiments suggest that these are likely to be responsible for the sensitivity of the females to odour, carbon dioxide and possibly temperature. However, experiments with male mosquitoes have not shown any correlation between the distribution of similar sense organs and the responses to these factors. In the male of *Aedes aegypti* thin-walled hairs are found on the 2 terminal segments of the flagella but not on the other segments. Blunt, thin-walled sensilla are found on the distal region of the maxillary palps in both males and females (Bässler, 1958). Amputation of the 2 distal, sensilla-bearing segments of the flagella in males of *Aedes aegypti* only slightly reduced their preference for the drier of 2 air streams in an olfactometer and the progressive amputation of the remaining segments, which bore no obvious sensilla, caused a similar steady decrease in the response to humidity as in the females where the thin-walled sensilla were present on all segments (Roth and Willis, 1952). The avoidance of carbon dioxide shown by males of *Aedes aegypti* in a small-cage olfactometer was not diminished at all by amputation of the two distal, sensilla-bearing segments of the flagella although further amputation led to a reduction and finally to elimination of the response as in the female (Willis and Roth, 1952; Bässler, 1958). Amputation of the distal region of the palps which bore blunt, thin-walled sensilla abolished the response to carbon dioxide in males with intact antennae although not in females (Bässler, 1958). From similar amputation experiments on *Anopheles labranchiae atroparvus* Ismail (1962) associated sensitivity to heat, odour and water vapour with particular sensilla of the female flagella.

Bässler (1958) has suggested that Johnston's organ is necessary for the control of equilibrium during flight and that the progressive reduction in sensitivity to moisture, carbon dioxide and other stimuli as successive flagellar segments are amputated is due to a progressive loss of control by the mosquito over its orientation. In the case of the females this hypothesis might seem to have little to recommend it over the view that the sense receptors were being removed by amputation, but when the results of amputation experiments with males are also considered it is clear that this hypothesis is the most satisfactory that has been proposed and that it is more plausible than the suggestion of Roth and Willis (1952) and Willis and Roth (1952) that sensitivity to moisture and carbon dioxide is mediated in the female by thin-walled sensilla and in the male by the extensive membranous regions which are found on the male flagella. If Bässler's hypothesis is accepted the visible sensilla of the antennae and palps may still be considered the probable receptors of airborne stimuli, although the palps are not necessary for the location of a hand by females over a short distance. This is supported by Bar-Zeev's (1960b) observation that greasing the antennae of females of *Aedes aegypti* abolished the response to water vapour.

Females which had suffered amputations that prevented them from locating a hand or some other test object would sometimes probe when placed on the object itself (Roth, 1951). For example, females of *Aedes aegypti* and *Anopheles quadrimaculatus* which had lost both antennal flagella would often probe if placed for a long enough time on the hand or over a heat source. Removal of proboscis and palps did not abolish the probing response under such conditions of stimulus, but removal of flagella and palps abolished probing in practically all *Aedes aegypti* although most *Anopheles quadrimaculatus* would still probe. More than half of the *Anopheles quadrimaculatus* which had had their antennal flagella, palpi and proboscis amputated and their eyes painted over would probe when placed on the hand or over a heat source, showing that the sense organs of the head were not essential. Antennectomized *Anopheles quadrimaculatus* would move their hind legs to touch a finger placed near them and would sometimes then walk to the finger and probe showing that the hind legs are sensitive to certain stimuli which lead to probing.

Until the importance of Johnston's organ in normal flight and orientation is better known, and the effect upon Johnston's organ of the removal of flagellar segments, the results of experiments involving amputation of the flagella will be impossible to interpret satisfactorily. The location of bait over short distances by females which retain the use of the antennae but which lack proboscis and palps suggests that the antennae are mediating the responses involved although the part played by the eyes in these responses is not known. In *Aedes aegypti* the antennae or the palps must be present for the normal probing response once the female has alighted on the host but the sense organs of the head are not essential for probing in *Anopheles quadrimaculatus*.

Field Observations

It is generally assumed that mosquitoes are able to locate human settlements or animal sheds over considerable distances by an active process and do not arrive simply through random flight. Certainly, on theoretical grounds, it appears that mosquitoes could be activated by windborne scent up to a mile from a host (p. 282), but few attempts have been made to investigate the attraction of mosquitoes over large distances. Ribbands (1949) found that 2–3 weeks after the removal of most of a village from its site the numbers of anopheline mosquitoes caught in the 2 huts, containing human bait, which were allowed to remain increased by only 25–50 per cent, although he estimated that if the local anopheline population had maintained its level the catch in the remaining huts would have increased tenfold. He concluded that most of the mosquitoes which had infested the village had been attracted from a distance and had not arrived by chance. The village was 1 mile from the probable larval habitat. Colless (1956b) argued that these results could be interpreted equally well as the result of random wandering and short-range attraction, and the same author (1957) analysed the rates at which females of *Culex annulus* appeared throughout the night in a stable containing a horse and found that the result corresponded to a theoretical depletion curve of mosquitoes arriving at the bait by random wandering in a closed domain, when the rate of arrival was proportional to the number remaining uncaught. Most workers would agree that mosquitoes can orientate to an upwind host over a short distance, but careful field experiments are needed to show how great that distance can be.

Kennedy (1939) has pointed out that although flying insects probably cannot orientate directly to a windborne scent mosquitoes downwind of distant hosts could reach the hosts through flying into the wind after being activated by windborne factors. There is evidence that mosquitoes orientate into a wind by visual means (Chapter 14) and it is likely that such orientation would still be possible at night since mosquitoes are sensitive to differences of light and shade in one-quarter starlight (Muirhead-Thomson, 1940a). Field observations support this view. For example, *Anopheles gambiae* and *Anopheles gambiae* var. *melas* were taken almost exclusively in the leeward entrance trap of a baited cattle shed at night when the wind blew from one direction only but they were taken in traps on both sides of the shed when the wind was variable or conditions calm; no mosquitoes entered unbaited traps (Bertram and McGregor, 1956). Similar observations have been made by Le Prince and Orenstein (1916) and van Thiel (1939). Rudolfs (1922) observed in the field by day that *Aedes sollicitans* and *Aedes cantator* always alighted on the leeward side of a host and even when a rather strong wind was blowing they could be seen flying upwind to the host.

The airborne factors which might activate mosquitoes to fly upwind are heat, moisture, carbon dioxide and body odour. Haddow (1942) found that the air in a hut with 10 occupants was 1°–2°C warmer than in a control hut with 1 occupant while the relative humidity was 4 per cent lower in the hut with 10 occupants than in the control. There is no indication over what distances windborne heat and moisture from a host are effective in stimulating mosquitoes but they are possibly most important as components of convection currents rising from the host which enable mosquitoes flying overhead to orientate to it. van Thiel and Weurman (1947) found that the carbon dioxide concentration inside a pigsty was 0·11 per cent and that just outside the door it was 0·07 per cent. It might be considered that the concentration would soon fall to the normal concentration of 0·03 per cent but the effectiveness of traps from which carbon dioxide issues in small amounts (p. 276) suggests that this may not be the case.

There is good evidence that odour is important in attraction from a distance. Huts containing 5 unwashed children were much more attractive to species of *Anopheles* and *Mansonia* than huts containing 5 washed children, and *Anopheles gambiae* and *Anopheles funestus* were attracted to huts containing dirty clothes in much larger numbers than to empty huts, although *Mansonia africana* and *Mansonia uniformis* were not (Haddow, 1942). The differences in attractiveness to mosquitoes of different individuals which have been demonstrated in the laboratory, and which have been ascribed to differences of odour, have also been found in the field by Ribbands (1949) who analysed the numbers of *Anopheles gambiae melas* biting 4 men who bathed frequently and who slept in separate huts, changing places each night. Individual attractiveness varied so that one man was significantly more attractive than the others for several nights after which another would become the most attractive. It has been claimed on rather a small number of observations that *Anopheles albimanus* and *Anopheles aquasalis* in the West Indies (Muirhead-Thomson, 1951a) and *Anopheles gambiae* in West Africa (Thomas, 1951) are attracted in large numbers to human adults but much less to children, particularly infants, even accounting for their smaller size. Freyvogel (1961) has established that the attractiveness of babies to *Aedes aegypti* is very low but that by the end of the first year of life attractiveness rises to a higher level, common to both sexes, and rises again in males at puberty.

Although many species are classified as zoophilic or anthropophilic, meaning *predominantly* animal biting or man biting, the degree of host selection exercised by any species is very difficult to ascertain since the use of precipitin tests to analyse host selection in mosquitoes which have fed in the wild is often invalidated by a failure to obtain a truly random sample of the mosquito population (Muirhead-Thomson, 1951b; Weitz, 1960), and host selection under artificial conditions may bear little relation to what happens in the field where availability will differ. When two men were exposed as bait with 8 animals (goats, pigs and a cow) they attracted 38 per cent of the total catch of *Anopheles gambiae*, but when 6 men were exposed with the same 8 animals the men attracted 98 per cent of the total catch (Muirhead Thomson, 1948). Studies by Wharton (1953a) suggest that by using a number of different methods the relative rate of attack on different hosts can be established approximately for a given locality. Colless (1959) concluded that most animals were attacked to some degree by most species of mosquitoes although fairly definite patterns of host selection could be distinguished. Certainly, striking examples of host selection are known; for example, in northern Europe *Culex pipiens* attacks birds almost exclusively but in the Mediterranean region it readily attacks man and other mammals (Mattingly *et al.*, 1951). Host smell doubtless plays an important part in such selection but what other factors are involved is not known. The factors which lead mosquitoes to a particular host probably differ from those which stimulate biting, for females of *Culex tarsalis* were caught in comparable numbers in traps containing birds of similar size, whether the birds were of the same species or not, but the number which fed on any bird was independent of its size and of the number attracted to it (Dow, Reeves and Bellamy, 1957).

Sight of the host is an important component of host finding in mosquitoes which bite by day and observations on *Eretmapodites* (Haddow, 1954, 1956) are typical. An easily-visible, standing bait attracted more *Eretmapodites* females than one lying down whereas a bait which moved slightly was more attractive than a motionless one. Indeed, a movement of the legs would stimulate many females to take off and fly directly to the bait with a fast, straight flight quite different from the vague and indirect approach of species for which olfactory stimuli were probably the most important. A curious limitation of biting behaviour was found in *Eretmapodites chrysogaster* in which biting was confined to a narrow band extending from about 6 to 18 inches above the forest floor. Of 335 caught biting a standing man 97 per cent were taken below the knee, almost entirely between the knee and the ankle, and 3 per cent between the hip and the knee. When a man lay on the forest floor the mosquitoes would approach in response to movement and circle over him but very few would bite although if he was raised 6 in. many would bite at once, attacking all parts of the body.

In describing the host-seeking behaviour of mosquitoes Provost (1952) and Laarman (1955) have used certain ethological terms which provide a new and useful way of considering this behaviour, as long as they do not merely conceal our ignorance of its physiological basis, and these terms are used in the following speculative account which attempts to summarize the present concept of host-seeking behaviour in mosquitoes. Females which are not gonoactive enter a state known as the biting drive during one or more periods in each 24 hr. The biting drive is almost certainly controlled by an endogenous mechanism responding to photoperiod but it is likely that the activity of the mosquito can be reduced or inhibited by unfavourable climatic conditions. How mosquitoes in nature behave during the period of their biting drive in the absence of a host is practically unknown but they may be said to display appetitive behaviour since an appropriate stimulus from the host releases an orientation response. In some day-flying mosquitoes sight of the host is the most important stimulus, leading the mosquito directly to the host; in night-flying mosquitoes, and probably in some day-flying mosquitoes also, windborne odours are probably the initial stimulus and the mosquitoes respond to them by flying into the wind and so towards the host, maintaining their orientation into the wind by visual means. When the female arrives in the vicinity of the host it is stimulated by other directional stimuli, such as gradients of heat and moisture, which lead it to alight on the host and probe when further stimuli lead to gorging, the consummatory act. Host seeking therefore consists of a chain of reactions, each a different form of appetitive behaviour released by a different stimulus, ending in alighting and gorging.

CHAPTER 16

REPRODUCTIVE BEHAVIOUR

Mating

It had been known for many years that mosquitoes react to sounds (Landois, 1874) and it was suspected that a response to sound was involved in mating (Maxim, 1901) but it was not until Roth (1948) investigated the mating behaviour of *Aedes aegypti* in detail that the significance of sound in mating was clearly demonstrated. The fact that a resting female might be surrounded by males, some even touching her, but that no male would attempt to copulate with her until she took to

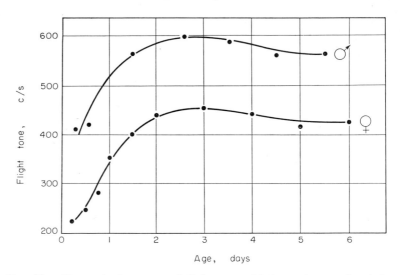

FIG. 90. Change in frequency of flight tone with increasing age in *Aedes aegypti* (at 23°C). (From Tischner and Schief, 1955).

flight convinced Roth that odour was not involved in mating behaviour. Sound was clearly implicated, however, since males were attracted to the source of sounds of certain frequencies and showed a characteristic mating response. Experiments with pure tones from tuning forks and audio oscillators showed that the range of frequencies which attracted males of *Aedes aegypti* was similar to the fundamental frequency of the flight tone

of the female (Roth, 1948; Wishart and Riordan, 1959). The flight tone
consists of a fundamental, which can be shown with a stroboscope to
correspond to the wingbeat frequency, and numerous harmonics thought
to result from vibrations of the surfaces, edges and tips of the wings
(Bugher, 1949; Offenhauser and Kahn, 1949; Tischner, 1953; Wishart
and Riordan, 1959). As only the fundamental falls within the range of
attractive frequencies the harmonics play no part in attraction to the
female. The wing-beat frequency of the male is about 150 c/s higher than

TABLE 21.   THE WING-BEAT FREQUENCIES OF DIFFERENT SPECIES
OF MOSQUITO.

Species	Frequency (c/s) Male	Female	Reference
Anopheles subpictus	520–580	330–385	Tischner (1953)
Anopheles maculipennis	330	165–247	Sotavalta (1947)
Culiseta alaskaensis	415–466	175–233	Sotavalta (1947)
Culiseta bergrothi	440–494	—	Sotavalta (1947)
Culiseta morsitans	247–392	196–220	Sotavalta (1947)
Culex pipiens		165–196	Sotavalta (1947)
Aedes aegypti	467	367	Christophers (1960)
Aedes aegypti	—	355–415	Tischner and Schief (1955)
Aedes aegypti	—	449–603	Wishart and Riordan (1959)
Aedes cantans	587	277–311	Sotavalta (1947)
Aedes punctor	330–523	247–311	Sotavalta (1947)
Aedes campestris	—	311–332	Hocking (1953a)
Aedes communis		349–370	Sotavalta (1947)
Aedes communis	—	213–230	Hocking (1953a)
Aedes impiger	—	305–380	Hocking (1953a)

that of the female and normally falls outside the range of attractive
frequencies. Both male and female wing-beat frequencies rise during the
first 2 days of adult life after which they maintain a more or less constant
value (Fig. 90), although the flight tone may fluctuate as much as 25 c/s
from one moment to another (Tischner and Schief, 1955). According to
Tischner and Schief (1955) the fundamental frequency of the female
flight tone in *Aedes aegypti* averages 385 c/s and ranges from 355 to 415 c/s;
Wishart and Riordan (1959) obtained an average value of 493 c/s and a
range of 449–603 c/s for females of the same species. A newly-emerged
male has a flight tone sufficiently low to attract other males and these will
attempt to copulate with it. The range of frequencies to which males of
Aedes aegypti respond rises with age reaching a maximum about 5 days
after emergence (Roth, 1948; Wishart and Riordan, 1959). Virgin males

will respond to a slightly wider band of frequencies than those which have mated (Roth, 1948). In the laboratory sounds of high intensity produce mating responses in the male of *Aedes aegypti* over a frequency range which includes the male wing-beat frequency (Roth, 1948; Wishart and Riordan, 1959) but there is little doubt that under natural conditions the flight tone of a mature male does not attract other males of the same species.

In all species in which it is known the wing-beat frequency of the male is 100–200 c/s higher than that of the female (Table 21). Differences of wing-beat frequency are encountered within each species, the frequency varying with size of individual and with wing length so that the larger mosquitoes produce a flight tone of lower pitch (Bugher, 1949). The female flight tones of different species of mosquitoes show insufficient diversity to act as an isolating mechanism; indeed, males of *Aedes aegypti* will try to copulate with females and even males of other species (Roth, 1948).

The mating response given by males of *Aedes aegypti* to a flying female consists of 4 stages: taking to flight, orientation to the source of the sound stimulus, seizing the female, and clasping the female's genitalia. The males will perform similar actions in response to sounds of appropriate frequency emitted by a tuning fork or a loudspeaker. The females appear to play an entirely passive role in mating and there is no evidence that they give any response to sound. Roth (1948) was able to show that the antennae form the hearing organs of the male, and the physiological characteristics of these organs are described in detail in Chapter 10.

Copulation is normally initiated during flight when the male approaches and seizes the female, and it may end with the pair still in flight or on the ground. The behaviour of both sexes during copulation has been described in most detail in *Aedes aegypti* (Roth, 1948). The male of *Aedes aegypti* normally first seizes the female by the legs and then moves to a ventral position so that the two are face to face with their ventral surfaces apposed. The female remains completely passive and does not grasp the male. The distal tarsal segments of the front and middle legs of the male are hollowed on the lower side and the female's legs can be held in these excavations by flexure of the male's pretarsal claws. The male usually uses his front tarsi to hold the hind legs of the female. With his middle and hind legs he pushes the abdomen or hind legs of the female upwards until contact of the genitalia is effected, after which the middle legs are usually used to push on the hind legs of the female to keep them raised in the air, although they are sometimes hooked over the female's wings; the hind legs normally hang down. Once in the proper position the male flexes his abdomen until he connects with the female's genitalia; insemination is rapid and the male soon releases the female and flies away. The average time for which the genitalia are connected in this species is 16 sec.

Aedes aegypti is probably atypical in remaining face to face throughout copulation for in many other species copulation is initiated in this position but the male subsequently releases his hold on the female and drops downwards, hanging by the interlocked genitalia, and finally faces in the opposite direction to the female.

In the great majority of species copulation is initiated in flight, the male probably being attracted to the female by her flight tone, but a few species are known in which copulation does not start on the wing. The males of *Opifex fuscus* dart about on the surface of rock pools and seize with their claspers any pupae which break the surface, struggling violently with them. The pupal cuticle splits a little to one side of the midline, apparently through the action of the male's claspers which work backwards extending the slit. The male then inserts the tip of his abdomen into the pupal case and if the emerging mosquito is a female achieves intromission before her abdomen is clear; if the emerging mosquito is a male the captor departs when emergence is almost complete (Kirk, 1923; Marks, 1958). Males of *Deinocerites cancer* spend a great deal of time on water where pupae occur, walking with their antennae directed towards the water surface, and when they come across a pupa they pass their antennae over and between its respiratory siphons. Female pupae appear to have a chemical attraction for the males which will try to copulate with an empty female skin. A female may be inseminated as soon as it is free from its pupal skin. The males also walk from one adult to another touching them with their front tarsi. Females which are not receptive will move away or raise their hind legs signalling the male to move on (Haeger and Phinizee, 1959). Males of *Culiseta inornata* give a mating response after accidentally touching with their legs males or females of their own or other species. Mechanical stimulation of the legs will also elicit a mating response. When copulation occurs the male hovers over a female, bends his abdomen under her and as soon as their genitalia are interlocked turns about so that copulation proceeds with the pair resting end to end. Swarming is not found in *Culiseta inornata* but both sexes make repeated short flights among the grass and mating occurs after a male touches a female or after a female flies within about 1 cm of a male without necessarily touching him; in the latter case mating occurs in flight (Rees and Onishi, 1951; Downes, 1958). In *Sabethes chloropterus* the male approaches a resting female and with a mid-tarsus taps one of her hind legs; this is repeated several times with the male fluttering from one side of the female to the other. Suddenly the male twists himself upside down and passes under the female, their genitalia interlock and copulation begins. During copulation the female remains motionless while the mid-tarsi of the male quiver rapidly, lightly tapping the tips of the female's antennae (Galindo, 1958). In all four species,

U

Opifex fuscus, Deinocerites cancer, Culiseta inornata and *Sabethes chloropterus,* the males lack the long hairs which characterize the male antennae in most species of mosquito and which are important in hearing (p. 205). In *Culiseta inornata,* at least, this sense appears not to be lost since the males are attracted to flying females over a very short distance. It appears, however, that mating at rest is not restricted to species in which the male antennae lack long hairs, for males of *Culex pipiens* var. *molestus,* which can copulate in flight, will also settle on resting females, force their way beneath them and copulate while the females remain at rest (Tate and Vincent, 1936). *Mansionia uniformis* in the field will mate on the wing or at rest (Jayewickreme, 1953) and in the laboratory males will pair with resting females and will even try to mate with dead females (Laurence, 1960).

Males of *Aedes aegypti* will attempt to copulate when their antennal fibrillae have become extended a few hours after emergence but they cannot copulate successfully until the rotation of their genitalia is almost complete. In some cases males can copulate 15–19 hr after emergence but most are not ready until 20–24 hr have elapsed (Roth, 1948). Males of *Culiseta inornata* are able to copulate 6–12 hr after emergence (Rees and Onishi, 1951). Males of *Opifex fuscus* may show searching behaviour within 10 min of emergence and usually do so within 20 min (Kirk, 1923) but it is not clear whether they are able to copulate at that age.

Most female mosquitoes are not attractive to males until maturation has raised the pitch of their flight tone. In *Aedes aegypti* this usually occurs 105–145 min after emergence (Roth, 1948). It is interesting that the females of *Culiseta inornata, Deinocerites cancer* and *Opifex fuscus* whose flight tones are of little or no importance in attracting males are able to copulate immediately after emergence. In contrast, not only are newly-emerged females of *Aedes aegypti* unattractive to males because the pitch of their flight tone is too low but their terminalia are too greatly retracted for successful copulation (Wheeler and Jones, 1960).

The terms 'eurygamy' and 'stenogamy' describe respectively the requirement for a large space for mating under laboratory conditions and the ability to mate in a small space such as a small cage or tube (Roubaud, 1932b). Some species appear to be stenogamous because the males will approach and seize a resting female, e.g. *Culiseta inornata,* but it seems likely that certain other species, in which copulation is always initiated in flight, are able to mate in a confined space because the female is inseminated before the pair come in contact with the sides or bottom of the container or because the mosquitoes do not fall apart when striking a surface. For example, it was observed with a stenogamous strain of *Culex pipiens* that if the pair were still face to face when they came to rest the male would fly away, but if the male had released his hold and the pair were interlocked end to end by their genitalia they would remain together until copulation was complete (Roth, 1948); also, the insemination rate could be raised substantially in caged *Anopheles multicolor* (Bates, 1941b) and *Aedes communis* (Beckel, 1958b) by increasing the height of the cages and so delaying contact with the ground. Breeding experiments with stenogamous and eurygamous strains of the *Culex pipiens* complex and the *Anopheles maculipennis* complex show that the F_1 generation is stenogamous in each case, but the number of loci involved in the inheritance of this character is not known (Kitzmiller, 1953).

During copulation the male of *Aedes aegypti* grasps the terminalia of the female with his claspers and inserts his aedeagus, which is now ventral owing to rotation, into the genital chamber (Wheeler and Jones, 1960). During copulation in *Culiseta inornata* the aedeagus is moved in and out of the female opening, articulating by the soft membrane at its base (Rees and Onishi, 1951). The time required for copulation varies considerably. Copulation lasts 2–4 sec in *Aedes taeniorhynchus,* up to 15 sec in *Anopheles culicifacies* (Russell and Rao, 1942b), from 10 to 25 sec in *Anopheles philippinensis* (Wharton, 1953b), from 4 to 59 sec in *Aedes aegypti* (Roth, 1948), and from 14 sec to 34 min, with an average of 6 min, in *Sabethes chloropterus* (Galindo, 1958). In *Culiseta inornata, Deinocerites cancer* and *Uranotaenia lowii* 45 min or more are required (Lum, 1961a).

Examination of the female reproductive tract immediately after copulation shows the presence of an elongate body or mating plug, sometimes bent in the shape of a U, in the genital chamber in *Anopheles* (Shute, 1958) and in the bursa copulatrix of those species that have one (Lum, 1961b). Mating plugs have been found in species of *Anopheles* (Gillies, 1956), *Aedes* and *Psorophora* (Lum, 1961b). The fact that in *Psorophora howardii* both the mating plug and the contents of the male accessory glands are bright yellow indicates that the mating plug is composed of secretions of the accessory glands, and this is confirmed by the loss of the contents of the accessory glands after 2 or more copulations (Lum, 1961b).

Immediately after copulation the bursa copulatrix of *Psorophora howardii* is distended with semen. The spermatozoa are dispersed and swim in a colourless, slightly-granular fluid surrounding a mating plug composed of large, pigmented granules. The mating plug starts to dissolve a few minutes after copulation and has disappeared almost completely 24 hr later. Spermatozoa enter the spermathecae within 15 min of copulation although some are still to be found in the bursa after 24 hr (Lum, 1961b). The average time for sperm to pass to the spermathecae after copulation in *Aedes aegypti* was found to be 100 sec although it could be as short as 40 sec. The sperm were transferred to the spermathecae without male accessory-gland secretion, and while there is little evidence to show whether the sperm reach the spermathecae by swimming or by some action of the female reproductive organs Schwartz (1961) considers the latter to be the more probable.

The functions of the accessory-gland secretions are not known. They do not appear to activate the spermatozoa since these are active when taken from the seminal vesicles and the addition of male accessory-gland secretion to the sperm of *Aedes aegypti* removed from the seminal vesicles has no effect on their locomotion (Schwartz, 1961). It has been suggested that the secretion furnishes a medium for the spermatozoa during ejaculation since even after several copulations the spermatozoa are still accompanied by some quantity of fluid from the accessory glands (Lum, 1961b); it is also possible that the secretion nourishes the spermatozoa, provided that some is transferred to the spermathecae, and there is some evidence that the secretion may stimulate the oviposition mechanism of the female (see p. 184).

In laboratory cultures of *Aedes aegypti* a female continues to be attractive after insemination and males will copulate with her repeatedly (Roth, 1948). Double mating plugs have been found in occasional females of *Anopheles gambiae* in a laboratory culture but they have not been found in nature (Gillies, 1956) and there is no other evidence for any species to indicate whether or not females are inseminated more than once in nature. Breeding experiments with genetically-marked individuals have shown that females of *Aedes aegypti* can use sperm from more than one male in fertilizing a single batch of eggs (VandeHey and Craig, 1958) but similar experiments with *Culex pipiens fatigans* and *Culex pipiens* var. *molestus* indicated that all the eggs in each egg raft were fertilized by sperm from a single male (Kitzmiller and Laven, 1958).

A single male will copulate with many females in quick succession — a male of *Aedes aegypti*, for example, placed with 16 females copulated 30 times in a 30 min period (Roth, 1948) — but it can inseminate only a relatively small number of females. A male of *Psorophora howardii* which copulated with 8 females in quick succession was found to have deposited sperm in 6 of them (Lum, 1961b). A male of *Aedes aegypti* mated to small batches of females over a period of days inseminated 4 out of 7 on one day, and in 3 short periods of activity over the following 4 days successfully inseminated 1 out of 3, 1 out of 4, and 1 out of 1, showing that there can be a certain recovery of reproductive potential (Roth, 1948). This is supported by the observation in a number of species that the maturation of spermatozoa in the testes continues for 25 days at least (Lum, 1961a). Repeated copulation in *Psorophora howardii* leads to depletion of the large pigmented granules in the accessory glands but never of the colourless secretion of these glands nor of sperm in the seminal vesicles, even after the male has ceased to transfer sperm on copulating (Lum, 1961b).

It seems likely that a single mating will provide sufficient sperm for the requirements of most females; certainly the longevity of the spermatozoa is not critical. Of a batch of females of *Anopheles labranchiae atroparvus* left with an equal number of males for 24 hours, two laid 15 batches of fertile eggs and one 17 batches without remating (Shute, 1936). Bacot (1916) recorded a female of *Aedes aegypti* laying 711 fertile eggs in 15 batches during a period of 62 days after pairing with a single male, and Goeldi (1905) found that periods of up to 102 days could elapse between mating and the laying of fertile eggs in this species. In species with over-wintering females the sperm must live for several months in the spermathecae, probably for 11 to 12 months in the case of *Culiseta impatiens* and *Culiseta alaskaensis* (Frohne, 1953, 1954).

Artificial insemination has been performed successfully with *Aedes aegypti* by the injection of spermatozoa and accessory-gland secretion into the bursa copulatrix (Burcham, 1957). Copulation, leading to insemination of the female, can be brought about in aedine mosquitoes by bringing together the tips of the abdomens of the male and female. McDaniel and Horsfall (1957) found that males of *Aedes vexans* would copulate more readily under these conditions if they were decapitated but Schwartz (1961) found that decapitation did not enhance the male's reaction in *Aedes aegypti*.

Swarming

The assembly of male mosquitoes in swarms at twilight is a very familiar sight. The swarms frequently develop a few feet above the ground over swarm markers, light or dark objects which contrast with the background. They also form over tall trees, chimneys and church steeples, which probably act as swarm markers, and they are occasionally found without obvious orientation to any object. When a female flies into or near a swarm her flight tone acts as a social releaser so that males are attracted to the source of the sound and seize the female, one copulating with her. Swarms develop when individual mosquitoes are attracted to the swarm markers and in most cases there appears to be no other cohesion between the individuals. If a swarm marker is moved the swarm moves with it. If the size of a marker is increased the mosquitoes dancing over it spread apart whereas if its size is diminished the swarm becomes more compact (Cambournac and Hill, 1940). By distributing many small markers Bässler (1958) was able to produce swarms consisting of single males of *Culex pipiens*. The cohesive factor of most swarms is clearly the marker and the only evidence for cohesion between the mosquitoes themselves is the occasional formation of swarms without obvious markers.

The behaviour patterns of males of *Aedes hexodontus* dancing over a swarm marker have been described by Downes (1958). At moderate wind speeds the mosquitoes fly upwind until they reach the upwind margin of the marker when they stop flying forward and allow themselves to be carried back for a short distance by the wind, still facing into the wind. They then fly forward again to the edge of the swarm marker. When the wind is very slight or absent the mosquitoes fly clockwise or counter-clockwise around the marker. Mating is frequently seen in swarms of this species.

Nielsen and Greve (1950) have described the swarming of *Aedes cantans*. In still air and at low wind speeds the swarming males fly in a circle of 20–50 cm diameter parallel to the ground. The direction of flight is normally reversed after each circuit, the mosquito turning at the most-downwind part of the circle and pausing momentarily at the turning point with its head pointing into the wind. After irregular intervals the plane of flight is elevated or depressed. As wind speed increases the circle is drawn out into an ellipse, and in strong winds the mosquitoes fly in a straight line, first into and then with the wind, reversing direction at each end of the line of flight. The swarms of *Aedes cantans* form over tree tops and over the ground, but it is not clear whether they form over swarm markers in the latter case. Mosquitoes constantly leave the swarm and others take their place. Copulation was very rarely seen to occur in the swarms although it was often observed at times of day when swarming did not take place. Males of *Aedes varipalpus* form small swarms over warm-blooded animals and mate with females when they approach to feed (Peyton, 1956). It is not clear whether the animals act purely as visual swarm markers or whether there is any other factor in their attractiveness to males.

The interaction of circadian rhythm and light intensity in controlling the onset of swarming has been described in Chapter 13. An experiment by Nielsen and Nielsen (1953) in which swarming males of *Aedes taeniorhynchus* were marked by dusting with eosin powder has provided further information of great interest and has shown how swarming can be investigated experimentally in the field. Four swarms were studied. Swarms I and II which were about 20 m apart were dusted, whereas swarms III and IV which were within about 50 m of swarms I and II were not dusted. Dusting was carried out on swarms I and II during five short, recorded periods between 19 42 and 19 52 hr on June 25 and collections were made from all four swarms during five recorded periods between 1939 and 1957 hr on June 26, all males swarming at the times of collection being caught. Of 101 males caught in swarms I and II 82 were marked while of 43 males caught in swarms III and IV only 1 was marked. Further analysis of the catch showed that collecting from swarms I and II during a period in which there had been no dusting the previous evening produced no marked mosquitoes, collecting during a period which partly coincided with a period of dusting produced mosquitoes of which a high proportion were marked, and collecting during a period which corresponded almost exactly to a period of dusting produced males which were all marked. Nielsen and Nielsen (1953) concluded that individual males swarmed at the same place each evening and that each was present for only a fraction of the total duration of the swarm, the time at which any individual swarmed being determined by its sensitivity to light. They suggested that if sensitivity to light determined the time of swarming of individual mosquitoes the duration of any swarm would reflect the range of variation in sensitivity to light, so that the duration of swarming would be proportional to the number of individuals participating, and in support of this theory they mentioned swarms of a small population of *Aedes taeniorhynchus* which lasted 12 minutes and swarms of a very large population which lasted 27 minutes. The same relationship between size of population and duration of swarming has been described in *Anopheles sinensis* (Ho and Lo, 1945). The continual replacement of swarming mosquitoes by mosquitoes from outside the swarm has also been described in *Aedes cantans* (Nielsen and Greve, 1950) and *Culex territans* (Frohne and Frohne, 1954) so it is possible that a turnover of this nature occurs in many species.

Two views have been expressed about the significance of swarming. One of these, widely held, has been expressed clearly by Downes (1958). According to this view not only males but females also are attracted by swarm markers, so that swarms concentrate a population which would otherwise be widely dispersed into small areas with obvious advantages for mating, a proportion of the population, although not all, mating in swarms. Although any marker may attract 2 or more species the different species are normally found to form separate swarms owing to differences in orientation to the marker, in height of swarm, or in time of swarming. The assembly of different species in separate swarms is particularly important as the female flight tones are attractive to males of other species. Haddow and Corbet (1961b), however, reported that in swarms above the forest canopy in Africa several species usually swarm together. The orientation of female mosquitoes to swarm markers has very rarely been seen although Hocking (1953a) on 4 occasions saw extremely large numbers of *Aedes punctor* females swarming over tents or huts, and Downes (1958) described females of *Aedes hexodontus* swarming regularly over the same markers as the males of their species, but in separate swarms. Goeldi (1905) described males and females of *Culex pipiens fatigans* in separate swarms indoors, individual females occasionally moving to the male swarm where they were seized by the males.

Nielsen and Haeger (1960) criticise on several points the theory that swarming is concerned entirely with mating. They point out that in many species which swarm regularly mating is very rarely seen in swarms although it is often seen away from them, and also that swarming is limited to periods of twilight whereas, in many species which swarm, mating can take place throughout the day. They emphasise that there is little evidence of females being attracted by swarm markers and they cite cases of compound swarms composed of more than one species. They conclude that swarming is an end in itself, a consummatory act, but that its function is not known.

The evidence is still insufficient to justify one or other view and it is to be hoped that more basic work, both observation and experiment, will be applied to this habit which is so widespread among Diptera. An observation of possible significance in this connection has been made by Shannon (1931) and Haddow and Corbet (1961b). It is that most of the species which swarm, in S. American and African forests at least, are essentially nocturnal and are drab in colour or at least without striking colour patterns. Day-flying mosquitoes of the forest are often brilliantly coloured as in *Haemagogus* and *Toxorhynchites*, or have striking adornments and conspicuous display behaviour as in *Anopheles implexus,* and such species do not swarm.

Oviposition

Egg laying is performed in many ways. The eggs may be laid singly on the water surface, as in *Anopheles* and *Toxorhynchites*, the female hovering over the water or resting on it. They may be laid in rafts on the water surface as in *Culex,* (subgenus) *Culiseta* and certain *Mansonia*. Females of *Aedes, Haemagogus, Psorophora, Heizmannia,* (subgenus) *Culicella* and (subgenus) *Armigeres* lay their eggs singly either in moist soil in situations liable to flooding or at the edge of small bodies of water such as those occurring in tree holes, and the eggs of these mosquitoes are resistant to desiccation. Aedine eggs are often coated with a sticky secretion which attaches them to the substrate. Females of (subgenus) *Mansonioides* lay their eggs in groups on the undersides of floating leaves, those of *Wyeomyia smithii* in the pitchers of *Sarracenia* which usually contain water at the time but which may be empty. Even in genera which have a fairly uniform method of oviposition individual species will often show a very specialized selection of oviposition site. This is seen rather strikingly in *Aedes apicoargenteus* which breeds in tree holes and other small bodies of water and which in East African forest lays most frequently at heights over

100 ft (Corbet, 1961a). Some species show extremely complex behaviour patterns at oviposition, for example certain of the species which breed in the internodes of damaged bamboos. In *Armigeres dolichocephalus* the thorax is laterally compressed and produced forward over the head, and this enables the females to penetrate holes 1–2 mm wide which are formed when certain 1st instar beetle larvae burrow into young bamboos. The damage caused by the beetle larvae not only permits entry of the mosquito but also causes a flow of sap into the internode which provides a suitable larval habitat (Macdonald, 1960). Females of *Sabethes chloropterus* hover in front of rather larger holes in bamboos and with a flick of the abdomen project an egg forwards into the cavity (Galindo, 1958). *Armigeres flavus*, which breeds in exposed cavities in bamboos and in tree holes, lays a batch of eggs on to its hind legs, holding them between the tibia and first tarsal segment, and deposits them some time later after alighting on water (Macdonald, 1960).

The restricted nature of the larval habitat of each species results from the discrimination of the ovipositing female, for eggs are rarely found outside the usual larval habitat and the larvae are tolerant of a wider range of water conditions than they are found in (Herms and Freeborn, 1920; Lewis, 1939; Bates, 1940; Muirhead-Thomson, 1940a; Macan, 1961). Oviposition therefore involves not only finding water and laying eggs but also selection of environment, whether shaded or open, stream, rice-field, pond, tree hole or artificial container, and examination of the water, whether moving or still, polluted, saline or fresh, each factor being finely discerned. Experiments with gravid females have shown that different species use different factors in selecting oviposition sites.

The preoviposition behaviour of mosquitoes gives some indication of the way in which oviposition sites are found and selected. Captive gravid females of *Anopheles labranchiae atroparvus* fly 2–4 cm above the ground, dipping again and again to touch the surface. On touching water their behaviour changes immediately to hovering, bobbing up and down or swinging from side to side through an arc; in each case the mosquito dips at intervals to touch the water surface with its 2nd and 3rd pairs of legs and it occasionally settles on the water. This behaviour normally precedes and accompanies laying (Kennedy, 1942). Similar behaviour has been described in a number of species of *Anopheles,* many of which scatter their eggs while in flight (Bates, 1940; Russell and Rao, 1942b). Under laboratory conditions, however, these females are often seen to lay while resting on the water surface, the tendency to lay in this manner increasing as cage size diminishes (Bates, 1940). Captive *Aedes aegypti* make explora-tory flights at all heights with frequent descents to the floor, the female settling on the surface when water is found. If the water is very salty the mosquito flies off within a few seconds but on fresh water it walks or flies about until a suitable edge is found. The hind legs are then raised and lowered in a fanning motion, a drop of clear liquid is wiped off the ovipositor and the hind legs rubbed together until they are wet. The mosquito then ranges over the substrate with its abdomen bent to bring the ovipositor close to the surface, eventually laying in this position (Kennedy, 1942; Wallis, 1954a). Similar behaviour is found in *Aedes polynesiensis* and *Aedes pseudoscutellaris* (Wallis, 1954a). Gravid females of *Culex pipiens* var. *molestus* fly close to the ground, dipping to touch it at frequent intervals. On finding water they settle on the surface for varying lengths of time, subsequently flying off to other water deposits or remaining to lay while resting on the surface (Hudson, 1956; Kennedy, 1942). The female of *Mansonia africana* and *Mansonia uniformis* walks on floating leaves testing the surface with her proboscis. When a small area of water is found at the leaf margin she bends her abdomen forwards beneath her head and thorax and when the abdomen touches water it is pushed downwards and backwards below the leaf where the eggs are laid (Laurence, 1959, 1960). Mosquitoes sometimes drink before laying (Detinova, 1936) but this is not essential for laying or for selection of water, both of which can be performed normally by females from which the proboscis has been removed (Wallis, 1954a; Hudson, 1956).

Attraction of gravid females of *Anopheles, Aedes* and *Culex* from a distance in the laboratory has only been obtained by displaying surfaces which are dark in contrast to their surroundings; in nature a water surface which is shaded appears darker than its surroundings when seen at night from near the ground (Kennedy, 1942). Mosquitoes are known to respond to differences of relative humidity (p. 254) but in still air in the laboratory gravid *Culex pipiens* var. *molestus* were not attracted to water from distances greater than 10 cm (Kennedy, 1942). So far as is known mosquitoes find water by flying towards areas which appear darker than their surroundings and by frequently dropping to touch the substrate. Whether in nature gravid mosquitoes fly upwind in response to high relative humidity is not known.

When water has been found certain factors stimulate the special activity which immediately precedes oviposition. Water vapour is strongly stimulating to gravid females of *Anopheles, Aedes* and *Culex* even when the mosquitoes are separated from the water by netting. The reflectiveness of the water surface is also stimulating, for females which fly over a mirror by chance remain to perform preoviposition behaviour patterns although the mirror has little power to attract from a distance, and females attracted from a distance to a patch of black paper are more likely to show preoviposition behaviour patterns if it is covered with glass (Kennedy, 1942).

Contact with water is essential for egg laying in *Aedes aegypti* and *Culex pipiens* var. *molestus,* and it is necessary for complete egg laying in *Anopheles labranchiae atroparvus*, although females of this species will occasionally lay in the absence of water if they have been deprived of water for some days after they are ready to lay and if they are in moist air (Kennedy, 1942).

The responses of captive, ovipositing females to water temperature appear to be correlated with the temperature range of the normal larval habitat. For example, larvae of *Aedes rubrithorax* are found in cool shaded pools, larvae of *Aedes rupestris* in warm sunlit pools; the females of *Aedes rubrithorax* select water at 15°C in preference to water at 30°C for oviposition whereas those of *Aedes rupestris* prefer the warmer water (Dobrotworsky, 1959). Similarly, *Anopheles maculipennis* females, whose larvae are normally found in sunlit ponds, prefer water at 22–29°C for oviposition, seldom laying on water below 20°C, whereas *Anopheles claviger* females, whose larvae live in shaded pools, prefer water at 12–20°C (Hecht, 1930). Muirhead-Thomson (1940c) has demonstrated the importance of water temperature to mosquito larvae, showing that larvae of *Anopheles barbirostris,* for example, can breed in rice fields where the water regularly reaches temperatures which would quickly be fatal to running-water breeders such as *Anopheles minimus*. Nevertheless, he found in Assam that breeding places which differed markedly in temperature by day showed little difference in the early part of the night when most oviposition occurred and it is probably true to say that in general oviposition sites are selected by factors other than temperature.

The importance of vision in water finding has already been mentioned and visual factors also affect selection of oviposition site. Sites which are shaded, whether in the field or in the laboratory, are more attractive to gravid females of many species than those which are not, shade being important at night as well as by day (Buxton and Hopkins, 1927; Jobling, 1935; de Zulueta and Bates, 1948). *Anopheles culicifacies* appears to be unusual in being neither attracted nor repelled by shade (Russell and Rao, 1942b). Background colour is generally important, a dark background being preferred to a light one (Jobling, 1935; Bates, 1940; Lund, 1942; O'Gower, 1957a). *Culex pipiens fatigans* can find water and lay normally in complete darkness (Jobling, 1935) but *Anopheles darlingi* is almost completely inhibited from oviposition by such conditions even when confined close to water (de Zulueta, 1950). An investigation by Wood (1961) suggests, however, that the influence of light on choice of oviposition site is more variable than has been assumed. When several laboratory strains of *Aedes aegypti* were given the choice between ovipositing at 0·02 lumen/ft² and 3·5–6·5 lumen/ft² certain strains showed a strong tendency to lay at the darker site, other strains at the brighter site. For example,

68 per cent of one strain and only 14 per cent of another laid their first egg batches at the darker site. These tendencies were inherited.

Many aedine species lay their eggs on a moist surface just above the edge of a body of water and the colour and texture of the surface affect the number of eggs laid. All species tested in the laboratory preferred a dark surface to a light one and a rough surface to a smooth (Beckel, 1955; O'Gower, 1955, 1957a, b, 1958) but under natural conditions *Aedes aegypti* showed no significant preference for a black surface over a white one (McClelland, 1958). The importance of surface texture is shown by the preference of *Aedes scutellaris* and *Aedes australis* in the laboratory for a grey rough surface over a black smooth one (O'Gower, 1955, 1958). *Aedes polynesiensis* in nature lays its eggs in cracks and crevices and in the laboratory it searches for angles and corners in which to lay its eggs (Wallis, 1954a, c).

Physical obstructions can deflect *Anopheles culicifacies* from otherwise suitable oviposition sites. Breeding of this species in rice fields stops after the plants have grown to a height of 12 in. and it has been found that glass rods or bamboo shoots arranged like growing rice will also greatly reduce oviposition, presumably by interfering with preoviposition behaviour. Other species, such as *Anopheles hyrcanus,* are not impeded by such obstructions and are able to breed among older rice (Russell and Rao, 1942b). Upright obstacles within an oviposition pan are repellent to captive *Anopheles darlingi* but similar obstacles around the outside of a pan are attractive (de Zulueta and Bates, 1948).

Salt solutions have been used in many experiments on selection of oviposition site. When offered a range of salinities *Culex pipiens pipiens* lays most egg rafts on distilled water whereas *Culex salinarius,* which breeds in fresh and brackish water, shows no preference below 0·129M (Table 22). *Aedes aegypti* prefers 0·021M–NaCl to both distilled water and 0·43M–NaCl and in the absence of 0·21M–NaCl it prefers 0·043M–NaCl to distilled water. The sensitivity to a difference of 0·02M–NaCl suggests that chemoreceptors are concerned rather than the common chemical sense (Wallis, 1954a, b). *Anopheles quadrimaculatus* and *Anopheles freeborni* while preferring distilled water lay a considerable percentage of their eggs on more concentrated solutions. This is partly due, at least in *Anopheles quadrimaculatus,* to the habit of scattering the eggs while in flight (Wallis, 1955) but field studies on a number of species of *Anopheles* have shown that in nature where a number of different habitats are close together eggs are found only in their normal habitat or with a very slight overlap (Muirhead-Thomson, 1940a, 1945). Work with salt solutions has helped very little towards an understanding of the attractive properties of natural oviposition sites, particularly where fresh-water species have been

TABLE 22. THE PERCENTAGE DISTRIBUTION OF EGGS AND EGG RAFTS LAID ON DIFFERENT CONCENTRATIONS OF SODIUM CHLORIDE. (FROM WALLIS, 1954a, b).

Species	0	0·021 M	0·043 M	0·086 M	0·128 M	0·171 M	0·257 M	0·342 M	>0·342 M
Culex pipiens pipiens	62	—	21	17	0	0	0	0	—
Culex salinarius	29	—	19	28	16	5	3	0	—
Aedes aegypti	12	—	50	20	12	5	1	0	—
Aedes aegypti	24	46	21	7	1	0	0	0	—
Aedes pseudoscutellaris	46	—	26	14	7	4	2	1	0
Anopheles quadrimaculatus	66	—	—	—	—	19	—	10	5
Anopheles freeborni	42	—	—	—	—	20	—	16	23

used. Moreover, the results of laboratory experiments cannot be used to predict behaviour in the field; a number of brackish-water breeders such as *Anopheles labranchiae atroparvus* and *Aedes australis* prefer to lay on fresh water in the laboratory (de Buck, Schoute and Swellengrebel, 1932; O'Gower, 1958) whereas the fresh-water species *Aedes aegypti* prefers dilute salt solutions (Wallis, 1954a).

In an investigation of the responses of gravid *Culex pipiens* var. *molestus* to different concentrations of various electrolytes it was found that the number of rafts laid on the different solutions was more closely related to their osmotic pressures than to their molarities, solutions with osmotic pressures of 0·8–3·0 atm being the most acceptable to the mosquitoes. When offered different concentrations of glucose, however, the mosquitoes laid almost at random (Hudson, 1956). Solutions of electrolytes are not ideal solutions, owing to the interaction of solute ions with one another and with the solvent, so it is not surprising that the responses of the mosquitoes do not vary directly with molarity. On the other hand osmotic pressure is a function of ionic activity and it is likely that the responses of chemoreceptors would be directly proportional to ionic activity. It seems possible therefore that the chemoreceptors are equally stimulated by solutions of different electrolytes which have equal ionic activities. In blowfly chemoreceptors different neurones are stimulated by electrolytes and sugars (Hodgson and Roeder, 1956) so that the different responses of gravid mosquitoes to electrolytes and sugars may have a similar basis.

The presence of organic matter, whether sterile or putrid, renders water highly attractive for oviposition to a number of species. *Culex pipiens fatigans, Aedes polynesiensis* and *Aedes aegypti* prefer such water to fresh water, the strength of the preference reflecting the extent of contamination normally found in the natural larval habitats (Buxton and Hopkins, 1927; Manefield, 1951). In contrast *Anopheles minimus,* a stream breeder, will avoid even slightly-polluted water in the laboratory (Muirhead-Thomson, 1941a). After organic compounds had been mixed with the soil beneath artificial, outdoor ponds, eggs of *Culex peus* were first deposited on the ponds when organic acids arising from fermentation started to accumulate in the water, while no rafts appeared on control ponds; *Culex peus* is a foul-water breeder. As the fermentation declined eggs of *Culex tarsalis* and *Anopheles freeborni* appeared (Gerhardt, 1959). Females are possibly attracted to foul water by smell. de Zulueta (1950) floated a petri dish containing organic infusion on a larger vessel of distilled water and compared the number of egg rafts laid by *Culex pipiens fatigans* on these with the number laid on a control consisting of a petri dish of distilled water floated on a larger vessel of distilled water. Fifty-seven rafts were laid on the petri dish containing infusion and 68 on the surrounding distilled water whereas only 1 raft was laid on the petri dish of the control and 45 on the surrounding water. The petri dish containing infusion was thus not only attractive itself but had attracted females to the surrounding distilled water.

Observations of preoviposition behaviour suggest that in most species only chemoreceptors on the legs are used in examining the water. Females of *Aedes aegypti,* for example, will quickly reject solutions of high salinity which they have touched with their tarsi and *Anopheles* females are able to discriminate between salt solutions which they have touched in flight (Wallis, 1954a). Females of 10 species or sub-species of *Anopheles, Aedes* and *Culex* in which the mouthparts had been amputated, the antennae coated with paraffin and in which the abdomen was prevented from touching water were able to distinguish distilled water from 0·52M–NaCl, yet otherwise normal females of *Aedes aegypti* in which the legs were coated with paraffin laid eggs at random on the 2 solutions. Amputation of the tarsi and the tips of the tibiae in the 10 species prevented discrimination whereas discrimination was possible in every case when the females retained only the fore, mid or hind tarsi. Further experiments with *Aedes aegypti* showed that the normal total avoidance of 0·52M–NaCl occurred when any single pair of tarsomeres was functional. It is most probable that the chemoreceptors are short, curved hairs found on the tarsi and the tips of the tibiae (p. 214), the only parts of the legs touching the water when the mosquito alights (Wallis, 1954a). It is important to remember that distilled water, which has been used extensively in experiments on selection of oviposition site by mosquitoes, renders similar chemosensory hairs on the labella of the blowfly electrically silent (Hodgson and Roeder, 1956).

The investigations of Muirhead-Thomson on the responses of egg-laying females on *Anopheles minimus* and their influence on the distribution of the larvae provide the most detailed analysis available on this subject and illustrate its complexity. In Assam the larvae occur along the edges of clear, slow-flowing, sunlit streams. By avoiding direct sunlight the larvae remain among the grass which grows thickly at the edges of the streams and within which the water is still. Shading by trees and shrubs will kill the grass and the larvae are then swept away. The larvae are never found in tanks or rice fields; indeed their thermal death point is low enough to make life in rice fields impossible. Factors which might, therefore, be expected to influence the ovipositing female are the temperature, purity and movement of the water, and shade. Experiments showed a strong preference of the laying female for shade. In the laboratory dishes exposed to $1·4 \times 10^{-5}$ ft-c, equivalent to one-quarter starlight, were avoided and most eggs were laid on those in deeper shade. No discrimination was shown, however, between dishes exposed to $0 \cdot 7 \times 10^{-5}$ ft-c and others more heavily shaded although the difference was easily appreciated by the dark-adapted human eye. In the field females would lay in shaded, artificial pools of still water adjacent to a stream but avoided unshaded pools (Muirhead-Thomson, 1940a). Water temperature is unlikely to influence ovipositing females since in the evenings, when most eggs are laid, water temperatures in rice fields have fallen to those of streams and are in a range within which the females show no selection (Muirhead-Thomson, 1940c). Captive females laid indiscriminately on stream water and water from stagnant tanks and borrow pits in which larvae were never found, showing that there is nothing intrinsically attractive in stream water itself, but they would avoid stream water polluted with very slight traces of decaying plant material although the larvae could grow well in water polluted more than 30 times this amount. Further observations showed that organic matter in the water of rice fields and tanks sometimes reached concentrations likely to be repellent but that in other cases it was well within the limits tolerated (Muirhead-Thomson, 1941a). Laboratory experiments showed a strong preference for still water, for with a choice of still water and water flowing only 1 ft in 20 sec 67 per cent of the eggs were laid on still water. In contrast the females were quite uninfluenced by surface ripples (Muirhead-Thomson, 1940b). Muirhead-Thomson concluded that the thick, grassy edges which harboured the larvae provided two important attractants for females, sufficient shade and a zone of still water. There appears to be a further, unknown factor which attracts females of *Anopheles minimus* to streams for the thick, grassy borders of unpolluted rice fields are unattractive and, moreover, once females have reached a stream the combined attraction of shade and still water in nearby pools will induce oviposition although such pools are normally unattractive (Muirhead-Thomson, 1940a, 1942).

These various investigations on oviposition illustrate the wide range of factors used by different species in discerning their oviposition sites. In no species has a simple chemical factor been found which typifies the breeding site and in most species it appears that a suitable site is discerned by a combination of particular physical factors and water of appropriate purity or pollution. A complete analysis for any species has yet to be made and it is clear that such an investigation will have to be made under field conditions owing to the abnormal behaviour of mosquitoes in the laboratory.

PLATES

PLATE I. FIG. 1. Fine structure of the midgut epithelium of an adult female of *Aedes aegypti*, 4 days old, fed only water. ×3000. BM basement membrane; ct connective tissue; ER endoplasmic reticulum; G Golgi apparatus; H haemocoele; ICB intercellular boundary; L midgut lumen; M mitochondria; MSL longitudinal muscle fibres; MST transverse muscle fibres; MV micro-villi; N nucleus; NE nuclear envelope; NU nucleolus; P possibly pores in nuclear envelope; S septa; TM thickenings along cell boundary; VES vesicle; W whorl of endoplasmic reticulum. The arrangement of the endoplasmic reticulum in whorls is characteristic of the blood-starved mosquito. (From Bertram and Bird, 1961).

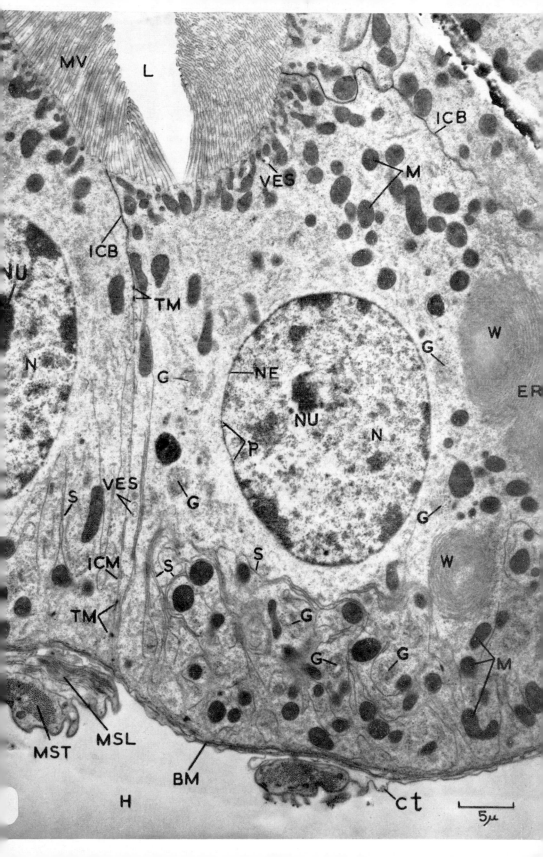

PLATE II. Fine structure of the midgut epithelium of an adult female of *Aedes aegypti*.

FIG. 2. Longitudinal section showing microvilli (MV), bifurcation of intercellular boundary (ICB) to form luminar cell surface continuing as microvillar surfaces, and mitochondrion (M) with cristae (cr). 24 hr after blood meal. $\times 48,000$. INSET. Cross section of microvilli, showing subcylindrical form. $\times 18,000$. 5 days old and fed sugar solution.

FIG. 3. Basal region of midgut cell showing intercellular boundary of paired membranes (ICB), with thickenings (TM), bifurcating to form basal cell membranes (BCM) of the adjacent cells. Also thick basement membrane (BM), longitudinal (MSL) and transverse (MST) muscle fibres. $\times 30,000$. 24 hr after a blood meal. INSET A. Tunica propria of ovariole showing alternate light and dark banding. $\times 30,000$. INSET B. Basement membrane of midgut epithelium. $\times 18,000$.

FIG. 4. Near basal region of midgut cell showing paired membranes of septa (S), mitochondria (M) and particles thought to be ribonucleoprotein (RP) in background of cytoplasm. $\times 48,000$. 7 days after a blood meal, fed sugar solution.

FIG. 5. Basal region of midgut cell showing basal cell membrane (BCM) and its invagination, presumably to form a septum (S). Also basement membrane (BM), tracheal end cell (tec), tracheole (t) and taenidia (tn). $\times 40,000$. 7 days after a blood meal, fed sugar solution. (From Bertram and Bird, 1961).

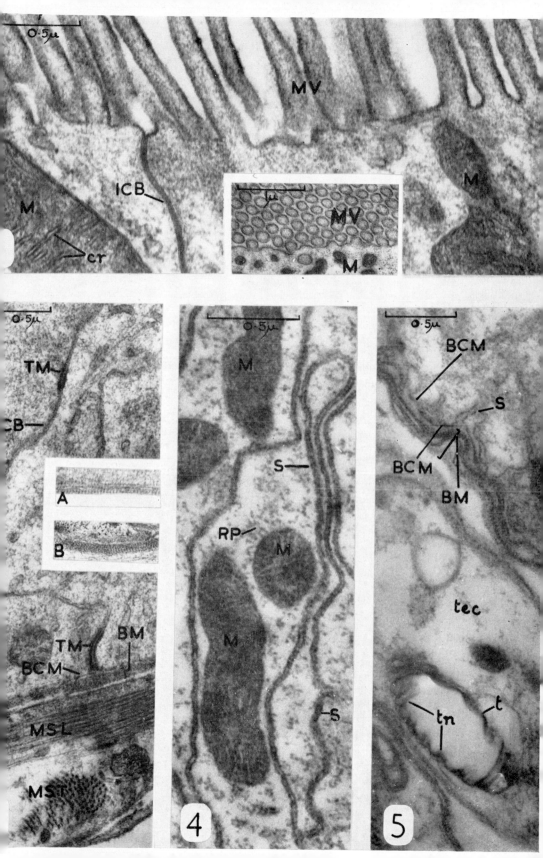

PLATE III.   Fine structure of the midgut epithelium of an adult female of *Aedes aegypti*.

FIG. 6.   Small and larger vesicles with dark amorphous content (VES), whorl (w) of granular endoplasmic reticulum, mitochondria (M) and modified mitochondrion (VP^1). $\times 25,000$.   72 hr after a blood meal, fed sugar solution.

FIG. 7.   Modified mitochondrion (M) with its cristae (cr). $\times 40,000$.   24 hr after a blood meal.

FIG. 8.   VP^2 is possibly a modified mitochondrion. $\times 39,000$.   Within 1 day of emergence, no food or water.

FIG. 9.   Transverse section of whorl (W) of granular endoplasmic reticulum (ER) showing ribonucleoprotein granules (RP) on the cytoplasmic surface of membrane limiting vesicles or cisternae (CIS) of whorl. $\times 40,000$.   6 days after blood meal, fed sugar solution. (From Bertram and Bird, 1961).

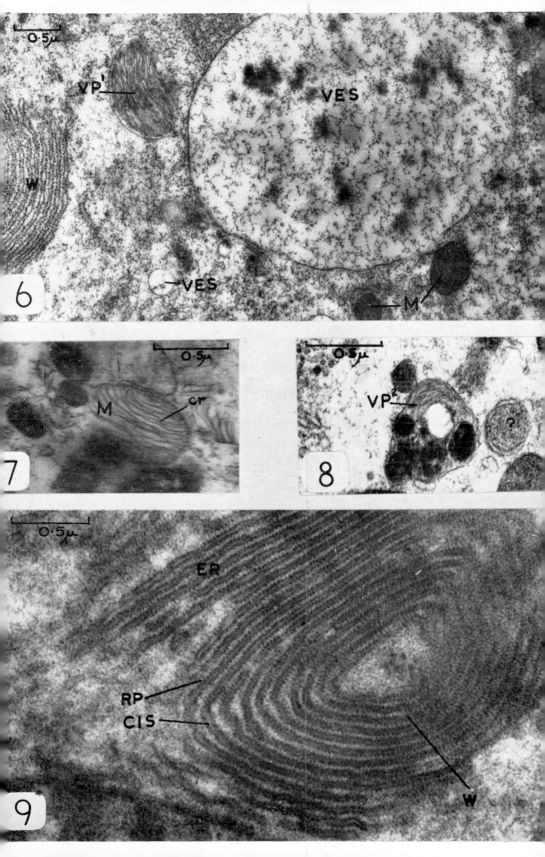

PLATE IV. Fine structure of the midgut epithelium of an adult female of *Aedes aegypti*.

FIG. 10. Secretion of matrix (sec) of peritrophic membrane; whorl (W) of endoplasmic reticulum beginning to unfold half an hour after a blood meal. ICB intercellular boundary; MV microvilli; M mitochondria. ×7500. After 2nd blood meal.

FIG. 11. Whorls of granular endoplasmic reticulum beginning to unfold half an hour after a blood meal. (Same specimen as Fig. 10). CIS cisterna. ×48,000.

FIG. 12. Midgut epithelial cells 24 hr after a blood meal showing absence of whorls and widely-dispersed endoplasmic reticulum (ER) ramifying throughout the cell. ICB intercellular boundary; BM basement membrane; M mitochondria; N nucleus; S septa; MV microvilli; VAC vacuole. ×6250.

(From Bertram and Bird, 1961).

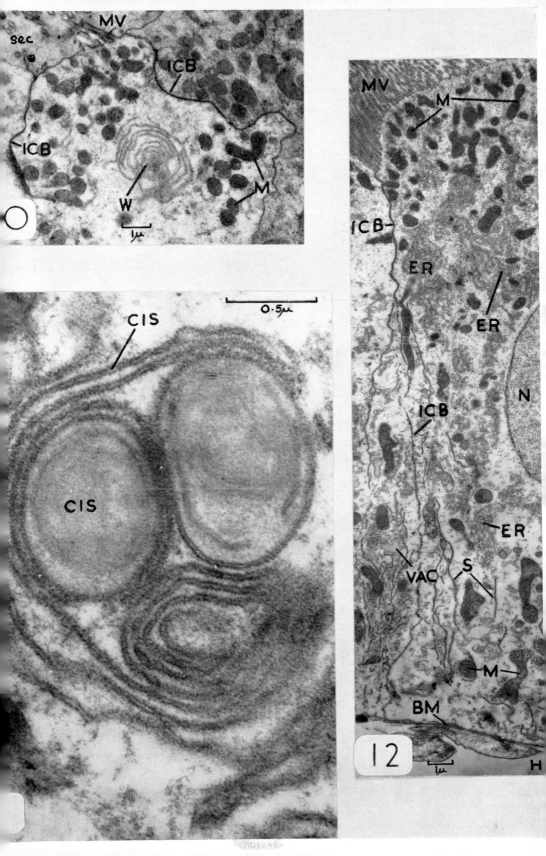

PLATE V. Fine structure of the midgut epithelium of an adult female of *Aedes aegypti*.

FIG. 13. Copious secretion (sec) of matrix of peritrophic membrane between and beyond microvilli (MV) within 1½ hr of blood meal. M mitochondria; N nucleus; rbc red blood corpuscles; L midgut lumen. ×7500.

FIG. 14. Secretion (sec) of matrix of peritrophic membrane between and beyond microvilli (MV) in cross section, and extending beyond them to a red blood corpuscle (rbc). M mitochondria; N nucleus; NE nuclear envelope; ER endoplasmic reticulum. ×30,000. 2 hr after blood meal.

FIG. 15. Formation of granular peritrophic membrane (PM) around the blood meal 15 hr after feeding. The amount of secretion of matrix between the microvilli is less than at earlier stages of digestion. L midgut lumen; MV microvilli. ×12,000.

FIG. 16. 24 hr after ingestion of blood; compact, granular peritrophic membrane surrounding blood. Secretion of matrix reduced. The micrograph has been altered to reduce the space between peritrophic membrane (PM) and microvilli (MV). L lumen; M mitochondria. ×7500.

FIG. 17. 24 hr after blood meal. Microvilli (MV) show protuberances; peritrophic membrane (PM) is granular and loosely layered; secretion (sec) of matrix is still apparent. ×60,000. (From Bertram and Bird, 1961).

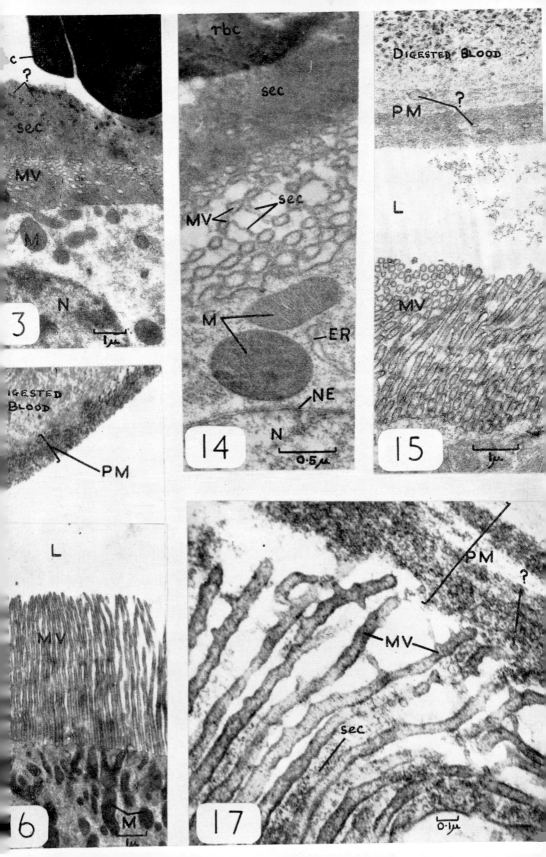

3

c
?
sec
MV
M
N
1μ

IGESTED
BLOOD
PM

14

rbc
sec
MV
sec
M
ER
NE
N
0.5μ

15

DIGESTER BLOOD
PM
?
L
MV
1μ

6

L
MV
M
1μ

17

PM
?
MV
sec
0.1μ

PLATE VI. FIG. 18. Fine structure of the midgut epithelium of an adult female of *Aedes togoi*. Transverse section through part of cell showing close resemblance to fine structure of *Aedes aegypti*. Three days old, no food or water. ER endoplasmic reticulum; G Golgi apparatus; M mitochondria; N nucleus; NE nuclear envelope; NU nucleolus; P possibly pores in nuclear envelope; VES vesicle; W whorl. ×30,000. (From Bertram and Bird, 1961).

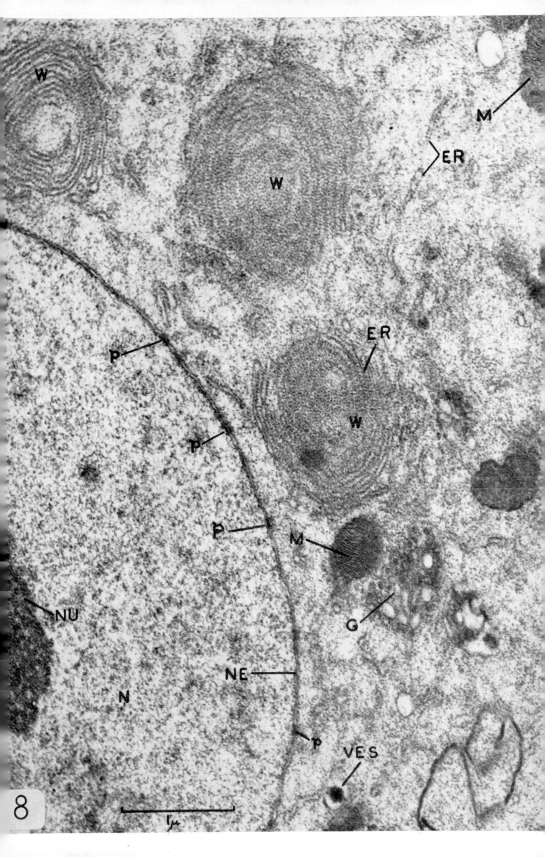

APPENDIX

Systematic List of Species Mentioned

(The usage follows that of Stone, Knight and Starcke (1959) and Stone (1961) except in a few cases).

CULICIDAE

Subfamily ANOPHELINAE

Anopheles (*Stethomyia*) *nimbus* (Theobald)
    (*Anopheles*) *algeriensis* Theobald
        aztecus Hoffmann
        bancroftii Giles
        barberi Coquillett
        barbirostris van der Wulp
        claviger (Meigen)
            syn. *bifurcatus* of authors, not Meigen
        coustani Laveran
        crucians Wiedemann
        freeborni Aitken
        hyrcanus (Pallas)
        implexus (Theobald)
        insulaeflorum (Swellengrebel and
            Swellengrebel de Graaf)
        labranchiae labranchiae Falleroni
        labranchiae atroparvus van Thiel
        lesteri Baisas and Hu
        maculipennis maculipennis Meigen
            syn. *typicus* Hackett and Missiroli
        maculipennis messeae Falleroni
        maculipennis melanoon Hackett
            syn. *subalpinus* Hackett and Lewis
        occidentalis Dyar and Knab
        plumbeus Stephens
        punctimacula Dyar and Knab
        punctipennis (Say)
        quadrimaculatus Say

W

sacharovi Favr
   syn. *elutus* Edwards
sinensis Wiedemann
walkeri Theobald
(*Nyssorhynchus*) *albimanus* Wiedemann
aquasalis Curry
albitarsis Lynch Arribálzaga
darlingi Root
evansae (Brèthes)
(*Kerteszia*) *bellator* Dyar and Knab
homunculus Komp
(*Cellia*) *aconitus* Dönitz
amictus hilli Woodhill and Lee
culicifacies Giles
   syn. *listoni* Giles
farauti Laveran
funestus Giles
gambiae Giles
   syn. *costalis* Giles
gambiae var. *melas* (Theobald)
koliensis Owen
leucosphyrus Dönitz
maculatus Theobald
minimus Theobald
multicolor Cambouliu
nili (Theobald)
pharoensis Theobald
philippinensis Ludlow
pulcherrimus Theobald
sergentii (Theobald)
stephensi Liston
subpictus Grassi
   syn. *rossi* Giles
superpictus Grassi
vagus Dönitz

Subfamily TOXORHYNCHITINAE

*Toxorhynchites (*Lynchiella*) *haemorrhoidalis* (Fabricius)

(*Toxorhynchites*) *splendens* (Wiedemann)

*syn. *Megarhinus*

Subfamily CULICINAE

Tribe Sabethini

Tripteroides Giles
Wyeomyia (*Wyeomyia*) *smithii* (Coquillett)
Sabethes (*Sabethes*) *chloropterus* (Humboldt)
**Malaya genurostris* Leicester
iacobsoni (Edwards)

Tribe Culicini

Ficalbia (*Mimomyia*) *hybrida* (Leicester)
pallida (Edwards)
†*Mansonia* (*Coquillettidia*) *fuscopennata* (Theobald)
richiardii (Ficalbi)
(*Mansonioides*) *africana* (Theobald)
uniformis (Theobald)
Uranotaenia campestris Leicester
lowii Theobald
Orthopodomyia signifera (Coquillett)
Aedeomyia africana Neveu-Lemaire
furfurea (Enderlein)
Psorophora (*Psorophora*) *ciliata* (Fabricius)
howardii Coquillett
(*Janthinosoma*) *ferox* (Humboldt)
(*Grabhamia*) *cingulata* (Fabricius)
confinnis (Lynch Arribálzaga)
Heizmannia stonei Mattingly
Eretmapodites chrysogaster Graham
silvestris conchobius Edwards
Aedes (*Ochlerotatus*) *campestris* Dyar and Knab
canadensis (Theobald)
cantans (Meigen)
cantator (Coquillett)
caspius (Pallas)
communis (Degeer)
syn. *nemorosus* Meigen
detritus (Haliday)
dorsalis (Meigen)
fitchii (Felt and Young)

*syn. *Harpagomyia*
†syn. *Taeniorhynchus*

flavescens (Müller)
hexodontus Dyar
impiger (Walker)
 syn. *nearcticus* Dyar
mariae (Sergent and Sergent)
nigromaculis (Ludlow)
punctor (Kirby)
rusticus (Rossi)
 syn. *maculatus* Meigen
sollicitans (Walker)
squamiger (Coquillett)
sticticus (Meigen)
stimulans (Walker)
taeniorhynchus (Wiedemann)
trivittatus (Coquillett)
varipalpus (Coquillett)
(*Finlaya*) *geniculatus* (Olivier)
 syn. *lateralis* Meigen
japonicus (Theobald)
notoscriptus (Skuse)
pulchrithorax Edwards
pulchriventer (Giles)
rubrithorax (Macquart)
 syn. *queenslandis* Strickland
rupestris Dobrotworsky
togoi (Theobald)
triseriatus (Say)
(*Pseudoskusea*) *australis* (Erichson)
 syn. *concolor* Taylor
(*Stegomyia*) *aegypti* (Linnaeus)
 syn. *argenteus* Poiret
 syn. *calopus* Meigen
 syn. *fasciatus* Fabricius
africanus (Theobald)
albopictus (Skuse)
apicoargenteus (Theobald)
flavopictus Yamada
luteocephalus (Newstead)
polynesiensis Marks
pseudoscutellaris (Theobald)
scutellaris scutellaris (Walker)
scutellaris katherinensis Woodhill

(*Aedimorphus*) *abnormalis* (Theobald)
  argenteopunctatus (Theobald)
  natronius Edwards
  tarsalis (Newstead)
  vexans (Meigen)
 (*Aedes*) *cinereus* Meigen
Armigeres (*Armigeres*) *subalbatus* (Coquillett)
 (*Leicesteria*) *dolichocephalus* (Leicester)
  flavus (Leicester)
Haemagogus (*Stegoconops*) *spegazzinii* Brèthes
  Opifex fuscus Hutton
*Culiseta (*Culiseta*) *alaskaensis* (Ludlow)
  annulata (Schrank)
  bergrothi (Edwards)
  impatiens (Walker)
  incidens (Thomson)
  inornata (Williston)
  subochrea (Edwards)
 (*Culicella*) *morsitans* (Theobald)
Culex (*Lutzia*) *vorax* (Edwards)
  fuscanus Wiedemann
   syn. *concolor* Robineau-Desvoidy
 (*Barraudius*) *pusillus* Macquart
 (*Neoculex*) *territans* Walker
   syn. *apicalis* of authors, not Adams
 (*Culex*) *annulus* Theobald
  bitaeniorhynchus Giles
  fuscocephalus Theobald
  peus Speiser
   syn. *stigmatosoma* Dyar
  pipiens pipiens Linnaeus
  pipiens fatigans Wiedemann
   syn. *pungens* Wiedemann
   ?syn. *quinquefasciatus* Say
  pipiens var. *pallens* Coquillett
  pipiens var. *molestus* Forskal
   syn. *autogenicus* Roubaud
   syn. *berbericus* Roubaud
  poicilipes (Theobald)
  restuans Theobald

  *syn. Theobaldia

salinarius Coquillett
sinaiticus Kirkpatrick
tarsalis Coquillett
thalassius Theobald
theileri Theobald
tritaeniorhynchus Giles
Deinocerites cancer Theobald

REFERENCES

ABDEL-MALEK, A. and GOULDING, R. L. (1948) A study of the rate of growth of two sclerotized regions within larvae of four species of mosquitoes. *Ohio J. Sci.* **48,** 119–128.

ABEDI, Z. H. and BROWN, A. W. A. (1961) Peritrophic membrane as vehicle for DDT and DDE excretion in *Aedes aegypti* larvae. *Ann. Ent. Soc. Amer.* **54,** 539–542.

ABUL-NASR, S. E. (1950) Structure and development of the reproductive system of some species of Nematocera (Order Diptera: Suborder Nematocera). *Phil. Trans.* (B) **234,** 339–396.

ACHUNDOW, I. (1928) Die Modifikation der Anophelen unter den äusseren Bedingungen und kritische Betrachtungen der Rassenfrage. *Arch. Schiffs-u. Tropenhyg.* **32,** 547–561.

AFRIDI, M. K., MAJID, A. and SHAH, I. A. (1940) Studies on the behaviour of adult *Anopheles culicifacies.* Part II. *J. Malar. Inst. India* **3,** 23–51.

AKOV, S. (1962a) A qualitative and quantitative study of the nutritional requirements of *Aedes aegypti* L. larvae. *J. Insect Physiol.* **8,** 319–335.

AKOV, S. (1962b) Antimetabolites in the nutrition of *Aedes aegypti* L. larvae. The substitution of choline by related substances and the effect of choline inhibitors. *J. Insect Physiol.* **8,** 337–348.

ALLEN, J. R., and WEST, A. S. (1962) Collection of oral secretion from mosquitoes. *Mosquito News* **22,** 157–159.

ANDREWARTHA, H. G. (1952) Diapause in relation to the ecology of insects. *Biol. Rev.* **27,** 50–107.

ANON. (1960) *Rep. Lond. Sch. Hyg.* 1958–1959, p. 49.

ANTONIPULLE, P., DAVID, H. V. and KARUNARATNE, M. D. R. (1958) Biology and control of *Taeniorhynchus (Mansonioides) uniformis* Theobald, the chief vector of rural filariasis in Ceylon. *Bull. World Hlth. Org.* **19,** 285–295.

ASCHOFF, J. (1960) Exogenous and endogenous components in circadian rhythms. *Cold Spr. Harb. Sym. Quant. Biol.* **25,** 11–28.

VAN DEN ASSEM, J. (1958) Some experimental evidence for the survival value of the rootpiercing habits of *Mansonia* larvae (Culicidae) to predators. *Ent. Exp. Appl.* **1,** 125–129.

VAN DEN ASSEM, J. (1959) Daily mortality in four species of New Guinea anophelines. *Trop. Geog. Med.* **11,** 223–236.

ATKIN, E. E. and BACOT, A. (1917) The relation between the hatching of the eggs and the development of the larvae of *Stegomyia fasciata (Aëdes calopus)* and the presence of bacteria and yeasts. *Parasitology* **9,** 482–536.

AUGENFELD, J. M. and NEESS, J. C. (1961) Observations on the respiratory enzymes of various life-stages of *Chironomus staegeri* and *Aedes aegypti. Biol. Bull. Wood's Hole* **120,** 129–139.

AVI-DOR, Y. and GONDA, O. (1959) Studies on the adenosine triphosphate-phosphate exchange and the hydrolysis of adenosine triphosphate catalysed by a particulate fraction from the mosquito. *Biochem. J.* **72,** 8–14.

317

AVI-DOR, Y., TRAUB, A. and MAGER, J. (1958) Inhibition studies on sarcosomal DPNH oxidase. *Biochim. Biophys. Acta* **30**, 164–168.

BACOT, A. W. (1916) Report of the Entomological Investigation Undertaken for the Commission for the year August, 1914 to July, 1915. *Rep. Yellow Fever Commission (West Africa)*, 119 pp.

BAKER, F. C. (1935) The effect of photoperiodism on resting, treehole mosquito larvae. *Canad. Ent.* **67**, 149–153.

BARBER, M. A. (1927) The food of anopheline larvae — food organisms in pure culture. *Publ. Hlth Rep., Wash.* **42**, 1494–1509.

BARLOW, C. A. (1955) The fecundity of *Aedes hexodontus* Dyar (Culicidae) in the laboratory. *Canad. J. Zool.* **33**, 420–427.

BARR, A. R. (1952) The thermal death times of the aquatic stages of some American dark-winged anophelines. *Amer. J. Hyg.* **55**, 170–181.

BARR, A. R., SMITH, T. A. and BOREHAM, M. M. (1960) Light intensity and the attraction of mosquitoes to light traps. *J. Econ. Ent.* **53**, 876–880.

BAR-ZEEV, M. (1957a) The effect of density on the larvae of a mosquito and its influence on fecundity. *Bull. Res. Coun. Israel* (B) **6**, 220–228.

BAR-ZEEV, M. (1957b) The effect of extreme temperatures on different stages of *Aedes aegypti* (L.). *Bull. Ent. Res.* **48**, 593–599.

BAR-ZEEV, M. (1958) The effect of temperature on the growth rate and survival of the immature stages of *Aedes aegypti* (L.). *Bull. Ent. Res.* **49**, 157–163.

BAR-ZEEV, M. (1960a) The reaction of mosquitoes to moisture and high humidity. *Ent. Exp. Appl.* **3**, 198–211.

BAR-ZEEV, M. (1960b) The location of hygroreceptors and moisture receptors in *Aedes aegypti* (L.). *Ent. Exp. Appl.* **3**, 251–256.

BÄSSLER, U. (1958) Versuche zur Orientierung der Stechmücken: die Schwarmbildung und die Bedeutung des Johnstonschen Organs. *Z. Vergl. Physiol.* **41**, 300–330.

BATES, M. (1939) The use of salt solutions for the demonstration of physiological differences between the larvae of certain European anopheline mosquitoes. *Amer. J. Trop. Med.* **19**, 357–384.

BATES, M. (1940) Oviposition experiments with anopheline mosquitoes. *Amer. J. Trop. Med.* **20**, 569–583.

BATES, M. (1941a) Studies in the technique of raising anopheline larvae. *Amer. J. Trop. Med.* **21**, 103–122.

BATES, M. (1941b) Laboratory observations on the sexual behavior of anopheline mosquitoes. *J. Exp. Zool.* **86**, 153–173.

BATES, M. (1947) The development and longevity of *Haemagogus* mosquitoes under laboratory conditions. *Ann. Ent. Soc. Amer.* **40**, 1–12.

BATES, M. (1949) *The Natural History of Mosquitoes*. MacMillan, New York.

BAUER, H. (1933) Die wachsenden Oocytenkerne einiger Insekten in ihrem Verhalten zur Nuklealfärbung. *Z. Zellforsch.* **18**, 254–298.

BAYLOR, E. R. and SMITH, F. E. (1953) The orientation of Cladocera to polarized light. *Amer. Nat.* **87**, 97–101.

BEADLE, L. C. (1939) Regulation of the haemolymph in the saline water mosquito larva *Aedes detritus* Edw. *J. Exp. Biol.* **16**, 346–362.

BEAMENT, J. W. L. (1961) The water relations of insect cuticle. *Biol. Rev.* **36**, 281–320.

BEATTIE, M. V. F. (1932) The physico-chemical factors of water in relation to mosquito breeding in Trinidad. *Bull. Ent. Res.* **23**, 477–500, 2 pl.

BECKEL, W. E. (1954) The lack of autolysis of the flight muscles of *Aedes communis* (De Geer) (Culicidae) in the laboratory. *Mosquito News* **14**, 124–127.

BECKEL, W. E. (1955) Oviposition site preference of *Aedes* mosquitoes (Culicidae) in the laboratory. *Mosquito News* **15**, 224–228.

BECKEL, W. E. (1958a) Investigations of permeability, diapause, and hatching in the eggs of the mosquito *Aedes hexodontus* Dyar. *Canad. J. Zool.* **36**, 541–554.

BECKEL, W. E. (1958b) Observations on the rearing of larvae, pupae, and adults of some *Aedes* mosquitoes of northern Canada. *Canad. J. Zool.* **36**, 797–808.

BEKLEMISHEV, W. (1930) Sur le rôle des particules colloïdales de l'eau dans l'alimentation des larves d'*Anopheles*. *Mag. Paras. Mus. Zool. Acad. Sci. URSS* **1**, 27–36.

BEKLEMISHEV, W. N., DETINOVA, T. S. and POLOVODOVA, V. P. (1959) Determination of physiological age in anophelines and of age distribution in anopheline populations in the USSR. *Bull. World Hlth. Org.* **21**, 223–232.

BEKLEMISHEV, W. N. and MITROFANOVA, J. G. (1926) The problem of distribution of the larvae of *Anopheles maculipennis* Mg. *Bull. Inst. Rech. Biol. Perm.* (*Molotov*) **4**, 285–332.

BEKMAN, A. M. (1935) Interruptions dans la nutrition des larves d'*Anopheles maculipennis*, occasionnées par les mues. *Med. Parasit., Moscow* **4**, 389–391.

BENJAMINI, E., FEINGOLD, B. F. and KARTMAN, L. (1960) Antigenic property of the oral secretion of fleas. *Nature, Lond.* **188**, 959–960.

BENNINGTON, E. E., BLACKMORE, J. S. and SOOTER, C. A. (1958) Soil temperature and the emergence of *Culex tarsalis* from hibernation. *Mosquito News* **18**, 297–298.

BENSON, R. L. (1936) Diagnosis and treatment of sensitization to mosquitoes. *J. Allergy* **8**, 47–59.

BERG, M. and LANG, S. (1948) Observations of hibernating mosquitoes in Massachusetts. *Mosquito News* **8**, 70–71.

BERGER, C. A. (1938a) Cytology of metamorphosis in the Culicinae. *Nature, Lond.* **141**, 834–835.

BERGER, C. A. (1938b) Multiplication and reduction of somatic chromosome groups as a regular developmental process in the mosquito, *Culex pipiens*. *Contr. Embryol. Carneg. Instn.* **27**, 209–232, 1 pl.

BERTRAM, D. S. (1962) The ovary and ovarioles of mosquitoes. Annex to Detinova (1962) pp. 195–210.

BERTRAM, D. S. and BIRD, R. G. (1961) Studies on mosquito-borne viruses in their vectors. I. The normal fine structure of the midgut epithelium of the adult female *Aedes aegypti* (L.) and the functional significance of its modification following a blood meal. *Trans. R. Soc. Trop. Med. Hyg.* **55**, 404–423, 12 pl.

BERTRAM, D. S. and McGREGOR, I. A. (1956) Catches in the Gambia, West Africa, of *Anopheles gambiae* Giles and *A. gambiae* var. *melas* Theobald in entrance traps of a baited portable wooden hut, with special reference to the effect of wind direction. *Bull. Ent. Res.* **47**, 669–681, 1 pl.

BERTRAM, D. S. and SAMARAWICKREMA, W. A. (1958) Age determination for individual *Mansonioides* mosquitoes. *Nature, Lond.* **182**, 444–446.

BHATIA, M. L., WATTAL, B. L. and KALRA, N. L. (1957) Structure of salivary glands in mosquitoes. A preliminary note. *Indian J. Malar.* **11**, 55–59.

BISHOP A. and GILCHRIST B. M. (1946) Experiments upon the feeding of *Aedes aegypti* through animal membranes with a view to applying this method to the chemotherapy of malaria. *Parasitology* **37**, 85–100.

BLISS, A. R. and GILL, J. M. (1933) The effects of freezing on the larvae of *Aedes aegypti*. *Amer. J. Trop. Med.* **13**, 583–588.

BODENSTEIN, D. (1945a) A study of the relationship between organ and organic environment in the post embryonic development of the yellow fever mosquito *Aedes aegypti*. *Bull. Conn. Agric. Exp. Sta.* **45**, 100–114.

BODENSTEIN, D. (1945b) The corpora allata of mosquitoes. *Bull. Conn. Agric. Exp. Sta.* **488,** 396–405.

BODENSTEIN, D. (1953) Embryonic development, in *Insect Physiology* (Edited by K. D. ROEDER), Wiley, New York.

DE BOISSEZON, P. (1930a) Contribution à l'étude de la biologie et de l'histophysiologie de *Culex pipiens* L. *Arch. Zool. Exp. Gén.* **70,** 281–431.

DE BOISSEZON, P. (1930b) Sur l'histologie et l'histophysiologie de l'intestin de la larve de *Culex pipiens* L. *C. R. Soc. Biol., Paris* **103,** 567–568.

DE BOISSEZON, P. (1930c) Le rôle du corps gras comme rein d'accumulation chez *Culex pipiens* L. et chez *Theobaldia annulata* M. *C. R. Soc. Biol., Paris* **103,** 1233–1235.

DE BOISSEZON, P. (1930d) Les réserves dans le corps gras de *Culex pipiens* L. et leur rôle dans la maturation des œufs. *C. R. Soc. Biol., Paris* **103,** 1232–1233.

DE BOISSEZON, P. (1932) Localisation du glycogène et du fer chez *Culex pipiens. C. R. Soc. Biol., Paris* **111,** 866–867.

DE BOISSEZON, P. (1934) L'accélération des multiplications cellulaires et de la phago-cytose sous l'action de l'élévation de la température chez *Culex pipiens* L. *Bull. Soc. Zool. Fr.* **58,** 384–388.

BOORMAN, J. P. T. (1960) Observations on the feeding habits of the mosquito *Aedes (Stegomyia) aegypti* (Linnaeus): the loss of fluid after a blood-meal and the amount of blood taken during feeding. *Ann. Trop. Med. Parasit.* **54,** 8–14.

BORG, A. F. and HORSFALL, W. R. (1953) Eggs of floodwater mosquitoes. II. Hatching stimulus. *Ann. Ent. Soc. Amer.* **46,** 472–477.

BRADBURY, F. R. and STANDEN, H. (1956) Benzene hexachloride metabolism in *Anopheles gambiae. Nature, Lond.* **178,** 1053–1054.

BRELAND, O. P. (1961) Studies on the chromosomes of mosquitoes. *Ann. Ent. Soc. Amer.* **54,** 360–375.

VON DER BRELJE, R. (1924) Die Anhangsorgane des weiblichen Geschlechtsganges der Stechmücken (Culicidae). *Zool. Anz.* **61,** 73–80.

BRESSLAU, E. (1920) Eier und Eizahn der einheimischen Stechmücken. *Biol. Zbl.* **40,** 337–355, 4 pl.

BRETT, G. A. (1938) On the relative attractiveness to *Aëdes aegypti* of certain coloured cloths. *Trans. R. Soc. Trop. Med. Hyg.* **32,** 113–124.

BROCHER, F. (1910) Les phénomènes capillaires. Leur importance dans la biologie aquatique. *Ann. Biol. Lacustre.* **4,** 89–138, 3 pl.

BROUWER, R. (1960a) The attraction of carbon dioxide excreted by the skin of the arm for malaria mosquitoes. *Trop. Geogr. Med.* **12,** 62–66.

BROUWER, R. (1960b) Variations in human body odour as a cause of individual differences of attraction for malaria mosquitoes. *Trop. Geogr. Med.* **12,** 186–192.

BROWN, A., GRIFFITTS, T. H. D., ERWIN, S. and DYRENFORTH, L. Y. (1938) Arthus's phenomenon from mosquito bites. Report of a case with experimental studies. *Sth. Med. J., Nashville* **31,** 590–596.

BROWN, A. W. A. (1951) Studies of the responses of the female *Aedes* mosquito. Part IV. Field experiments on Canadian species. *Bull. Ent Res.* **42,** 575–582, 1 pl.

BROWN, A. W. A. (1954) Studies on the responses of the female *Aedes* mosquito. Part VI. The attractiveness of coloured cloths to Canadian species. *Bull. Ent. Res.* **45,** 67–78.

BROWN, A. W. A. (1958) Factors which attract *Aedes* mosquitos to humans. *Proc. Tenth Int. Congr. Ent.* **3,** 757–763.

BROWN, A. W. A. (1960) Mechanisms of resistance against insecticides. *Annu. Rev. Ent.* **5,** 301–326.

BROWN, A. W. A. (1961) Protective mechanisms against nerve poisons in insects. *Trans. Roy. Soc. Can.* **55,** 25–35.

BROWN, A. W. A. and CARMICHAEL, A. G. (1961a) Lysine as a mosquito attractant. *Nature, Lond.* **189,** 508–509.

BROWN, A. W. A. and CARMICHAEL, A. G. (1961b) Lysine and alanine as mosquito attractants. *J. Econ. Ent.* **54,** 317–324.

BROWN, A. W. A., SARKARIA, D. S. and THOMPSON, R. P. (1951) Studies on the responses of the female *Aedes* mosquito. Part I. The search for attractant vapours. *Bull. Ent. Res.* **42,** 105–114, 1 pl.

BRUCK, R. (1930) Zur Frage über die Ernährung der Larven von *Anopheles maculipennis*. *Trav. Soc. Nat. Leningrad* **60,** 15–28.

BRUMPT, E. (1941) Mécanisme d'éclosion des moustiques. *Ann. Parasit. Hum. Comp.* **18,** 75–94.

BRYUKHANOVA, L. V. (1960) Functional changes of Malpighian tubes in *Anopheles maculipennis sacharovi* Favre in connection with the age difference of females. *Med. Parasit., Moscow* **29,** 549–552. (In Russian with English summary).

DE BUCK, A. (1935) Beitrag zur Rassenfrage bei *Culex pipiens*. *Z. angew. Ent.* **22,** 242–252.

DE BUCK, A. (1937) Some observations on the salivary and stomach secretion of *Anopheles* and other mosquitoes. *Proc. Acad. Sci. Amst.* **40,** 217–223.

DE BUCK, A. (1938) Das Exochorion der *Stegomyia*-Eier. *Verh. Akad. Wet. Amst.* **41,** 677–683, 1 pl.

DE BUCK, A., SCHOUTE, E. and SWELLENGREBEL, N. H. (1932) Further investigations on the racial differentiation of *Anopheles maculipennis* in the Netherlands and its bearing on malaria. *Riv. Malariol.* **11,** 137–156, 1 pl.

DE BUCK, A. and SWELLENGREBEL, N. H. (1934) Behaviour of Dutch *Anopheles atroparvus* and *messeae* in winter under artificial conditions. *Riv. Malariol.* **13,** 404–416.

VON BUDDENBROCK, W. (1952) *Vergleichende Physiologie. Band I: Sinnesphysiologie.* Birkhäuser, Basel.

BUDDINGTON, A. R. (1941) The nutrition of mosquito larvae. *J. Econ. Ent.* **34,** 275–281.

BUGHER, J. C. (1949) Responses of mosquitoes to changes in microclimate. *Rep. Yellow Fever Res. Inst. Lagos* 1948, pp. 166–175.

BURCHAM, E. (1957) Artificial insemination of *Aedes aegypti* (L.). *Canad. Ent.* **89,** 494–495.

BURGESS, L. (1959) Probing behaviour of *Aedes aegypti* (L.) in response to heat and moisture. *Nature, Lond.* **184,** 1968–1969.

BURGESS, L. and BROWN, A. W. A (1957) Studies on the responses of the female *Aëdes* mosquito. Part VIII. The attractiveness of beef blood to *Aedes aegypti* (L.). *Bull. Ent. Res.* **48,** 783–793.

BURGESS, R. W. and YOUNG, M. D. (1944). Methods of handling and feeding *Anopheles quadrimaculatus* upon malarious patients. *J. Nat. Malar. Soc.* **3,** 241–247.

BÜTTIKER, W. (1958) Observations on the physiology of adult anophelines in Asia. *Bull. World Hlth Org.* **19,** 1063–1071.

BUXTON, A. P. (1952) Observations on the diurnal behaviour of the redtail monkey (*Cercopithecus ascanius schmidti* Matschie) in a small forest in Uganda. *J. Anim. Ecol.* **21,** 25–58.

BUXTON, P. A. (1935) Changes in the composition of adult *Culex pipiens* during hibernation. *Parasitology* **27,** 263–265.

BUXTON, P. A. and HOPKINS, G. H. E. (1927) Researches in Polynesia and Melanesia. Parts I–IV. *Mem. Lond. Sch. Hyg. Trop. Med.,* no. **1**, xi+260 pp., 12 pl.

CALLOT, J. (1943) Sur *Culex hortensis* et *Culex apicalis* à Richlieu (Indre-et-Loire). *Ann. Parasit. Hum. Comp.* **19**, 129–141.

CAMBOURNAC, F. J. C. and HILL, R. B. (1940) Observation on the swarming of *Anopheles maculipennis,* var. *atroparvus. Amer. J. Trop. Med.* **20**, 133–140.

CANTRELL, W. (1939) Relation of size to sex in pupae of *Aedes aegypti* (Linn.), *A. triseriatus* (Say) and *A. vexans* Meigen. *J. Parasit.* **25**, 448–449.

CARPENTER, P. L. (1956) *Immunology and Serology.* Saunders, Philadelphia and London.

CASIDA, J. E. (1955) Toxicity of aromatic acids to the larvae of the mosquito *Aedes aegypti* L. and the counteracting influence of amino acids. *Biochem. J.* **59**, 216–221.

CAZAL, P. (1948) Les glandes endocrines rétro-cérébrales des insectes (étude morphologique). *Bull Biol. Fr. Belg.* Suppl. **32**, 1–227.

CHABAUD, M. A., GHELELOVITCH, S. and DE LALUN, E. (1960) Apparition de contractions rythmées sur des explants de disques imaginaux thoraciques de larves d'*Aedes (Stegomyia) aegypti* (L.), cultivés *in vitro. Bull. Soc. Pat. Exot.* **53**, 170–172.

CHEN, P. S. (1958a) Studies on the protein metabolism of *Culex pipiens* L. I. Metabolic changes of free amino acids during larval and pupal development. *J. Insect Physiol.* **2**, 38–51.

CHEN, P. S. (1958b) Studies on the protein metabolism of *Culex pipiens* L. II. Quantitative differences in free amino acids between male and female adult mosquitoes. *J. Insect Physiol.* **2**, 128–136.

CHEN, P. S. (1959) Trennung der Blut proteine von *Drosophila-* und *Culex-*Larven mittels Stärke-Gel-Elektrophorese. *Rev. Suisse Zool.* **66**, 280–289.

CHRISTOPHERS, S. R. (1911) The development of the egg follicle in anophelines. *Paludism* no. 2, 73–88, 1 pl.

CHRISTOPHERS, S. R. (1922) The development and structure of the terminal abdominal segments and hypopygium of the mosquito, with observations on the homologies of the terminal segments of the larva. *Indian J. Med. Res.* **10**, 530–572, 4 pl.

CHRISTOPHERS, S. R. (1923) The structure and development of the female genital organs and hypopygium of the mosquito. *Indian J. Med. Res.* **10**, 698–720, 2 pl.

CHRISTOPHERS, S. R. (1945) Structure of the *Culex* egg and egg-raft in relation to function (Diptera). *Trans. R. Ent. Soc. Lond.* **95**, 25–34, 4 pl.

CHRISTOPHERS, S. R. (1960) *Aedes aegypti* (L.) *the Yellow Fever Mosquito. Its Life History, Bionomics and Structure.* Cambridge University Press.

CHRISTOPHERS, S. R. and PURI, I. M. (1929) Why do *Anopheles* larvae feed at the surface, and how? *Trans. Far-East. Ass. Trop. Med.* **2**, 736–739, 1 pl.

CLARK, E. W. and BALL, G. H. (1952) The free amino acids in the whole bodies of culicid mosquitoes. *Exp. Parasit.* **1**, 339–346.

CLEMENTS, A. N. (1955) The sources of energy for flight in mosquitoes. *J. Exp. Biol.* **32**, 547–554.

CLEMENTS, A. N. (1956a) Hormonal control of ovary development in mosquitoes. *J. Exp. Biol.* **33**, 211–223.

CLEMENTS, A. N. (1956b) The antennal pulsating organs of mosquitoes and other Diptera. *Quart. J. Micr. Sci.* **97**, 429–433.

COGGESHALL, L. T. (1926) Relationship of plankton to anopheline larvae. *Amer. J. Hyg.* **6**, 556–569.

COLLESS, D. H. (1956a) Environmental factors affecting hairiness in mosquito larvae. *Nature, Lond.* **177**, 229–230.

COLLESS, D. H. (1956b) The *Anopheles leucosphyrus* group. *Trans. R. Ent. Soc. Lond.* **108**, 37–116.

COLLESS, D. H. (1957) Components of the catch curve of *Culex annulus* in Singapore. *Nature, Lond.* **180**, 1496–1497.

COLLESS, D. H. (1958) Recognition of individual nulliparous and parous mosquitoes. *Trans. R. Soc. Trop. Med. Hyg.* **52**, 187.

COLLESS, D. H. (1959) Notes on the culicine mosquitoes of Singapore. VII. Host preferences in relation to the transmission of disease. *Ann. Trop. Med. Parasit.* **53**, 259–267.

COLLESS, D. H. and CHELLAPAH, W. T. (1960) Effects of body weight and size of blood-meal upon egg production in *Aedes aegypti* (Linnaeus) (Diptera, Culicidae). *Ann. Trop. Med. Parasit.* **54**, 475–482.

CONSTANTINEAUNU, M. J. (1930) Der Aufbau der Sehorgane bei den im Süsswasser lebenden Dipterenlarven und bei Puppen und Imagines von *Culex*. *Zool. Jb.* (*Anat. Ont.*). **52**, 253–346, 12 pl.

COOK, E. F. (1944) The morphology of the larval heads of certain Culicidae (Diptera). *Microentomology*. **9**, 38–68.

CORBET, P. S. (1959) Recognition of individual nulliparous and parous mosquitoes. *Trans. R. Soc. Trop. Med. Hyg.* **53**, 297.

CORBET, P. S. (1960) Recognition of nulliparous mosquitoes without dissection. *Nature, Lond.* **187**, 525–526.

CORBET, P. S. (1961a) Entomological studies from a high tower in Mpanga forest, Uganda. IV. Mosquito breeding at different levels in and above the forest. *Trans. R. Ent. Soc. Lond.* **113**, 275–283.

CORBET, P. S. (1961b) Entomological studies from a high tower in Mpanga forest, Uganda. VI. Nocturnal flight activity of Culicidae and Tabanidae as indicated by light-traps. *Trans. R. Ent. Soc. Lond.* **13**, 301–314.

CORBET, P. S. (1961c) Entomological studies from a high tower in Mpanga forest, Uganda. VIII. The age-composition of biting mosquito populations according to time and level. *Trans. R. Ent. Soc. Lond.* **113**, 336–345.

CORBET, P. S., HADDOW, A. J. and GILLETT, J. D. (1960) Observations on the oviposition-cycle of *Aedes* (*Stegomyia*) *aegypti* (Linnaeus), IV. *Ann. Trop. Med. Parasit.* **54**, 156–164.

CORNWALL, J. W. and PATTON, W. S. (1914) Some observations on the salivary secretion of the commoner blood-sucking insects and ticks. *Indian J. Med. Res.* **2**, 569–593.

CORRADETTI, A. (1930) Sulle modificazioni delle larve di *Anopheles* in relazione col colore dell'ambiente. *Riv. Malariol.* **9**, 35–39. (English summary p. 95).

COUNCE, S. J. (1961) The analysis of insect embryogenesis. *Annu. Rev. Ent.* **6**, 295–312.

CRAIG, G. B. (1957) Parthenogenesis in *Aedes aegypti* (L.). *Bull. Ent. Soc. Amer.* **3** (3), 36.

CRAIG, G. B., HICKEY, W. A. and VANDEHEY, R. C. (1960) An inherited male-producing factor in *Aedes aegypti*. *Science* **132**, 1887–1889.

CRAIG, G. B., VANDEHEY, R. C. and HICKEY, W. A. (1961) Genetic variability in populations of *Aedes aegypti*. *Bull. World Hlth. Org.* **24**, 527–539.

CURRY, D. P. (1939) A documented record of a long flight of *Aedes sollicitans*. *Proc. N. J. Mosq. Ext. Ass.* **26**, 36–39.

CURTIN, T. J. and JONES, J. C. (1961) The mechanism of ovulation and oviposition in *Aedes aegypti*. *Ann. Ent. Soc. Amer.* **54**, 298–313.

DAKSHINAMURTY, S. and SHARMA, M. I. D. (1951a) The humidity preferences of mosquitoes. *Indian J. Malar.* **5**, 209–219.

DAKSHINAMURTY, S. and SHARMA, M. I. D. (1951b) The temperature preferences of mosquitoes. *Indian J. Malar.* **5**, 221–227.

DANILEVSKIĬ, A. S. and GLINYANAYA, E. I. (1958) The dependence of the gonotrophic cycle and imaginal diapause of blood-sucking mosquitoes on changes in day length, pp. 34–51. In Danilevskiĭ, A. S. (ed.). The Ecology of Insects (1958) *Uchen. Zap. Leningr. Gosud. Univ.*, no. 240 (*Ser. Biol. Nauk* no 46) 160 pp. (In Russian) (Cited from *Rev. Appl. Ent.* (B) (1960) **48**, 88).

DANILOVA, M. I. and ZUBAREVA, S. P. (1932) On the influence of light on the larval development of *Anopheles maculipennis. Bull. Inst. Rech. Biol. Perm. (Molotov).* **8**, 57–64.

DARROW, E. M. (1949) Factors in the elimination of the immature stages of *Anopheles quadrimaculatus* Say in a water level fluctuation cycle. *Amer. J. Hyg.* **50**, 207–235.

DARSIE, M. L., PERRY, S. M., ROSENFELD, D. and ZARO, J. A. (1945) Size of histamine wheal in relation to dose and to animal species. *Proc. Soc. Exp. Biol. Med.* **59**, 278–281.

DAVIDSON, G. (1954) Estimation of the survival-rate of anopheline mosquitoes in nature. *Nature, Lond.* **174**, 792–793.

DAVIDSON, G. (1955) Measurement of the ampulla of the oviduct as a means of determining the natural daily mortality of *Anopheles gambiae. Ann. Trop. Med. Parasit.* **49**, 24–36.

DAVIS, H. (1957) Biophysics and physiology of the inner ear. *Physiol. Rev.* **37**, 1–49.

DAVIS, N. C. (1932) The effects of heat and cold upon *Aedes (Stegomyia) aegypti. Amer. J. Hyg.* **16**, 177–191.

DAY, M. F. (1954) The mechanism of food distribution to midgut or diverticula in the mosquito. *Aust. J. Biol. Sci.* **7**, 515–524, 1 pl.

DEANE, M. P. and CAUSEY, O. R. (1943) Viability of *Anopheles gambiae* eggs and morphology of unusual types found in Brazil. *Amer. J. Trop. Med.* **23**, 95–102.

DECOURSEY, J. D. and WEBSTER, A. P. (1952) Effect of insecticides and other substances on oviposition by *Aedes sollicitans. J. Econ. Ent.* **45**, 1030–1034.

DECOURSEY, J. D., WEBSTER, A. P. and LEOPOLD, R. S. (1953) Studies on the effect of insecticides on the oviposition of *Anopheles quadrimaculatus* Say. *Ann. Ent. Soc. Amer.* **46**, 359–365.

DÉDUIT, Y. (1957) Etudes sur la ponte par autogénèse des Culicides. II. Données numériques sur l'acte de ponte chez la femelle fecondée de *Culex pipiens autogenicus* Roubaud. *C. R. Soc. Biol., Paris* **151**, 974–977.

DETHIER, V. G. (1947) *Chemical Insect Attractants and Repellents.* Blakiston, Philadelphia.

DETHIER, V. G. (1955) The physiology and histology of the contact chemoreceptors of the blowfly. *Quart. Rev. Biol.* **30**, 348–371.

DETHIER, V. G. and CHADWICK, L. E. (1948) The stimulating effect of glycols and their polymers on the tarsal receptors of blowflies. *J. Gen. Physiol.* **32**, 139–151.

DETINOVA, T. (1936) Certain éléments de la conduite des femelles d'*Anopheles maculipennis messeae* Fall. *Med. Parasit., Moscow* **5**, 525–543

DETINOVA, T. S. (1944) The relationship between the size of female *Anopheles maculipennis atroparvus* van Thiel and the stage of development of the ovaries on emergence. *Med. Parasit., Moscow* **13**, 52–55. (In Russian).

DETINOVA, T. S. (1945a) On the influence of glands of internal secretion upon the ripening of the gonads and the imaginal diapause in *Anopheles maculipennis. Zool. Zh.* **34**, 291–298. (In Russian with English summary).

DETINOVA, T. S. (1945b) Determination of the physiological age of the females of *Anopheles* by the changes in the tracheal system of the ovaries. *Med. Parasit., Moscow* **14**, 45–49. (In Russian) (Cited from *Rev. Appl. Ent.* (B). **34**, 180–181 (1946)).

DETINOVA, T. S. (1949) Physiological changes in the ovaries of female *Anopheles maculipennis*. *Med. Parasit., Moscow* **18**, 410–420. (In Russian).

DETINOVA, T. S. (1953a) On the changes in the ovarioles of *Anopheles maculipennis*, when retention of an egg developed on the previous gonotrophic cycle has occurred. *Med. Parasit., Moscow* **22**, 279–280. (In Russian).

DETINOVA, T. S. (1953b) Mechanism of gonotrophic harmony in the common malarial mosquito. *Zool. Zh.* **32**, 1178–1188. (In Russian).

DETINOVA, T. S. (1953c) The age composition and epidemiological significance of populations of *Anopheles maculipennis* under the conditions found in the Province of Moscow. *Med. Parasit., Moscow* **22**, 486–495. (In Russian).

DETINOVA, T. S. (1955) Fertility of the common malarial mosquito *Anopheles maculipennis*. *Med. Parasit., Moscow* **24**, 6–11. (In Russian).

DETINOVA, T. S. (1962) Age-grouping methods in Diptera of medical importance with special reference to some vectors of malaria. *Monogr. World Hlth Org. No. 47*, 216 pp.

DIMOND, J. B., LEA, A. O. and DELONG, D. M. (1958) Nutritional requirements for reproduction in insects. *Proc. Tenth Int. Congr. Ent.* (1956) **2**, 135–137.

DIMOND, J. B., LEA, A. O., HAHNERT, W. F. and DELONG, D. M. (1956) The amino acids required for egg production in *Aedes aegypti*. *Canad. Ent.* **88**, 57–62.

DOBROTWORSKY, N. V. (1955) The *Culex pipiens* group in south-eastern Australia. III. Autogeny in *Culex pipiens* form *molestus*. *Proc. Linn. Soc. N.S.W.* **79**, 193–195.

DOBROTWORSKY, N. V. (1959) Notes on Australian mosquitoes (Diptera, Culicidae). IV. *Aedes alboannulatus* complex in Victoria. *Proc. Linn. Soc. N.S.W.* **84**, 131–145.

DOW, R. P., REEVES, W. C. and BELLAMY, R. E. (1957) Field tests of avian host preference of *Culex tarsalis* Coq. *Amer. J. Trop. Med. Hyg.* **6**, 294–303.

DOWNES, J. A. (1958) Assembly and mating in the biting Nematocera. *Proc. Tenth Int. Congr. Ent.* (1956) **2**, 425–434.

DOWNS, W. G. (1951) Growth changes of anopheline eggs in water and in saline solutions. *J. Nat. Malar. Soc.* **10**, 17–22.

DUNCAN, J. T. (1926) On a bactericidal principle present in the alimentary canal of insects and arachnids. *Parasitology* **18**, 238–252.

ECKERT, D., PAASONEN, M. and VARTIAINEN, A. (1950) On histamine in gnat (*Culex pipiens*). *Ann. Med. Exp. Fenn.* **28**, 84–85.

ECKERT, D., PAASONEN, M. and VARTIAINEN, A. (1951) On histamine in the gnat (*Culex pipiens*). *Acta. Pharm. Tox., Kbh.* **7**, 16–22.

EDWARDS, F. W. (1941) *Mosquitoes of the Ethiopian Region.* III. *Culicinae Adults and Pupae.* British Museum (Natural History), London.

EGGERS, F. (1924) Zur Kenntnis der antennalen stiftführenden Sinnesorgane der Insekten. *Z. Morph. Ökol. Tiere* **2**, 259–349.

EICHLER, W. (1951) *Anopheles*-Beobachtungen in Südrussland. *Riv. Malariol.* **30**, 29–38.

ELZINGA, R. J. (1961) A comparison in time of egg hatching between male and female *Aedes aegypti* (L.). *Mosquito News* **21**, 307–310.

EVANS, D. R. and MELLON, DEF. (1962) Electrophysiological studies of a water receptor associated with the taste sensilla of the blowfly. *J. Gen. Physiol.* **45**, 487–500.

EYLES, D. E. and BISHOP, L. K. (1943) The microclimate of diurnal resting places of *Anopheles quadrimaculatus* Say in the vicinity of Reelfoot Lake. *Publ. Hlth. Rep., Wash.* **58**, 217–230.

FARID, M. A. (1949) Relationships between certain populations of *Culex pipiens* Linnaeus and *Culex quinquefasciatus* Say in the United States. *Amer. J. Hyg.* **49**, 83–100.

FARNSWORTH, M. W. (1947) The morphology and musculature of the larval head of *Anopheles quadrimaculatus* Say. *Ann. Ent. Soc. Amer.* **40**, 137–151.

FEIR, D., LENGY, J. I. and OWEN, W. B. (1961) Contact chemoreception in the mosquito, *Culiseta inornata* (Williston); sensitivity of the tarsi and labella to sucrose and glucose. *J. Insect Physiol.* **6**, 13–20.

FELDBERG, W. (1927) The action of histamine on the blood vessels of the rabbit. *J. Physiol.* **63**, 211–216.

FERGUSON M. J. and MICKS, D. W. (1961) Microorganisms associated with mosquitoes: I. Bacteria isolated from the mid-gut of adult *Culex fatigans* Wiedemann. *J. Insect Pathol.* **3**, 112–119.

FIELDING, J. W. (1919) Notes on the bionomics of *Stegomyia fasciata,* Fabr. (Part I). *Ann. Trop. Med. Parasit.* **13**, 259–296.

FISK, F. W. (1941) *Deinocerites spanius* at Brownsville, Texas, with notes on its biology and a description of the larva. *Ann. Ent. Soc. Amer.* **34**, 543–550.

FISK, F. W. (1950) Studies on proteolytic digestion in adult *Aedes aegypti* mosquitoes. *Ann. Ent. Soc. Amer.* **43**, 555–572.

FISK, F. W. and SHAMBAUGH, G. F. (1952) Protease activity in adult *Aedes aegypti* mosquitoes as related to feeding. *Ohio J. Sci.* **52**, 80–88.

FISK, F. W. and SHAMBAUGH, G. F. (1954) Invertase activity in adult *Aedes aegypti* mosquitoes. *Ohio J. Sci.* **54**, 237–239.

FOLGER, H. T. (1946) The reactions of *Culex* larvae and pupae to gravity, light, and mechanical shock. *Physiol. Zool.* **19**, 190–202.

FORD, E. B. (1961) The theory of genetic polymorphism. *Symp. R. Ent. Soc. Lond.* no. 1, 11–19.

FRAENKEL, G. S. and GUNN, D. L. (1940) *The Orientation of Animals. Kineses, Taxes and Compass Reactions.* Clarendon Press, Oxford.

FREEBORN, S. B. (1921) The seasonal history of *Anopheles occidentalis* D. & K. in California. *J. Econ. Ent.* **14**, 415–421.

FREEBORN, S. B. (1932) The seasonal life history of *Anopheles maculipennis* with reference to humidity requirements and "hibernation". *Amer. J. Hyg.* **16**, 215–223.

DE FREITAS, J. R. and DA SILVEIRA GUEDES, A. (1961) Determination by radioactive iron (^{59}Fe) of the amount of blood ingested by insects. *Bull. World Hlth Org.* **25**, 271–273.

FREYVOGEL, T. A. (1961) Ein Beitrag zu den Problemen um die Blutmahlzeit von Stechmücken. *Acta Trop., Basel* **18**, 201–251.

FRINGS, H. and HAMRUM, C. L. (1950) The contact chemoreceptors of adult yellow fever mosquitoes, *Aedes aegypti. J. N. Y. Ent. Soc.* **58**, 133–142.

FRIZZI, G. (1947a) Salivary gland chromosomes of *Anopheles. Nature, Lond.* **160**, 226–227.

FRIZZI, G. (1947b) Determinazione del sesso nel genere *Anopheles. Sci. Genet.* **3**, 80–88. (English summary).

FRIZZI, G. and KITZMILLER, J. B. (1959) The salivary gland chromosomes of *Anopheles punctipennis* compared with those of the *Anopheles maculipennis* complex Diptera: Culicidae. *Ent. News* **70**, 33–39.

FROHNE, W. C. (1953) Natural history of *Culiseta impatiens* (Wlk.), (Diptera, Culicidae), in Alaska. *Trans. Amer. Micr. Sci.* **72,** 103–118.

FROHNE, W. C. (1954) Biology of an Alaskan mosquito, *Culiseta alaskaensis* (Ludl.). *Ann. Ent. Soc. Amer.* **47,** 9–24.

FROHNE, W. C. and FROHNE, R. G. (1954) Diurnal swarms of *Culex territans* Walker, and the crepuscular swarming of *Aedes* about a small glade in Alaska. *Mosquito News* **14,** 62–64.

FROST, F. M., HERMS, W. B. and HOSKINS, W. M. (1936) The nutritional requirements of the larva of the mosquito, *Theobaldia incidens* (Thom.). *J. Exp. Zool.* **73,** 461–479.

FÜLLER, H. B. (1960) Morphologische und experimentelle Untersuchungen über die neurosekretorischen Verhältnisse im Zentralnervensystem von Blattiden und Culiciden. *Zool. Jb. (Allg. Zool. Physiol.)* **69,** 223–250.

GALINDO, P. (1958) Bionomics of *Sabethes chloropterus* Humboldt, a vector of sylvan yellow fever in middle America. *Amer. J. Trop. Med. Hyg.* **7,** 429–440.

GALUN, R. (1960) Respiration of decapitated mosquitoes. *Nature, Lond.* **185,** 391–392.

GALUN, R. and FRAENKEL, G. (1957) Physiological effects of carbohydrates in the nutrition of a mosquito, *Aedes aegypti* and two flies, *Sarcophaga bullata* and *Musca domestica*. *J. Cell. Comp. Physiol.* **50,** 1–23.

GANDER, R. (1951) Experimentelle und oekologische Untersuchungen über das Schlüpfvermögen der Larven von *Aedes aegypti* L. *Rev. Suisse Zool.* **58,** 215–278.

GARRETT-JONES, C. (1950) A dispersion of mosquitoes by wind. *Nature, Lond.* **165,** 285.

GASCHEN, H. (1932) Influence de la température et de la nutrition larvaire sur le développement de *Culex pipiens* (race autogène). *Bull. Soc. Pat. Exot.* **25,** 577–581.

GEBERT, S. (1937) Notes on the viability of *Anopheles costalis* ova subjected to natural desiccation. *Trans. R. Soc. Trop. Med. Hyg.* **31,** 115–117.

GEIGER, H. R. (1961) Untersuchungen über freie Aminosäuren während der Adultentwicklung von *Culex pipiens* und *Culex fatigans* und deren Einfluss auf die Eireifung. *Rev. Suisse Zool.* **68,** 583–626.

GEIGY, R. and GANDER, R. (1959) Aeussere Einwirkungen beim Schlüpfen von *Aedes aegypti* aus dem Ei. *Acta Trop., Basel* **6,** 97–104.

GERHARDT, R. W. (1959) The influence of soil fermentation on oviposition site selection by mosquitoes. *Mosquito News* **19,** 151–155.

GHELELOVITCH, S. (1950) Étude génétique de deux charactères de pigmentation chez *Culex autogenicus* Roubaud. *Bull. Biol. Fr. Belg.* **84,** 217–224.

GIBBINS, E. G. (1932) A note on the relative size of the anal gills of mosquito larvae breeding in salt and fresh water. *Ann. Trop. Med. Parasit.* **26,** 551–554.

GIGLIOLI, M. E. C. (1959) Observations on the structure of the ovariole and the follicular residue body or corpus luteum in *Anopheles gambiae*. *Trans. R. Soc. Trop. Med. Hyg.* **53,** 310–311.

GILBERT, I. H. and GOUCK, H. K. (1957) Influence of surface color on mosquito landing rates. *J. Econ. Ent.* **50,** 678–680.

GILCHRIST, B. M. and HALDANE, J. B. S. (1947) Sex linkage and sex determination in a mosquito, *Culex molestus*. *Hereditas* **33,** 175–190.

GILL, C. A. (1921) The influence of humidity on the life history of mosquitoes and on their power to transmit infection. *Trans. R. Soc. Trop. Med. Hyg.* **14,** 77–87.

GILLETT, J. D. (1955a) Variation in the hatching-response of *Aedes* eggs (Diptera: Culicidae). *Bull. Ent. Res.* **46,** 241–254.

GILLETT, J. D. (1955b) The inherited basis of variation in the hatching-response of *Aëdes* eggs (Diptera: Culicidae). *Bull. Ent. Res.* **46,** 255–265.

GILLETT, J. D. (1955c) Behaviour differences in two strains of *Aedes aegypti*. *Nature, Lond.* **176**, 124.

GILLETT, J. D. (1956a) Genetic differences affecting egg-laying in the mosquito *Aedes (Stegomyia) aegypti* (Linnaeus). *Ann. Trop. Med. Parasit.* **50**, 362–374.

GILLETT, J. D. (1956b) Initiation and promotion of ovarian development in the mosquito *Aedes (Stegomyia) aegypti* (Linnaeus). *Ann. Trop. Med. Parasit.* **50**, 375–380.

GILLETT, J. D. (1957a) Variation in the time of release of the ovarian development hormone in *Aedes aegypti*. *Nature, Lond.* **180**, 656–657.

GILLETT, J. D. (1957b) Age analysis in the biting-cycle of the mosquito *Taeniorhynchus (Mansonioides) africanus* Theobald, based on the presence of parasitic mites. *Ann. Trop. Med. Parasit.* **51**, 151–158.

GILLETT, J. D. (1958) Induced ovarian development in decapitated mosquitoes by transfusion of haemolymph. *J. Exp. Biol.* **35**, 685–693.

GILLETT, J. D. (1959) Control of hatching in the prediapause eggs of *Aedes* mosquitoes. *Nature, Lond.* **184**, 1621–1623.

GILLETT, J. D. (1961) Cyclical feeding-activity in colonized mosquitoes. *Nature, Lond.* **190**, 881–883.

GILLETT, J. D., CORBET, P. S. and HADDOW, A. J. (1959) Observations on the oviposition-cycle of *Aedes (Stegomyia) aegypti* (Linnaeus), III. *Ann. Trop. Med. Paras.* **53**, 132–136.

GILLETT, J. D., CORBET, P. S. and HADDOW, A. J. (1961) Observations on the oviposition-cycle of *Aëdes (Stegomyia) aegypti* (Linnaeus), VI. *Ann. Trop. Med. Parasit.* **55**, 427–431.

GILLETT, J. D., HADDOW, A. J. and CORBET, P. S. (1959) Observations on the oviposition-cycle of *Aedes (Stegomyia) aegypti* (Linnaeus), II. *Ann. Trop. Med. Paras.* **53**, 35–41.

GILLIES, M. T. (1953) The duration of the gonotrophic cycle in *Anopheles gambiae* and *Anopheles funestus*, with a note on the efficiency of hand catching. *E. Afr. Med. J.* **30**, 129–135.

GILLIES, M. T. (1954) The recognition of age-groups within populations of *Anopheles gambiae* by the pre-gravid rate and the sporozoite rate. *Ann. Trop. Med. Parasit.* **48**, 58–74.

GILLIES, M. T. (1955) The pre-gravid phase of ovarian development in *Anopheles funestus*. *Ann. Trop. Med. Parasit.* **49**, 320–325.

GILLIES, M. T. (1956) A new character for the recognition of nulliparous females of *Anopheles gambiae*. *Bull. World Hlth Org.* **15**, 451–459.

GILLIES, M. T. (1957) Age-groups and the biting cycle in *Anopheles gambiae*. A preliminary investigation. *Bull. Ent. Res.* **48**, 553–559.

GILLIES, M. T. (1958) A modified technique for the age-grading of populations of *Anopheles gambiae*. *Ann. Trop. Med. Parasit.* **52**, 261–273.

GILLIES, M. T. (1961) Studies on the dispersion and survival of *Anopheles gambiae* Giles in East Africa, by means of marking and release experiment. *Bull Ent. Res.* **52**, 99–127, 2 pl.

GILLIES, M. T. and SHUTE, G. T. (1954) Environmental influences and the maxillary index in *Anopheles gambiae*. *Nature, Lond.* **173**, 409.

GILMOUR, D. (1961) *The Biochemistry of Insects*. Academic Press, New York and London.

GJULLIN, C. M. (1947) Effect of clothing color on the rate of attack of *Aedes* mosquitoes. *J. Econ. Ent.* **40**, 326–327.

GJULLIN, C. M., HEGARTY, C. P. and BOLLEN, W. B. (1941) The necessity of a low oxygen concentration for the hatching of *Aedes* mosquito eggs. *J. Cell. Comp. Physiol.* **17**, 193–202.

GJULLIN, C. M., YATES, W. W. and STAGE, H. H. (1950) Studies on *Aedes vexans* (Meig.) and *Aedes sticticus* (Meig.), flood-water mosquitoes, in the Lower Columbia River Valley. *Ann. Ent. Soc. Amer.* **43**, 262–275.

GOELDI, E. A. (1905) Os mosquitos no Pará. *Mem. Mus. Goeldi (paraense)* no. IV, 154 pp. (Quoted from KNAB, 1906).

GOLBERG, L. and DE MEILLON, B. (1948a) The nutrition of the larva of *Aedes aegypti* Linnaeus. 3. Lipid requirements. *Biochem. J.* **43**, 372–379.

GOLBERG, L. and DE MEILLON, B. (1948b) The nutrition of the larva of *Aedes aegypti* Linnaeus. 4. Protein and amino-acid requirements. *Biochem. J.* **43**, 379–387.

GOLBERG, L., DE MEILLON, B. and LAVOIPIERRE, M. (1945) The nutrition of the larva of *Aedes aegypti* L. II. Essential water-soluble factors from yeast. *J. Exp. Biol.* **21**, 90–96.

GOMA, L. K. H. (1959) Periodic pupation in *Anopheles gambiae* Giles. *J. Ent. Soc. S. Afr.* **22**, 275–276.

GONDA, O., TRAUB, A. and AVI-DOR, Y. (1957) The oxidative activity of particulate fractions from mosquitoes. *Biochem. J.* **67**, 487–493.

GORDON, R. M. and CREWE, W. (1948) The mechanisms by which mosquitoes and tsetse-flies obtain their blood-meal, the histology of the lesions produced, and the subsequent reactions of the mammalian host; together with some observations on the feeding of *Chrysops* and *Cimex*. *Ann. Trop. Med. Parasit.* **42**, 334–356, 4 pl.

GORDON, R. M. and LUMSDEN, W. H. R. (1939) A study of the behaviour of the mouth-parts of mosquitoes when taking up blood from living tissue; together with some observations on the ingestion of microfilariae. *Ann. Trop. Med. Parasit.* **33**, 259–278.

GOUCK, H. K. and BOWMAN, M. C. (1959) Effect of repellents on the evolution of carbon dioxide and moisture from human arms. *J. Econ. Ent.* **52**, 1157–1159.

GRABOWSKI, C. T. and DETHIER, V. G. (1954) The structure of the tarsal chemoreceptors of the blowfly, *Phormia regina* Meigen. *J. Morph.* **94**, 1–19.

GRACHEVA, L. I. and SHEVKUNOVA, E. A. (1959) Materials on the study of blood-sucking mosquitoes in the Archangelsk region. *Zool. Zh.* **38**, 1751–1753. (In Russian with English summary).

GREENBERG, J. (1951) Some nutritional requirements of adult mosquitoes (*Aedes aegypti*) for oviposition. *J. Nutrit.* **43**, 27–35.

GRELL, M. (1946a) Cytological studies in *Culex*. I. Somatic reduction divisions. *Genetics.* **31**, 60–76, 3 pl.

GRELL, M. (1946b) Cytological studies in *Culex*. II. Diploid and meiotic divisions. *Genetics.* **31**, 77–94, 1 pl.

GRIFFITHS, R. B. and GORDON, R. M. (1952) An apparatus which enables the process of feeding by mosquitoes to be observed in the tissues of a live rodent; together with an account of the ejection of saliva and its significance in malaria. *Ann. Trop. Med. Parasit.* **46**, 311–319.

HAAS, G. (1956) Entwicklung des Komplexauges bei *Culex pipiens* und *Aedes aegypti*. *Z. Morph. Ökol. Tiere.* **45**, 198–216.

HADDOW, A. J. (1942) The mosquito fauna and climate of native huts at Kisumu, Kenya. *Bull. Ent. Res.* **33**, 91–142.

HADDOW, A. J. (1943) Measurements of temperature and light in artificial pools with reference to the larval habitat of *Anopheles (Myzomyia) gambiae*, Giles, and *A. (M.) funestus*, Giles. *Bull. Ent. Res.* **34**, 89–93.

HADDOW, A. J. (1945) The mosquitoes of Bwamba County, Uganda. II. Biting activity with special reference to the influence of microclimate. *Bull. Ent. Res.* **36**, 33–73.

HADDOW, A. J. (1954) Studies of the biting-habits of African mosquitoes. An appraisal of methods employed, with special reference to the twenty-four-hour catch. *Bull. Ent. Res.* **45**, 199–242.

HADDOW, A. J. (1956) Observations on the biting-habits of African mosquitoes in the genus *Eretmapodites* Theobald. *Bull. Ent. Res.* **46**, 761–772.

HADDOW, A. J. (1960) Studies on the biting habits and medical importance of East African mosquitoes in the genus *Aëdes*. I. Subgenera *Aëdimorphus, Banksinella* and *Dunnius*. *Bull. Ent. Res.* **50**, 759–779.

HADDOW, A. J. (1961a) Studies on the biting habits and medical importance of East African mosquitoes in the genus *Aëdes*. II. Subgenera *Mucidus, Diceromyia, Finlaya* and *Stegomyia*. *Bull. Ent. Res.* **52**, 317–351.

HADDOW, A. J. (1961b) Entomological studies from a high tower in Mpanga forest, Uganda. VII. The biting behaviour of mosquitoes and tabanids. *Trans. R. Ent. Soc. Lond.* **113**, 315–335.

HADDOW, A. J. and CORBET, P. S. (1961a) Entomological studies from a high tower in Mpanga forest, Uganda. II. Observations on certain environmental factors at different levels. *Trans. R. Ent. Soc. Lond.* **113**, 257–269.

HADDOW, A. J. and CORBET, P. S. (1961b) Entomological studies from a high tower in Mpanga forest, Uganda. V. Swarming activity above the forest. *Trans. R. Ent. Soc. Lond.* **113**, 284–300.

HADDOW, A. J., CORBET, P. S. and GILLETT, J. D. (1960) Laboratory observations on the oviposition-cycle in the mosquito *Aedes (Stegomyia) apicoargenteus* Theobald. *Ann. Trop. Med. Parasit.* **54**, 392–396.

HADDOW, A. J. and DICK, G. W. A. (1948) Catches of biting Diptera in Uganda, with anaesthetized monkeys as bait. *Ann. Trop. Med. Parasit.* **42**, 271–277.

HADDOW, A. J. and GILLETT, J. D. (1957) Observations on the oviposition-cycle of *Aedes (Stegomyia) aegypti* (Linnaeus). *Ann. Trop. Med. Parasit.* **51**, 159–169.

HADDOW, A. J. and GILLETT, J. D. (1958) Laboratory observations on the oviposition-cycle in the mosquito *Taeniorhynchus (Coquillettidia) fuscopennatus* Theobald. *Ann. Trop. Med. Parasit.* **52**, 320–325.

HADDOW, A. J., GILLETT, J. D. and CORBET, P. S. (1959) Laboratory observations on pupation and emergence in the mosquito *Aedes (Stegomyia) aegypti* (Linnaeus). *Ann. Trop. Med. Parasit.* **53**, 123–131.

HADDOW, A. J., GILLETT, J. D. and CORBET, P. S. (1961) Observations on the oviposition-cycle of *Aedes (Stegomyia) aegypti* (Linnaeus), V. *Ann. Trop. Med. Parasit.* **55**, 343–356.

HADDOW, A. J., GILLETT, J. D. and HIGHTON, R. B. (1947) The mosquitoes of Bwamba county, Uganda. V. The vertical distribution and biting-cycle of mosquitoes in rain-forest, with further observations on microclimate. *Bull Ent. Res.* **37**, 301–330, 2 pl.

HAEGER, J. S. (1955) The non-blood feeding habits of *Aedes taeniorhynchus* (Diptera, Culicidae) on Sanibel Island, Florida. *Mosquito News* **15**, 21–26.

HAEGER, J. S. (1960) Behavior preceding migration in the salt-marsh mosquito, *Aedes taeniorhynchus* (Wiedemann). *Mosquito News* **20**, 136–147.

HAEGER, J. S. and PHINIZEE, J. (1959) The biology of the crabhole mosquito, *Deinocerites cancer* Theobald. *Rep. Fla Antimosq. Ass.* **30**, 34–37.

HALCROW, J. G. (1953) Preliminary observations on some possible tarsal sensillae of English mosquitoes. *Entomologist* **86**, 104–105.

HAMON, J., CHAUVET, G. and THÉLIN, L. (1961) Observations sur les méthodes d'évaluation de l'âge physiologique des femelles d'anophèles. *Bull. World Hlth Org.* **24**, 437–443.

HANCE, R. T. (1917) The somatic mitoses of the mosquito *Culex pipiens. J. Morph.* **28**, 579–591.

VAN HANDEL, E. and LUM, P. T. M. (1961) Sex as regulator of triglyceride metabolism in the mosquito. *Science* **134**, 1979–1980.

HARDEN, F. W. and CHUBB, H. S. (1960) Observations of *Aedes taeniorhynchus* dispersal in extreme south Florida and the Everglades National Park. *Mosquito News* **20**, 249–255.

HARKER, J. E. (1958) Diurnal rhythms in the animal kingdom. *Biol. Rev.* **3**, 1–52.

HARKER, J. E. (1961) Diurnal rhythms. *Annu. Rev. Ent.* **6**, 131–144.

HARWOOD, R. F. (1958) Development, structure, and function of coverings of eggs of floodwater mosquitoes. II. Postovarian structure. *Ann. Ent. Soc. Amer.* **51**, 464–471.

HARWOOD, R. F. and HORSFALL, W. R. (1957) Development, structure, and function of covering of eggs of floodwater mosquitoes. I. Ovarian development. *Ann. Ent. Soc. Amer.* **50**, 555–561.

HARWOOD, R. F. and HORSFALL, W. R. (1959) Development, structure, and function of coverings of eggs of floodwater mosquitoes. III. Functions of coverings. *Ann. Ent. Soc. Amer.* **52**, 113–116.

HASSAN, A. A. G. (1944) The structure and mechanism of the spiracular regulatory apparatus in adult Diptera and certain other groups of insects. *Trans. R. Ent. Soc. Lond.* **94**, 103–153, 22 pl.

HASSETT, C. C., DETHIER, V. G. and GANS, J. (1950) A comparison of nutritive values and taste thresholds of carbohydrates for the blowfly. *Biol. Bull. Wood's Hole* **99**, 446–453.

HASSETT, C. C. and JENKINS, D. W. (1951) The uptake and effect of radiophosphorus in mosquitoes. *Physiol. Zoöl.* **24**, 257–266.

HAUFE, W. O. (1952) Observations on the biology of mosquitoes (Diptera: Culicidae) at Goose Bay, Labrador. *Canad. Ent.* **84**, 254–263.

HAUFE, W. O. (1954) The effects of atmospheric pressure on the flight responses of *Aedes aegypti* (L.). *Bull. Ent. Res.* **45**, 507–526.

HAUFE, W. O. (1957) Physical environment and behaviour of immature stages of *Aedes communis* (Deg.) (Diptera: Culicidae) in subarctic Canada. *Canad. Ent.* **89**, 120–139.

HAUFE, W. O. (1958) Quantitative study of the stimulation of flight activity in adult mosquitoes by interaction of physical factors in the environment. *Ph.D. Thesis, University of London.*

HAUFE, W. O. and BURGESS, L. (1956) Development of *Aedes* (Diptera: Culicidae) at Fort Churchill, Manitoba, and prediction of dates of emergence. *Ecology* **37**, 500–519.

HAUFE, W. O. and BURGESS, L. (1960) Design and efficiency of mosquito traps based on visual response to patterns. *Canad. Ent.* **92**, 124–140.

HAYES, R. O. (1953) Studies on the artificial insemination of the mosquito *Aedes aegypti* (Linnaeus). *Mosquito News* **13**, 145–152.

HEADLEE, T. J. (1942) A continuation of the studies of the relative effects on insect metabolism of temperature derived from constant and varied sources. *J. Econ. Ent.* **35,** 785–786.

HEARLE, E. (1929) The life history of *Aedes flavescens* Müller — a contribution to the biology of mosquitoes of the Canadian prairies. *Trans. Roy. Soc. Can.* **23,** 85–102, 6 pl.

HECHT, O. (1929) Die Hautreaktionen auf Insektenstiche als allergische Erscheinungen. *Arch. Schiffs-u. Tropenhyg.* **33,** 364–366.

HECHT, O. (1930) Ueber den Wärmesinn der Stechmücken bei der Eiablage. *Riv. Malariol.* **9,** 706–724.

HECHT, O. (1933) Die Blutnahrung, die Erzeugung der Eier und die Überwinterung der Stechmückenweibchen. *Arch. Schiffs-u. Tropenhyg.* **37,** 125–211.

HEILESEN, G. (1949) Studies on mosquito bites. *Acta Allerg., Kbh.* **2,** 244–267.

HENDERSON, B. E. and SENIOR, L. (1961) Attack rate of *Culex tarsalis* on reptiles, amphibians and small mammals. *Mosquito News* **21,** 29–32.

HENSON, H. (1946) The theoretical aspect of insect metamorphosis. *Biol. Rev.* **21,** 1–14.

HERMS, W. B. and FREEBORN, S. B. (1920) The egg-laying habits of Californian anophelines. *J. Parasit.* **7,** 69–79.

HERMS, W. B. and FROST, F. M. (1932) A comparative study of the eggs of Californian anophelines. *J. Parasit.* **18,** 240–244, 3 pl.

VAN DEN HEUVEL, M. J. (1961) The effect of breeding conditions on the morphology of the adult mosquito, *Aedes aegypti* (L.). *M.Sc. Thesis, University of London.*

HINKE, W. (1961) Das relative postembryonale Wachstum der Hirnteile von *Culex pipiens, Drosophila melanogaster* und *Drosophila*-mutanten. *Z. Morph. Ökol. Tiere* **50,** 81–118.

HINMAN, E. H. (1930) A study of the food of mosquito larvae (Culicidae). *Amer. J. Hyg.* **12,** 238–270.

HINMAN, E. H. (1932) The rôle of solutes and colloids in the nutrition of anopheline larvae. *Amer. J. Trop. Med.* **12,** 263–271.

HINMAN, E. H. (1933a) The rôle of bacteria in the nutrition of mosquito larvae. The growth-stimulating factor. *Amer. J. Hyg.* **18,** 224–236.

HINMAN, E. H. (1933b) Enzymes in the digestive tract of mosquito larvae. *Ann. Ent. Soc. Amer.* **26,** 45–52.

HINTON, H. E. (1959) Origin of indirect flight muscles in primitive flies. *Nature, Lond.* **183,** 557–558.

HO, C. and LO, S. C. (1945) Observations on the swarming behaviour of *Anopheles hyrcanus* var. *sinensis. Exp. Hyg.* **2,** 9–12. (Cited from *Acta Brevia Sinensia* (1945), no. 9, p. 14).

HOCKING, B. (1953a) The intrinsic range and speed of flight of insects. *Trans. R. Ent. Soc. Lond.* **104,** 223–345, 6 pl.

HOCKING, B. (1953b) Notes on the activities of *Aedes* larvae. *Mosquito News* **13,** 77–81.

HOCKING, B. (1954) Flight muscle autolysis in *Aedes communis* (De Geer). *Mosquito News* **14,** 121–123.

HODAPP, C. J. (1960) The mechanism of terminalia rotation in male *Aedes aegypti* (Linnaeus). *M.S. Thesis, University of Maryland,* 43 pp.

HODAPP, C. J. and JONES, J. C. (1961) The anatomy of the adult male reproduction system of *Aedes aegypti* (Linnaeus) (Diptera, Culicidae). *Ann. Ent. Soc. Amer.* **54,** 832–844.

HODGSON, E. S. (1957) Electrophysiological studies of arthropod chemoreception. II. Responses of labellar chemoreceptors of the blowfly to stimulation by carbo-hydrates. *J. Insect. Physiol.* **1**, 240–247.

HODGSON, E. S. and ROEDER, K. D. (1956) Electrophysiological studies of arthropod chemoreception. I. General properties of the labellar chemoreceptors of Diptera. *J. Cell. Comp. Physiol.* **48**, 51–75.

HOLMES, S. J. (1911) The reactions of mosquitoes to light in different periods of their life history. *J. Anim. Behav.* **1**, 29–32.

HOLSTEIN, M. H. (1952) Biologie d'*Anopheles gambiae*. Recherches en Afrique-Occidentale Française. *Monogr. World Hlth Org.* no. 9, 176 pp.

HOOGSTRAAL, H. and KNIGHT, K. L. (1951) Observations on *Eretmapodites silvestris conchobius* Edwards (Culicidae) in the Anglo-Egyptian Sudan. *Amer. J. Trop. Med.* **31**, 659–664.

HOPKINS, G. H. E. (1938) Function of the 'gills' in mosquito larvae. *Nature, Lond.* **142**, 482.

HORSFALL, W. R. (1943) Some responses of the malaria mosquito to light. *Ann. Ent. Soc. Amer.* **36**, 41–45.

HORSFALL, W. R. (1956) Eggs of floodwater mosquitoes III (Diptera, Culicidae). Conditioning and hatching of *Aedes vexans*. *Ann. Ent. Soc. Amer.* **49**, 66–71.

HORSFALL. W. R. and ANDERSON, J. F. (1961) Suppression of male characteristics of mosquitoes by thermal means. *Science* **133**, 1830.

HORSFALL, W. R. and FOWLER, H. W. (1961) Eggs of floodwater mosquitoes. VIII. Effect of serial temperatures on conditioning of eggs of *Aedes stimulans* Walker (Diptera: Culicidae). *Ann. Ent. Soc. Amer.* **54**, 664–666.

HORSFALL, W. R., HENDERSON, L. M. and LUM, P. T. M. (1957) Eggs of floodwater mosquitoes (Diptera: Culicidae) VI. Effect of metabolites on latent embryos in uncapped eggs. *Proc. Soc. Exp. Biol. Med.* **95**, 828–830.

HORSFALL, W. R., LUM, P. T. M. and HENDERSON, L. M. (1958) Eggs of floodwater mosquitoes (Diptera:Culicidae). V. Effect of oxygen on hatching of intact eggs. *Ann. Ent. Soc. Amer.* **51**, 209–213.

HOSOI, T. (1954a) Egg production in *Culex pipiens pallens* Coquillett. III. Growth and degeneration of ovarian follicles. *Jap. J. Med. Sci. Biol.* **7**, 111–127.

HOSOI, T. (1954b) Egg production in *Culex pipiens pallens* Coquillett. IV. Influence of breeding conditions on wing length, body weight and follicle production. *Jap. J. Med. Sci. Biol.* **7**, 129–134.

HOSOI, T. (1954c) Mechanism enabling the mosquito to ingest blood into the stomach and sugary fluids into the oesophageal diverticula. *Annot. Zool. Jap.* **27**, 82–90.

HOSOI, T. (1959) Identification of blood components which induce gorging of the mosquito. *J. Insect Physiol.* **3**, 191–218.

HOSSELET, C. (1925) Les oenocytes de *Culex annulatus* et l'étude de leur chondriome au cours de la sécrétion. *C. R. Acad. Sci., Paris* **180**, 399–401.

HOVANITZ, W. (1946) Comparisons of mating behaviour, growth rate, and factors influencing egg-hatching in South American *Haemagogus* mosquitoes. *Physiol. Zoöl.* **19**, 35–53.

HOWARD, L. O., DYAR, H. G. and KNAB, F. (1912) *The Mosquitoes of North and Central America and the West Indies*. Vol. I. Carnegie Institution, Washington.

HOWLAND, L. J. (1930) The nutrition of mosquito larvae, with special reference to their algal food. *Bull. Ent. Res.* **21**, 431–440, 1 pl.

HOWLETT, F. M. (1910) The influence of temperature upon the biting of mosquitoes. *Parasitology* **3**, 479–484.

HUDSON, B. N. A. (1956) The behaviour of the female mosquito in selecting water for oviposition. *J. Expl Biol.* **33**, 478–492.

HUDSON, A., BOWMAN, L. and ORR, C. W. M. (1960) Effects of absence of saliva on blood feeding by mosquitoes. *Science* **131**, 1730–1731.

HUDSON, A., McKIEL, J. A., WEST, A. S. and BOURNS, T. K. R. (1958) Reactions to mosquito bites. *Mosquito News* **18**, 249–252.

HUFF, C. G. (1934) Comparative studies on susceptible and insusceptible *Culex pipiens* in relation to infections with *Plasmodium cathemerium* and *P. relictum*. *Amer. J. Hyg.* **19**, 123–147.

HUFFAKER, C. B. (1944) The temperature relations of the immature stages of the malarial mosquito, *Anopheles quadrimaculatus,* Say, with a comparison of the developmental power of constant and variable temperatures in insect metabolism. *Ann. Ent. Soc. Amer.* **37**, 1–27.

HULST, F. A. (1906) The histolysis of the musculature of *Culex pungens* during metamorphosis. *Biol. Bull. Wood's Hole* **11**, 277–304, 2 pl.

HUNDERTMARK, A. (1938) Ueber das Luftfeuchtigkeitsunterscheidungsvermögen und die Lebensdauer der 3 in Deutschland vorkommenden Rassen von *Anopheles maculipennis (atroparvus, messeae, typicus)* bei verschiedenen Luftfeuchtigkeitsgraden. *Z. Angew. Ent.* **25**, 125–141.

HUNDERTMARK, A. (1941) Versuche und Beobachtungen über das Verhalten von *Anopheles maculipennis* bei verschiedener Luftfeuchtigkeit und Temperatur. *Z. Angew. Ent.* **27**, 667–696.

HUNDERTMARK, A. and MARTINI, E. (1938) Ueber das Helligkeitsunterscheidungsvermögen von *Anopheles maculipennis. Anz. Schädlingsk.* **14**, 25–30.

HURLBUT, H. S. (1938) Further notes on the overwintering of the eggs of *Anopheles walkeri* with a description of the eggs. *J. Parasit.* **24**, 521–526.

HURLBUT, H. S. (1943) The rate of growth of *Anopheles quadrimaculatus* in relation to temperature. *J. Parasit.* **29**, 107–113.

HURST, C. H. (1890a) The pupal stage of *Culex. Stud. Biol. Lab. Owens Coll.* **2**, 47–71, 1 pl.

HURST, C. H. (1890b) The post-embryonic development of a gnat (*Culex*). *Proc. Lpool. Biol. Soc.* **4**, 170–191, 1 pl.

HUXLEY, J. S. (1932) *Problems of Relative Growth*. Methuen, London.

IDRIS, B. E. M. (1960a) Die Entwicklung im normalen Ei von *Culex pipiens* L. (Diptera). *Z. Morph. Ökol. Tiere.* **49**, 387–429.

IDRIS, B. E. M. (1960b) Die Entwicklung im geschnürten Ei von *Culex pipiens* L. (Diptera). *Wilhelm Roux' Arch. Entw.Mech. Organ.* **152**, 230–262.

ILTIS, W. G. and ZWEIG, G. (1962) Surfactant in apical drop of eggs of some culicine mosquitoes. *Ann. Ent. Soc. Amer.* **55**, 409–415.

IMMS, A. D. (1907) On the larval and pupal stages of *Anopheles maculipennis,* Meigen. Part I. The larva. *J. Hyg.* **7**, 291–318, 2 pl.

IMMS, A. D. (1908) On the larval and pupal stages of *Anopheles maculipennis,* Meigen. Part II. The larva. *Parasitology* **1**, 103–133, 2 pl.

INGRAM, R. L. (1954) A study of the bionomics of *Aedes (Stegomyia) polynesiensis* Marks under laboratory conditions. *Amer. J. Hyg.* **60**, 169–185.

IRREVERRE, F. and TERZIAN, L. A. (1959) Nitrogen partition in excreta of three species of mosquitoes. *Science* **129**, 1358–1359.

ISMAIL, I. A. H. (1962) Sense organs in the antennae of *Anopheles maculipennis atroparvus* (v. Thiel), and their possible function in relation to the attraction of female mosquito to man. *Acta Trop., Basel* **19**, 1–58.

IVANOVA, L. V. (1936a) État de repos et mouvements de la larve d'*Anopheles maculipennis messeae* Fall. *Med. Parasit., Moscow* **5**, 474–484. (In Russian with French summary).

IVANOVA, L. V. (1936b) Sur l'influence de la lumière sur la conduite des larves d'*Anopheles maculipennis* Mg. *Med. Parasit., Moscow* **5**, 485–499. (In Russian with French summary).

IVANOVA, L. V. (1940) The influence of temperature on the behaviour of the *Anopheles maculipennis* larvae. *Med. Parasit., Moscow* **9**, 58–70. (In Russian with English summary).

IVANOVA-KAZAS, O. M. (1949) Embryonic development of *Anopheles maculipennis* Mg. *Izv. Akad. Nauk SSSR* (ser. Biol.) 1949 (2), 140–170.

IYENGAR, M. O. T. and MENON, M. A. U. (1948) Notes on *Harpagomyia genurostris* Leicester (Dipt. Culicidae). *Proc. R. Ent. Soc. Lond.* (A). **23**, 39–43.

JACKSON, N. (1953) Observations on the feeding habits of a predaceous mosquito larva, *Culex (Lutzia) tigripes* Granpré and Charmoy (Diptera). *Proc. R. Ent. Soc. Lond.* (A). **28**, 153–159.

JANISCH, E. (1932) The influence of temperature on the life-history of insects. *Trans. Ent. Soc. Lond.* **8**, 137–168.

JAYEWICKREME, S. H. (1953) Nocturnal mating in *Taeniorhynchus (Mansonioides) uniformis* (Theobald). *Nature, Lond.* **171**, 577.

JEFFERY, G. M. (1956) Blood meal volume in *Anopheles quadrimaculatus, A. albimanus* and *Aedes aegypti. Exp. Parasit.* **5**, 371–375.

JENSEN, D. V. and JONES, J. C. (1957) The development of the salivary glands in *Anopheles albimanus* Wiedemann (Diptera, Culicidae). *Ann. Ent. Soc. Amer.* **50**, 464–469.

JETTMAR, H. M., LIEB, F. and EXNER, H. (1949) Über die Beeinflussung der winterlichen Einstellung von Anophelenlarven durch entwicklungsfördernde Substanzen. *Z. Vit. Horm. Fermentforsch.* **3**, 213–235.

JOBLING, B. (1935) The effect of light and darkness on oviposition in mosquitoes. *Trans. R. Soc. Trop. Med. Hyg.* **29**, 157–166.

JOBLING, B. (1937) The development of mosquitoes in complete darkness. *Trans. R. Soc. Trop. Med. Hyg.* **30**, 467–474.

JOHNSTON, C. (1855) Auditory apparatus of the *Culex* mosquito. *Quart. J. Micr. Sci.* **3**, 97–102, 1 pl.

JONES, J. C. (1952) Prothoracic aortic sinuses in *Anopheles, Culex,* and *Aedes. Proc. Ent. Soc. Wash.* **54**, 244–246.

JONES, J. C. (1953a) On the heart in relation to circulation of hemocytes in insects. *Ann. Ent. Soc. Amer.* **46**, 366–372.

JONES, J. C. (1953b) Some biometrical constants for *Anopheles quadrimaculatus* Say larvae in relation to age within stadia. *Mosquito News* **13**, 243–247.

JONES, J. C. (1954) The heart and associated tissues of *Anopheles quadrimaculatus* Say (Diptera: Culicidae). *J. Morph.* **94**, 71–123.

JONES, J. C. (1956a) A study of normal heart rates in intact *Anopheles quadrimaculatus* Say larvae. *J. Exp. Zool.* **131**, 223–233.

JONES, J. C. (1956b) Effects of different gas concentrations on heart rates of intact *Anopheles quadrimaculatus* Say larvae. *J. Exp. Zool.* **131**, 257–265.

JONES, J. C. (1956c) Effects of salts on *Anopheles* heart rates. *J. Exp. Zool.* **133**, 125–144.

JONES, J. C. (1956d) Effects of drugs on *Anopheles* heart rates. *J. Exp. Zool.* **133**, 573–588.

JONES, J. C. (1957) Effects of various poisons on *Anopheles* heart rates. *Mosquito News* **17**, 214–215.

JONES, J. C. (1960) The anatomy and rhythmical activities of the alimentary canal of *Anopheles* larvae. *Ann. Ent. Soc. Amer.* **53**, 459–474.

JUDSON, C. L. (1960) The physiology of hatching of aedine mosquito eggs: hatching stimulus. *Ann. Ent. Soc. Amer.* **53**, 688–691.

KALMUS, H. (1946) Lack of optomotor reactions in a white-eyed mutant of *Culex molestus*. *Nature, Lond.* **157**, 512.

KALMUS, H. (1958) Responses of insects to polarized light in the presence of dark reflecting surfaces. *Nature, Lond.* **182**, 1526–1527.

KALMUS, H. and HOCKING, B. (1960) Behaviour of *Aedes* mosquitos in relation to blood-feeding and repellents. *Ent. Exp. appl.* **3**, 1–26.

KARAMCHANDANI, P. V. (1935) The effect of heat and atmospheric humidity on all stages of *Culex fatigans*. *Rec. Malar. Surv. India* **5**, 23–38.

KARTMAN, L. and REPASS, R. P. (1952) The effects of desiccation on the eggs of *Anopheles quadrimaculatus* Say. *Mosquito News* **12**, 107–110.

KEENER, G. G. (1945) Detailed observations on the life history of *Anopheles quadrimaculatus*. *J. Nat. Malar. Soc.* **4**, 263–270.

KEILIN, D. (1932) On the water reservoir of a horse-chestnut tree. *Parasitology* **24**, 280–282, 1 pl.

KEILIN, D., TATE, P. and VINCENT, M. (1935) The perispiracular glands of mosquito larvae. *Parasitology* **27**, 257–262.

KENNEDY, J. S. (1939) The visual responses of flying mosquitoes. *Proc. Zool. Soc. Lond.* (A) **109**, 221–242.

KENNEDY, J. S. (1942) On water-finding and oviposition by captive mosquitoes. *Bull. Ent. Res.* **32**, 279–301.

KENNEDY, J. S. (1961) A turning point in the study of insect migration. *Nature, Lond.* **189**, 785–791.

KEPPLER, E. (1958a) Über das Richtungshören von Stechmücken. *Z. Naturf.* **13b**, 280–284.

KEPPLER, E. (1958b) Zum Hören von Stechmücken. *Z. Naturf.* **13b**, 285–286.

KERSHAW, W. E., CHALMERS, T. A. and LAVOIPIERRE, M. M. J. (1954) Studies on arthropod survival. I. The pattern of mosquito survival in laboratory conditions. *Ann. Trop. Med. Parasit.* **48**, 442–450.

KETTLE, D. S. (1948) The growth of *Anopheles sergenti* Theobald (Diptera, Culicidae), with special reference to the growth of the anal papillae in varying salinities. *Ann. Trop. Med. Parasit.* **42**, 5–29.

KHELEVIN, N. V. (1958a) The effect of environmental factors on the induction of embryonic diapause and on the number of generations in a season of *Aedes caspius dorsalis* Mg. (Diptera, Culicidae). Effect of temperature on the induction of embryonic diapause in *Aedes caspius dorsalis* Mg. *Ent. Rev.* **37**, 19–35.

KHELEVIN, N. V. (1958b) Biology of the eggs of *Aedes flavescens*. *Med. Parasit., Moscow* **27**, 51–57. (In Russian with English summary).

KHELEVIN, N. V. (1959) The seasonal character of hatching and the embryonic diapause in *Aedes caspius dorsalis* Mg. (Diptera, Culicidae). *Ent. Rev.* **38**, 355–365.

KHELEVIN, N. V. (1961) External factors influencing hatching of the larvae and the number of generations of *Aedes vexans* Meig. (Diptera, Culicidae). *Med. Parasit., Moscow* **30**, 43–48. (In Russian, English summary p. 122).

KING, W. V., BRADLEY, G. H., SMITH, C. N. and McDUFFIE, W. C. (1960) *A Handbook of the Mosquitoes of the Southeastern United States.* U.S. Dept. Agric. Handbook No. 173, 188 pp.

KINGSCOTE, A. A. and FRANCIS, J. D. (1954) Studies on the attractancy of laboratory rats to *Aedes aegypti* L. *Tech. Rep. no. 5, Environmental Protection Section, Defence Res. Board, Canada.* 23 pp.

KIRK, H. B. (1923) Notes on the mating-habits and early life-history of the culicid *Opifex fuscus* Hutton. *Trans. Proc. N. Z. Inst.* **54,** 400–406.

KIRKPATRICK, T. W. (1925) *The Mosquitoes of Egypt.* Government Press, Cairo.

KITZMILLER, J. B. (1953) Mosquito genetics and cytogenetics. *Rev. bras. Malariol.* **5,** 285–359.

KITZMILLER, J. B. (1959) Parthenogenesis in *Culex fatigans. Science* **129,** 837–838.

KITZMILLER, J. B. and LAVEN, H. (1958) Tests for multiple fertilization in *Culex* mosquitoes by the use of genetic markers. *Amer. J. Hyg.* **67,** 207–213.

KLIGLER, I. J. (1928) Further studies on the epidemiology of malaria in Palestine. *Amer. J. Trop. Med.* **8,** 183–198.

KLIGLER, I. J. (1932) Flight of *Anopheles* mosquitoes. *Trans. R. Soc. Trop. Med. Hyg.* **26,** 73–88.

KLIGLER, I. J. and MER, G. (1930) Studies on malaria: VI. Long-range dispersion of *Anopheles* during the prehibernating period. *Riv. Malariol.* **9,** 363–374.

KLIGLER, I. J. and THEODOR, O. (1925) Effect of salt concentration and reaction on the development of *Anopheles* larvae. *Bull. Ent. Res.* **16,** 45–49.

KNAB, F. (1906) Goeldi's "Os mosquitos no Pará". *J. N.Y. Ent. Soc.* **14,** 57–76.

KOCH, A. (1956) The experimental elimination of symbionts and its consequences. *Exp. Parasit.* **5,** 481–518.

KOCH, H. J. (1938) The absorption of chloride ions by the anal papillae of Diptera larvae. *J. Exp. Biol.* **15,** 152–160.

KOZHEVNIKOVA, S. M. (1953) The survival of mosquitoes of the genus *Anopheles* to an epidemiologically dangerous age under the conditions found in Stalingrad. *Med. Parasit., Moscow* **22,** 500–505. (In Russian).

KRISHNAMURTHY, B. S. and LAVEN, H. (1961) A note on inheritance of autogeny in *Culex* mosquitos. *Bull. World Hlth Org.* **24,** 675–677.

KROGH, A. (1941) *The Comparative Physiology of Respiratory Mechanisms.* University of Pennsylvania Press.

KÜHLHORN, F. (1958) Untersuchungen über die Ernährung der Larven von *Anopheles bifurcatus* Meigen (Dipt. Culicidae). *Nachr. Bayer. Ent.* **7,** 118–124.

KURIHARA, Y. (1959) Synecological analysis of the biotic community in microcosm. VIII. Studies on the limiting factor in determining the distribution of mosquito larvae in the polluted water of bamboo container, with special reference to relation of larvae to bacteria. *Jap. J. Zool.* **12,** 391–400.

LAARMAN, J. J. (1955) The host-seeking behaviour of the malaria mosquito *Anopheles maculipennis atroparvus. Acta Leidensia* **25,** 1–144.

LAARMAN, J. J. (1958) The host-seeking behaviour of anopheline mosquitoes. *Trop. Geogr. Med.* **10,** 293–305.

LAARMAN, J. J. (1959) Host-seeking behaviour of malaria mosquitoes. *Proc. Fifteenth Int. Congr. Zool.* (1958) pp. 648–649.

LACOUR, P. (1937) Étude biologique de la race rurale de *Culex pipiens* L. *Thesis, Clermont-Ferrand.*

LAIRD, M. (1956) Studies of mosquitoes and freshwater ecology in the south Pacific. *Bull. Roy. Soc. N.Z.* no. 6, 213 pp.

LAL, R. (1953) Notes on the effect of temperature on the developmental stages of *Anopheles subpictus* Grassi and *Anopheles stephensi* Liston. *Indian J. Ent.* **15**, 97–106.

LAMBORN, W. A. (1922) The bionomics of some Malayan anophelines. *Bull. Ent. Res.* **13**, 129–149.

LAMBREMONT, E. N. (1960) Postemergence changes of enzyme activity in the mosquito, *Aedes aegypti* (L.). *Ann. Ent. Soc. Amer.* **53**, 86–91.

LANDOIS, H. (1874) *Thierstimmen.* Freiburg.

LANG, C. A. (1956) The influence of mating on egg production by *Aedes aegypti*. *Amer. J. Trop. Med. Hyg.* **5**, 909–914.

LANG, C. A. (1958) Zinc uptake by the mosquito. *Anat. Rec.* **132**, 468.

LANG, C. A. (1959) Cytochrome *c* reductase activities during development. *Exp. Cell Res.* **17**, 516–518.

LANG, C. A. (1961) TPNH-cytochrome *c* reductase in the mosquito. *Fed. Prod.* **20** (1), 47b.

LANG, W. D. (1920) *A Handbook of British Mosquitoes.* British Museum (Natural History), London.

LARSEN, E. B. (1948) Observations on the activity of some culicids. Studies on the activity of insects IV. *Ent. Medd.* **25**, 263–277.

LARSEN, J. R. (1958) Hormone-induced ovarian development in mosquitoes. *Science* **127**, 587–588.

LARSEN, J. R. and BODENSTEIN, D. (1959) The humoral control of egg maturation in the mosquito. *J. Exp. Zool.* **140**, 343–381.

LAURENCE, B. R. (1959) Oviposition by *Mansonioides* mosquitoes in the Gambia, West Africa. *Proc. R. Ent. Soc. Lond.* (A) **34**, 161–170.

LAURENCE, B. R. (1960) The biology of two species of mosquito, *Mansonia africana* (Theobald) and *Mansonia uniformis* (Theobald), belonging to the subgenus *Mansonioides* (Diptera, Culicidae). *Bull. Ent. Res.* **51**, 491–517.

LAVEN, H. (1955) Erbliche Intersexualität bei *Culex pipiens*. *Naturwissenschaften* **42**, 517.

LAVEN, H. (1956) Induzierte Parthenogenese bei *Culex pipiens*. *Naturwissenschaften* **43**, 116–117.

LAVEN, H. (1957a) Vererbung durch Kerngene und das Problem der ausserkaryotischen Vererbung bei *Culex pipiens*. I. Kernvererbung. *Z. Indukt. Abstamm.-u. Vererb Lehre.* **88**, 443–477.

LAVEN, H. (1957b) Vererbung durch Kerngene und das Problem der ausserkaryotischen Vererbung bie *Culex pipiens*. II. Ausserkaryotische Vererbung. *Z. Indukt. Abstamm.-u. Vererb Lehre.* **88**, 478–516.

LAVEN, H. (1959) Speciation by cytoplasmic isolation in the *Culex pipiens*-complex. *Cold Spr. Harb. Sym. Quant. Biol.* **24**, 166–173.

LAVEN, H. and CHEN, P. S. (1956) Genetische und papierchromatographische Untersuchungen an einer letalen Mutante von *Culex pipiens*. *Z. Naturf.* **11b**, 273–276.

LAVOIPIERRE, M. M. J. (1958a) Biting behaviour of mated and unmated females of an African strain of *Aedes aegypti*. *Nature, Lond.* **181**, 1781–1782.

LAVOIPIERRE, M. M. J. (1958b) Presence of a factor inhibiting biting in *Aedes aegypti*. *Nature, Lond.* **182**, 1567–1568.

LAVOIPIERRE, M. M. J. (1961) Blood-feeding, fecundity and ageing in *Aedes aegypti* var. *queenslandensis. Nature, Lond.* **191**, 575–576.

LEA, A. O. and DELONG, D. M. (1958) Studies on the nutrition of *Aedes aegypti* larvae. *Proc. Tenth Int. Congr. Ent.* (1956) **2**, 299–302.

LEA, A. O., DIMOND, J. B. and DELONG, D. M. (1956) A chemically defined medium for rearing *Aedes aegypti* larvae. *J. Econ. Ent.* **49**, 313–315.

LEA, A. O., DIMOND, J. B. and DeLONG, D. M. (1958) Some nutritional factors in egg production by *Aedes aegypti*. *Proc. Tenth Int. Congr. Ent.* (1956) **3**, 793–796.

LEES, A. D. (1955) *The Physiology of Diapause in Arthropods*. Cambridge University Press.

LEESON, H. S. (1931) Anopheline mosquitos in Southern Rhodesia 1926–1928. *Mem. Lond. Sch. Hyg. Trop. Med.* no. 4, ix+55 pp., 15 pl.

LEESON, H. S. (1939) Longevity of *Anopheles maculipennis* race *atroparvus,* van Thiel, at controlled temperature and humidity after one blood meal. *Bull. Ent. Res.* **30**, 295–301.

LEFTWICH, A. W. (1954) Vision and blindness in mosquito larvae as indicated by the submerging reflex. *Proc. R. Ent. Soc. Lond.* (A) **29**, 156–162.

LE PRINCE, J. A. and ORENSTEIN, A. J. (1916) *Mosquito Control in Panama*. Putnam's, New York and London.

LEWIS, D. J. (1933) Observations on *Aedes aegypti, L.* (Dipt. Culic.) under controlled atmospheric conditions. *Bull. Ent. Res.* **24**, 363–372.

LEWIS, D. J. (1939) The seasonal and geographical distribution of *Anopheles maculipennis* in Albania. *Riv. Malariol.* **18**, 237–248, 2 pl.

LEWIS, D. J. (1949) Tracheal gills in some African culicine mosquito larvae. *Proc. R. Ent. Soc. Lond.* (A) **24**, 60–66.

LICHTENSTEIN, E. P. (1948) Growth of *Culex molestus* under sterile conditions. *Nature, Lond.* **162**, 227.

LILES, J. N. and DeLONG, D. M. (1960) The longevity and productivity of adult male and female *Aedes aegypti* when reared separately and together on three different diets. *Ann. Ent. Soc. Amer.* **53**, 277–280.

LOVE, G. J. and SMITH, W. W. (1957) Preliminary observations on the relation of light trap collections to mechanical sweep net collections in sampling mosquito populations. *Mosquito News* **17**, 9–14.

LOVE, G. J. and WHELCHEL, J. G. (1955) Photoperiodism and the development of *Aedes triseriatus* (Diptera: Culicidae). *Ecology* **36**, 340–342.

LOVE, G. J. and WHELCHEL, J. G. (1957) Lethal effects of high temperatures on the immature stages of *Anopheles quadrimaculatus*. *Ecology* **38**, 570–576.

LUM, P. T. M. (1961a) The reproductive system of some Florida mosquitoes. I. The male reproductive tract. *Ann. Ent. Soc. Amer.* **54**, 397–401.

LUM, P. T. M. (1961b) The reproductive system of some Florida mosquitoes. II. The male accessory glands and their role. *Ann. Ent. Soc. Amer.* **54**, 430–433.

LUMSDEN, W. H. R. (1947) Observations on the effect of micro-climate on biting by *Aëdes aegypti* (L.) (Dipt., Culicid.), *J. Exp. Biol.* **24**, 361–373.

LUMSDEN, W. H. R. (1951) The night-resting habits of monkeys in a small area on the edge of the Semliki Forest, Uganda. A study in relation to the epidemiology of sylvan yellow fever. *J. Anim. Ecol.* **20**, 11–32.

LUMSDEN, W. H. R. (1952) The crepuscular biting activity of insects in the forest canopy in Bwamba, Uganda. A study in relation to the sylvan epidemiology of yellow fever. *Bull. Ent. Res.* **42**, 721–760.

LUND, H. O. (1942) Studies on the choice of a medium for oviposition by *Anopheles quadrimaculatus* Say. *J. Nat. Malar. Soc.* **1**, 101–111.

MACAN, T. T. (1950) The anopheline mosquitoes of Iraq and North Persia. *Mem. Lond. Sch. Hyg. Trop. Med.* no. 7, 109–223.

MACAN, T. T. (1961) Factors that limit the range of freshwater animals. *Biol. Rev.* **36**, 151–198.

McCLELLAND, G. A. H. (1958) Studies on oviposition of mosquitoes in the field by the use of bamboo pots. *Rep. E. Afr. Virus Res. Inst.* 1957–1958, 22–24.

McClelland, G. A. H. (1959) Observations on the mosquito, *Aedes* (*Stegomyia*) *aegypti* (L.), in East Africa. I. The biting cycle in an outdoor population at Entebbe, Uganda. *Bull. Ent. Res.* **50**, 227–235.

McClelland, G. A. H. (1960a) Observations on the mosquito, *Aedes* (*Stegomyia*) *aegypti* (L.) in East Africa. II. The biting cycle in a domestic population on the Kenya coast. *Bull. Ent. Res.* **50**, 687–696.

McClelland, G. A. H. (1960b) A preliminary study of the genetics of abdominal colour variations in *Aedes aegypti* (L.) (Diptera, Culicidae). *Ann. Trop. Med. Parasit.* **54**, 305–320.

McClelland, G. A. H. (1962) Sex-linkage in *Aedes aegypti*. *Trans. R. Soc. Trop. Med. Hyg.* **56**, 4.

McDaniel, I. N. and Horsfall, W. R. (1957) Induced copulation of aedine mosquitoes. *Science* **125**, 745.

Macdonald, G. (1952a) The analysis of the sporozoite rate. *Trop. Dis. Bull.* **49**, 569–586.

Macdonald, G. (1952b) The objectives of residual insecticide campaigns. *Trans. R. Soc. Trop. Med. Hyg.* **46**, 213–274.

Macdonald, G. (1957) *The Epidemiology and Control of Malaria*. Oxford University Press, London.

Macdonald, W. W. (1956) *Aëdes aegypti* in Malaya. II. Larval and adult biology. *Ann. Trop. Med. Parasit.* **50**, 399–414.

Macdonald, W. W. (1960) On the systematics and ecology of *Armigeres* subgenus *Leicesteria* (Diptera, Culicidae). *Stud. Inst. Med. Res. F.M.S.* no. 29, pp. 110–153.

Macdonald, W. W. and Traub, R. (1960) An introduction to the ecology of the mosquitoes of the lowland dipterocarp forest of Selangor, Malaya. *Stud. Inst. Med. Res. F.M.S.* no. 29, pp. 79–109.

MacFie, J. W. S. (1915) Observations on the bionomics of *Stegomyia fasciata*. *Bull. Ent. Res.* **6**, 203–229.

MacFie, J. W. S. (1917) The limitations of kerosene as a larvicide, with some observations on the cutaneous respiration of the mosquito larvae. *Bull. Ent. Res.* **7**, 277–295.

MacGregor, M. E. (1921) The influence of the hydrogen-ion concentration in the development of mosquito larvae (preliminary communication). *Parasitology* **13**, 348–351.

MacGregor, M. E. (1929) The significance of the *p*H in the development of mosquito larvae. *Parasitology* **21**, 132–157.

MacGregor, M. E. (1932) The ova of *Aedes* (*Finlaya*) *geniculatus* Olivier. *Parasitology* **24**, 183–184.

MacKenna, R. M. B., Wheatley, V. R. and Wormall, A. (1950) The composition of the surface skin fat ('sebum') from the human forearm. *J. Invest. Derm.* **15**, 33–47.

McKiel, J. A. (1959) Sensitization to mosquito bites. *Canad. J. Zool.* **37**, 341–351.

McKiel, J. A. and Clunie, J. C. (1960) Chromatographic fractionation of the non-dialyzable portion of mosquito extract and intracutaneous reactions of mosquito-bite-sensitive subjects to the separated components. *Canad. J. Zool.* **38**, 479–487.

McKiel, J. A. and West, A. S. (1961a) Nature and causation of insect bite reactions. *Pediatric Clinics N. America* **8**, 795–816.

McKiel, J. A. and West, A. S. (1961b) Effects of repeated exposures of hypersensitive humans and laboratory rabbits to mosquito antigens. *Canad. J. Zool.* **39**, 597–603.

McKINLEY, E. B. and DOUGLASS, M. (1930) Further note on the salivary gland poison of *Aedes aegypti*. *Proc. Soc. Exp. Biol. Med.* **27**, 845–846.

MANEFIELD, T. (1951) Investigations of the preferences shown by *Aëdes (Stegomyia) aegypti* Linn. and *Culex (Culex) fatigans* Wied. for specific types of breeding water. *Proc. Linn. Soc. N.S.W.* **76**, 149–154.

MARCOVITCH, S. (1960) Experiments on prolongation of the life of mosquito larvae by underfeeding. *J. Econ. Ent.* **53**, 169.

MARKOVICH, N. YA. (1941) New data on the biology of *A. bifurcatus* (Observations in North Caucasus). *Med. Parasit., Moscow* **10**, 24–34. (In Russian) (Cited from *Rev. Appl. Ent.* (B) (1943) **31**, 155).

MARKS, E. N. (1954). A review of the *Aedes scutellaris* subgroup with a study of variation in *Aedes pseudoscutellaris* (Theobald) (Diptera: Culicidae). *Bull. Brit. Mus. (Nat. Hist.) Ent.* **3**, 349–414, 1 pl.

MARKS, E. N. (1958) Notes on *Opifex fuscus* Hutton (Diptera: Culicidae) and the scope for further research on it. *New Zealand Ent.* **2**, 20–25.

MARSHALL, J. F. (1938) *The British Mosquitoes*. British Museum (Natural History), London.

MARSHALL, J. F. and STALEY, J. (1932) On the distribution of air in the oesophageal diverticula and intestine of mosquitoes. Its relation to emergence, feeding and hypopygial rotation. *Parasitology* **24**, 368–381.

MARSHALL, J. F. and STALEY, J. (1935) Generic and subgeneric differences in the mouth-parts of male mosquitoes. *Bull. Ent. Res.* **26**, 531–532.

MARSHALL, J. F. and STALEY, J. (1936) Exhibition of 'autogenous' and 'stenogamous' characteristics by *Theobaldia subochrea,* Edwards (Diptera, Culicidae). *Nature, Lond.* **137**, 580–581.

MARTINI, E. and TEUBNER, E. (1933) Ueber das Verhalten von Stechmücken, besonders von *Anopheles maculipennis,* bei verschiedenen Temperaturen und Luftfeuchtigkeiten. *Arch. Schiffs-u. Tropenhyg.* **37**, 1–80.

MASLOW, A. W. (1930) Das kritische Temperaturminimum der überwinternden Mücken. *Arch. Schiffs-u. Tropenhyg.* **34**, 170–173.

MATHESON, R. and HURLBUT, H. S. (1937) Notes on *Anopheles walkeri* Theobald. *Amer. J. Trop. Med.* **17**, 237–243.

MATHIS, M. (1935) Sur la nutrition sanguine et la fécondité de *Stegomyia: Aëdes aegypti*. *Bull. Soc. Pat. Exot.* **28**, 231–234.

MATSUMURA, F. and BROWN, A. W. A. (1961a) Biochemical study of a malathion-tolerant strain of *Aedes aegypti*. *Mosquito News* **21**, 192–194.

MATSUMURA, F. and BROWN, A. W. A. (1961b) Biochemistry of malathion resistance in *Culex tarsalis*. *J. Econ. Ent.* **54**, 1176–1185.

MATTINGLY, P. F. (1957) *The Culicine Mosquitoes of the Indomalayan Area. Part I. Genus Ficalbia Theobald.* British Museum (Natural History), London.

MATTINGLY, P. F., ROZEBOOM, L. E., KNIGHT, K. L., LAVEN, H., DRUMMOND, F. H., CHRISTOPHERS, S. R. and SHUTE, P. G. (1951) The *Culex pipiens* complex. *Trans. R. Ent. Soc. Lond.* **102**, 331–382.

MAXIM, HIRAM S. (1901) Mosquitoes and musical notes. *The Times,* 28 October, p. 11.

MAYER, A. M. (1874) Experiments on the supposed auditory apparatus of the mosquito. *Amer. Nat.* **8**, 577–592.

MAYNE, B. (1926a) Notes on the influence of temperature and humidity on oviposition and early life of *Anopheles*. *Publ. Hlth. Rep., Wash.* **41**, 986–990.

MAYNE, B. (1926b) Report of a survey to determine the malaria prevalence in the Okefenokee swamp. *Publ. Hlth. Rep., Wash.* **41**, 1652–1660.

MAYNE, B. (1928) The influence of relative humidity on the presence of parasites in the insect carrier and the initial seasonal appearance of malaria in a selected area in India. *Indian J. Med. Res.* **15**, 1073–1084.

MAYNE, B. (1930) A study of the influence of relative humidity on the life and infectibility of the mosquito. *Indian J. Med. Res.* **17**, 1119–1137.

MEDNIKOVA, M. V. (1952) Endocrine glands corpora allata and corpora cardiaca of mosquitoes (Fam. Culicidae). *Zool. Zh.* **31**, 676–685. (In Russian).

MEHTA, D. R. (1934) Studies on the longevity of some Indian anophelines. Part I. Survival of *Anopheles subpictus* Grassi under controlled conditions of temperature and humidity. *Rec. Malar. Surv. India* **4**, 261–272.

DE MEILLON, B. (1934) Observations on *Anopheles funestus* and *Anopheles gambiae* in the Transvaal. *Publ. S. Afr. Inst. Med. Res.* **6**, 195–248.

MELLANBY, K. (1932) The influence of atmospheric humidity on the thermal death point of a number of insects. *J. Exp. Biol.* **9**, 222–231.

MELLANBY, K. (1940) The activity of certain arctic insects at low temperatures. *J. Anim. Ecol.* **9**, 296–301.

MELLANBY, K. (1946) Man's reaction to mosquito bites. *Nature, Lond.* **158**, 554.

MELLANBY, K. (1954) Acclimatization and the thermal death point in insects. *Nature, Lond.* **173**, 582.

MELLANBY, K. (1958) The alarm reaction of mosquito larvae. *Ent. Exp. Appl.* **1**, 153–160.

MELLANBY, K. (1960) Acclimatization affecting the position of the cold and heat death points of larvae of *Aedes aegypti* (L.). *Bull. Ent. Res.* **50**, 821–823.

MENON, M. A. U. (1951) On certain little-known external characters of adult mosquitoes and their taxonomic significance. *Proc. R. Ent. Soc. Lond.* (B) **20**, 63–71.

MENON, M. A. U. and TAMPI, M. R. V. (1959) Notes on the feeding and egg-laying habits of *Ficalbia (Mimomyia) chamberlaini,* Ludlow 1904. (Diptera, Culicidae). *Indian J. Malar.* **13**, 13–18.

MER, G. (1931) Notes on the bionomics of *Anopheles elutus,* Edw. (Dipt., Culic.). *Bull. Ent. Res.* **22**, 137–145.

MER, G. (1932) The determination of the age of *Anopheles* by differences in the size of the common oviduct. *Bull. Ent. Res.* **23**, 563–566.

MER, G. G. (1936) Experimental study on the development of the ovary in *Anopheles elutus,* Edw. (Dipt. Culic.). *Bull. Ent. Res.* **27**, 351–359.

MER, G. (1937) Variations saisonnières des caractères de *Anopheles elutus* en Palestine. II. *Bull. Soc. Pat. Exot.* **30**, 38–42.

MER, G., BIRNBAUM, D. and AIOUB, A. (1947) The attraction of mosquitoes by human beings. *Parasitology* **38**, 1–9.

METCALF, R. L. (1945) The physiology of the salivary glands of *Anopheles quadrimaculatus. J. Nat. Malar. Soc.* **4**, 271–278.

METZ, C. W. (1919) Observations on the food of *Anopheles* larvae. *Publ. Hlth. Rep., Wash.* **34**, 1783–1791.

MICKS, D. W., DE CAIRES, P. F. and FRANCO, L. B. (1948) The relationship of exflagellation in avian plasmodia to *p*H and immunity in the mosquito. *Amer. J. Hyg.* **48**, 182–190.

MICKS, D. W., JULIAN, S. R., FERGUSON, M. J. and DUNCAN, D. (1961) Microorganisms associated with mosquitoes: II. Location and morphology of microorganisms in the mid-gut of *Culex fatigans* Wiedemann and certain other species. *J. Insect Path.* **3**, 120–128.

MICKS, D. W., STARR, C. F. and PARTRIDGE, M. H. (1959) The vitamin B content of mosquitoes. *Ann. Ent. Soc. Amer.* **52**, 26–28.

MITROFANOVA, J. (1929) On the growth of the head in the larva of *Anopheles maculipennis,* Meig. *Bull. Ent. Res.* **19**, 361–366.

MÖLLRING, F. K. (1956) Autogene und anautogene Eibildung bei *Culex* L. Zugleich ein Beitrag zur Frage der Unterscheidung autogener und anautogener Weibchen an Hand von Eiröhrenzahl und Flügellänge. *Z. Tropenmed. u. Parasit.* **7**, 15–48.

MORTENSON, E. W. (1950) The use of sodium hypochlorite to study *Aedes nigromaculis* (Ludlow) embryos (Diptera: Culicidae). *Mosquito News* **10**, 211–212.

MUIRHEAD-THOMSON, R. C. (1938) The reactions of mosquitoes to temperature and humidity. *Bull. Ent. Res.* **29**, 125–140.

MUIRHEAD-THOMSON, R. C. (1940a) Studies on the behaviour of *Anopheles minimus.* Part I. The selection of the breeding place and the influence of light and shade. *J. Malar. Inst. India* **3**, 265–294, 9 pl.

MUIRHEAD-THOMSON, R. C. (1940b) Studies on the behaviour of *Anopheles minimus.* Part II. The influence of water movement on the selection of the breeding place. *J. Malar. Inst. India* **3**, 295–322, 4 pl.

MUIRHEAD-THOMSON, R. C. (1940c) Studies on the behaviour of *Anopheles minimus.* Part. III. The influence of water temperature on the choice and suitability of the breeding place. *J. Malar. Inst. India* **3**, 323–348, 3 pl.

MUIRHEAD-THOMSON, R. C. (1941a) Studies on the behaviour of *Anopheles minimus.* Part IV. The composition of the water and the influence of organic pollution and silt. *J. Malar. Inst. India* **4**, 63–102, 2 pl.

MUIRHEAD-THOMSON, R. C. (1941b) Studies on the behaviour of *Anopheles minimus.* Part V. The behaviour of adults in relation to blood feeding and resting in houses. *J. Malar. Inst. India* **4**, 217–245.

MUIRHEAD-THOMSON, R. C. (1942) Studies on the behaviour of *Anopheles minimus.* Part VIII. The naturalistic control of *A. minimus* in shallow earth wells. *J. Malar. Inst. India* **4**, 611–614.

MUIRHEAD-THOMSON, R. C. (1945) Studies on the breeding places and control of *Anopheles gambiae* and *A. gambiae* var. *melas* in coastal districts of Sierra Leone. *Bull. Ent. Res.* **36**, 185–252, 13 pl.

MUIRHEAD-THOMSON, R. C. (1948) Studies on *Anopheles gambiae* and *A. melas* in and around Lagos. *Bull. Ent. Res.* **38**, 527–558, 1 pl.

MUIRHEAD-THOMSON, R. C. (1951a) The distribution of anopheline mosquito bites among different age groups. A new factor in malaria epidemiology. *Brit. Med. J.* **1**, 1114–1117.

MUIRHEAD-THOMSON, R. C. (1951b) *Mosquito Behaviour in Relation to Malaria Transmission and Control in the Tropics.* Arnold, London.

MURTHY, M. R. V. and MICKS, D. W. (1961) Intracellular distribution of TPN-isocitric dehydrogenase activity in susceptible and insecticide-resistant strains of *Aedes aegypti. J. Econ. Ent.* **54**, 513–517.

MUSPRATT, J. (1952) The bionomics of an African *Megarhinus* (Dipt., Culicidae) and its possible use in biological control. *Bull. Ent. Res.* **42**, 355–370.

NATH, V. (1924) Egg-follicle of *Culex. Quart. J. Micr. Sci.* **69**, 151–175, 2 pl.

NATH, V. (1929) Studies on the shape of the Golgi apparatus. 1. Egg-follicle of *Culex. Z. Zellforsch.* **8**, 655–670.

NEVEU-LEMAIRE, M. (1902) Sur les réceptacles séminaux de quelques culicides. *Bull. Soc. Zool. Fr.* **22**, 172–175.

NEWKIRK, M. R. (1955) On the eggs of some man-biting mosquitoes. *Ann. Ent. Soc. Amer.* **48,** 60–66.

NICHOLSON, A. J. (1921) The development of the ovary and ovarian egg of a mosquito, *Anopheles maculipennis,* Meig. *Quart. J. Micr. Sci.* **65,** 395–448, 4 pl.

NIELSEN, E. T. (1958) The initial stage of migration in salt-marsh mosquitoes. *Bull. Ent. Res.* **49,** 305–313, 2 pl.

NIELSEN, E. T. and EVANS, D. G. (1960) Duration of the pupal stage of *Aedes taeniorhynchus* with a discussion of the velocity of development as a function of temperature. *Oikos* **11,** 200–222.

NIELSEN, E. T. and GREVE, H. (1950) Studies on the swarming habits of mosquitoes and other Nematocera. *Bull. Ent. Res.* **41,** 227–258, 3 pl.

NIELSEN, E. T. and HAEGER, J. S. (1954) Pupation and emergence in *Aedes taeniorhynchus* (Wied.). *Bull. Ent. Res.* **45,** 757–768.

NIELSEN, E. T. and HAEGER, J. S. (1960) Swarming and mating in mosquitoes. *Misc. Publ. Ent. Soc. Amer.* **1,** 71–95.

NIELSEN, E. T. and NIELSEN, A. T. (1953) Field observations on the habits of *Aedes taeniorhynchus*. *Ecology* **34,** 141–156.

NIELSEN, E. T. and NIELSEN, H. T. (1958) Observations on mosquitoes in Iraq. *Ent. Medd.* **28,** 282–321.

NIELSEN, H. T. and NIELSEN, E. T. (1962) Swarming of Mosquitoes. Laboratory experiments under controlled conditions. *Ent. Exp. Appl.* **5,** 14–32.

NUTTALL, G. H. F. and SHIPLEY, A. E. (1901, 1902 and 1903) Studies in relation to Malaria. II. The structure and biology of *Anopheles* (*Anopheles maculipennis*). *J. Hyg.* **1,** 45–77 (2 pl.); **1,** 269–276; **1,** 451–484 (3 pl.); **2,** 58–84; **3,** 166–215 (4 pl.).

OELHAFEN, F. (1961) Zur Embryogenese von *Culex pipiens:* Markierungen und Exstirpationen mit UV-Strahlenstich. *Wilhelm Roux' Arch. EntwMech. Organ.* **153,** 120–157.

OFFENHAUSER, W. H. and KAHN, M. C. (1949) The sounds of disease carrying mosquitoes. *J. Acoust. Soc. Amer.* **21,** 259–263.

O'GOWER, A. K. (1955) The influence of the physical properties of a water container surface upon its selection by the gravid females of *Aedes scutellaris scutellaris* (Walker) for oviposition (Diptera, Culicidae). *Proc. Linn. Soc. N.S.W.* **79,** 211–218.

O'GOWER, A. K. (1956) The rate of digestion of human blood by certain species of mosquitoes. *Aust. J. Biol. Sci.* **9,** 125–129.

O'GOWER, A. K. (1957a) The influence of the surface on oviposition by *Aedes aegypti* (Linn.) (Diptera, Culicidae). *Proc. Linn. Soc. N.S.W.* **82,** 240–244.

O'GOWER, A. K. (1957b) The influence of the surface on oviposition by *Aedes albopictus* (Skuse) and *Aëdes scutellaris katherinensis* Woodhill (Diptera, Culicidae). *Proc. Linn. Soc. N.S.W.* **82,** 285–288.

O'GOWER, A. K. (1958) The oviposition behaviour of *Aedes australis* (Erickson) (Diptera, Culicidae). *Proc. Linn. Soc. N.S.W.* **83,** 245–250.

OKA, H. (1955) A morphological study on the growth of the mosquito larvae. *Bull. Yamaguchi Med. School.* **2,** 137–147.

OLIFAN, V. I. (1947) Periodicity in the postembryonic development of *Anopheles maculipennis*. *Dokl. Akad. Nauk SSSR.* **55,** 169–172.

OLIFAN, V. I. (1949) Some regularities in changes of gas exchange in *Anopheles* pupae. *Dokl. Akad. Nauk SSSR.* **65,** 577–580. (In Russian).

OMARDEEN, T. A. (1957) The behaviour of larvae and pupae of *Aedes aegypti* (L.) in light and temperature gradients. *Bull. Ent. Res.* **48,** 349–357.

Omori, N. (1954) On the swarming of *Culex pipiens pallens*. *Jap. J. San. Zool.* **4,** 342–350.

Onishi, A. (1959) Influence of moonlight on mosquito collection with the light trap. *Shikoku Acta Med.* **15,** 1993–1998. (In Japanese with English summary).

O'Rourke, F. J. (1956) Observations on pool and capillary feeding in *Aedes aegypti* (L.). *Nature, Lond.* **177,** 1087–1088.

O'Rourke, F. J. and Murnaghan, M. F. (1953) The cutaneous reaction to the bite of the mosquito *Aedes aegypti* (L.) and its alleviation by the topical application of an antihistaminic cream (pyribenzamine). *J. Allergy* **24,** 120–125.

Orr, C. W. M., Hudson, A. and West, A. S. (1961) The salivary glands of *Aedes aegypti*. Histological-histochemical studies. *Canad. J. Zool.* **39,** 265–272.

Otsuru, M. and Ohmori, Y. (1960) Malaria studies in Japan after World War II. Part II. The research for *Anopheles sinensis* sibling species group. *Jap. J. Exp. Med.* **30,** 33–65.

Owen, W. B. (1937) The mosquitoes of Minnesota, with special reference to their biologies. *Tech. Bull. Minn. Agric. Exp. Sta.* No. 126, 75 pp.

Pal, R. (1943a) On the bionomics of *Anopheles culicifacies*. Pt. I. Longevity under controlled conditions of temperature and humidity. *J. Malar. Inst. India* **5,** 77–85.

Pal, R. (1943b) On the histological structure of the midgut of mosquitoes. *J. Malar. Inst. India* **5,** 247–250, 1 pl.

Pal, R. (1944) Nephrocytes in some Culicidae-Diptera. *Indian J. Ent.* **6,** 143–148, 2 pl.

Pal, R. (1945) On the bionomics of *Anopheles culicifacies* Giles. Part II. The ecology of the immature stages. *J. Malar. Inst. India* **6,** 53–74.

Parker, A. H. (1948) Stimuli involved in the attraction of *Aedes aegypti*, L., to man. *Bull. Ent. Res.* **39,** 387–397.

Peters, H. T. (1943) Studies on the biology of *Anopheles walkeri* Theobald (Diptera: Culicidae). *J. Parasit.* **29,** 117–122.

Peterson, D. G. and Brown, A. W. A. (1951) Studies on the responses of the female *Aëdes* mosquito. Part III. The response of *Aedes aegypti* (L.) to a warm body and its radiation. *Bull. Ent. Res.* **42,** 535–541, 1 pl.

Peyton, E. L. (1956) Biology of the Pacific coast tree hole mosquito *Aedes varipalpus* (Coq.). *Mosquito News* **16,** 220–224.

Phifer, K. O. (1962) A comparative study of the aldolase systems of *Aedes aegypti, Anopheles quadrimaculatus,* and *Culex quinquefasciatus*. *J. Parasit.* **48,** 368–372.

Pittendrigh, C. S. (1950) The ecoclimatic divergence of *Anopheles bellator* and *A. homunculus. Evolution* **4,** 43–63.

Platt, R. B., Collins, C. L. and Witherspoon, J. P. (1957) Reactions of *Anopheles quadrimaculatus* Say to moisture, temperature and light. *Ecol. Monogr.* **27,** 303–324.

Platt, R. B., and Love, G. J. and Williams, E. L. (1958) A positive correlation between relative humidity and the distribution and abundance of *Aedes vexans. Ecology* **39,** 167–169.

Polovodova, V. P. (1947) Changes with age in the female genitalia of *Anopheles* and the age composition of mosquito populations. *Thesis, Moscow.* (Cited by Detinova, 1962).

Polovodova, V. P. (1949) The determination of the physiological age of female *Anopheles,* by the number of gonotrophic cycles completed. *Med. Parasit., Moscow* **18,** 352–355. (In Russian).

Polovodova, V. P. (1953) Innervation of the sexual apparatus and of the hind-gut of the female malarial mosquito. *Zool. Zh.* **32,** 635–637. (In Russian).

POLYZHAEV, V. (1936) La réaction à la lumière chez les femelles hibernantes d'*Anopheles messeae* Fall. *Med. Parasitol., Moscow* **5**, 519–524. (In Russian with French summary).

POWERS, G. E. and HEADLEE, T. J. (1939) How petroleum oil kills certain mosquito eggs. *J. Econ. Ent.* **32**, 219–222.

PRADHAN, S. (1945) Insect population studies. II. Rate of insect development under variable temperature of the field. *Proc. Nat. Inst. Sci. India* **11**, 74–80.

PRADHAN, S. (1946) Insect population studies. IV. Dynamics of temperature effect on insect development. *Proc. Nat. Inst. Sci. India* **12**, 385–404.

PRASHAD, B. (1916a) The halteres of mosquitoes and their function. *Indian J. Med. Res.* **3**, 503–509.

PRASHAD, B. (1916b) Male generative organs of some Indian mosquitoes. *Indian J. Med. Res.* **3**, 497–502, 2 pl.

PRASHAD, B. (1918) The development of the dorsal series of thoracic imaginal buds of the mosquito, and certain observations on the phylogeny of the insects. *Indian J. Med. Res.* **5**, 641–655, 5 pl.

PRATT, H. D. (1944) Studies on the comparative attractiveness of 25-, 50- and 100-watt bulbs for Puerto Rican *Anopheles*. *Mosquito News* **4**, 17–18.

PRATT, H. D. (1948) Influence of the moon on light trap collections of *Anopheles albimanus* in Puerto Rico. *J. Nat. Malar. Soc.* **7**, 212–220.

PRICE, R. D. (1958a) Observations on a unique monster embryo of *Wyeomyia smithii* (Coquillett) (Diptera: Culicidae). *Ann. Ent. Soc. Amer.* **51**, 600–604.

PRICE, R. D. (1958b) Notes on the biology and laboratory colonization of *Wyeomyia smithii* (Coquillett) (Diptera: Culicidae). *Canad. Ent.* **90**, 473–478.

PRINGLE, J. W. S. (1948) The gyroscopic mechanism of the halteres of Diptera. *Phil. Trans.* (B) **233**, 347–384, 1 pl.

PROVOST, M. W. (1952) The dispersal of *Aedes taeniorhynchus*. I. Preliminary studies. *Mosquito News* **12**, 174–190.

PROVOST, M. W. (1957) The dispersal of *Aedes taeniorhynchus*. II. The second experiment. *Mosquito News* **17**, 233–247.

PROVOST, M. W. (1958) Mating and male swarming in *Psorophora* mosquitoes. *Proc. Tenth. Int. Congr. Ent.* (1956) **2**, 553–561.

PROVOST, M. W. (1959) The influence of moonlight on light-trap catches of mosquitoes. *Ann. Ent. Soc. Amer.* **52**, 261–271.

PROVOST, M. W. (1960) The dispersal of *Aedes taeniorhynchus*. III. Study methods for migratory exodus. *Mosquito News* **20**, 148–161.

PROVOST, M. W., LUM, P. T. M. and BRANCH, N. (1961) Rotation of male terminalia in *Aedes taeniorhynchus* (Diptera: Culicidae) as affected by temperature. *Ann. Ent. Soc. Amer.* **54**, 896–900.

PUTNAM, P. and SHANNON, R. C. (1934) The biology of *Stegomyia* under laboratory conditions. II. Egg-laying capacity and longevity of adults. *Proc. Ent. Soc. Wash.* **36**, 217–242.

QUTUBUDDIN, M. (1953) The emergence and sex ratio of *Culex fatigans* Wied. (Diptera, Culicidae) in laboratory experiments. *Bull. Ent. Res.* **43**, 549–565.

RAHM, U. (1956) Zum Problem der Attraktion von Stechmücken durch den Menschen. *Acta. Trop., Basel* **13**, 319–344.

RAHM, U. (1957a) Wichtige Faktoren bei der Attraktion von Stechmücken durch den Menschen. *Rev. Suisse Zool.* **64**, 236–246.

RAHM, U. (1957b) Zur Bedeutung des Duftes und des Schweisses bei der Attraktion von *Aedes aegypti* durch den Menschen. *Acta Trop., Basel* **14**, 208–217.

RAHM, U. (1958a) Die attraktive Wirkung der vom Menschen abgegebenen Duft-stoffe auf *Aedes aegypti* L. *Z. Tropenmed. u. Parasit.* **9**, 146–156.

RAHM, U. (1958b) Die Funktion der Antennen, Palpen und Tarsen von *Aedes aegypti* L. beim Aufsuchen des Wirtes. *Rev. Suisse Zool.* **65**, 779–792.

RAMSAY, J. A. (1950) Osmotic regulation in mosquito larvae. *J. Exp. Biol.* **27**, 145–157, 1 pl.

RAMSAY, J. A. (1951) Osmotic regulation in mosquito larvae: the role of the Malpighian tubules. *J. Exp. Biol.* **28**, 62–73.

RAMSAY, J. A. (1953a) Exchanges of sodium and potassium in mosquito larvae. *J. Exp. Biol.* **30**, 79–89.

RAMSAY, J. A. (1953b) Active transport of potassium by the Malpighian tubules of insects. *J. Exp. Biol.* **30**, 358–369.

RAMSAY, J. A. (1956) Excretion by the Malpighian tubules of the stick insect, *Dixippus morosus* (Orthoptera, Phasmidae): calcium, magnesium, chloride, phosphate and hydrogen ions. *J. Exp. Biol.* **33**, 697–708.

RAO, T. R. (1947) Visual responses of mosquitoes artificially rendered flightless. *J. Exp. Biol.* **24**, 64–78.

RAO, T. R. and RUSSELL, P. F. (1938) Some field observations on the swarming and pairing of mosquitoes, particularly *A. annularis,* in south India. *J. Malar. Inst. India.* **1**, 395–403.

RAO, V. V. (1947) On gonotrophic discordance among certain Indian *Anopheles*. *Indian J. Malar.* **1**, 43–50.

REES, D. M. and ONISHI, K. (1951) Morphology of the terminalia and internal reproductive organs, and copulation in the mosquito, *Culiseta inornata* (Williston). *Proc. Ent. Soc. Wash.* **53**, 233–246.

REEVES, W. C. (1953) Quantitative field studies on a carbon dioxide chemotropism of mosquitoes. *Amer. J. Trop. Med. Hyg.* **2**, 325–331.

REMINGTON, C. L. (1945) The feeding habits of *Uranotaenia lowii* Theobald (Diptera: Culicidae). *Ent. News.* **56**, 32–37 and 64–68.

RENN, C. E. (1941) The food economy of *Anopheles quadrimaculatus* and *A. crucians* larvae. Relationships of the air-water interface and the surface-feeding mechanism. In *A Symposium on Hydrobiology.* University of Wisconsin Press, Madison.

REUTER, J. (1936) Oriënteerend onderzoek naar de oorzaak van het gedrag van *Anopheles maculipennis* Meigen bij de voedselkeuze. *Thesis, Leiden.* 118 pp.

RIBBANDS, C. R. (1946) Moonlight and house-haunting habits of female anophelines in West Africa. *Bull. Ent. Res.* **36**, 395–415.

RIBBANDS, C. R. (1949) Studies on the attractiveness of human populations to anophelines. *Bull. Ent. Res.* **40**, 227–238.

RICHINS, C. A. (1938) The metamorphosis of the digestive tract of *Aedes dorsalis* Meigen. *Ann. Ent. Soc. Amer.* **31**, 74–87.

RICHINS, C. A. (1945) The development of the midgut in the larva of *Aedes dorsalis* Meigen. *Ann. Ent. Soc. Amer.* **38**, 314–320.

RISLER, H. (1953) Das Gehörorgan der Männchen von *Anopheles stephensi* Liston (Culicidae). *Zool. Jb. (Anat. Ont.).* **73**, 165–186.

RISLER, H. (1955) Das Gehörorgan der Männchen von *Culex pipiens* L., *Aedes aegypti* L. und *Anopheles stephensi* Liston (Culicidae), eine vergleichend morphologische Untersuchung. *Zool. Jb. (Anat. Ont.).* **74**, 478–490.

RISLER, H. (1959) Polyploidie und somatische Reduktion in der Larvenepidermis von *Aedes aegypti* L. (Culicidae). *Chromosoma* **10**, 184–209.

RISLER, H. (1961) Untersuchungen zur somatischen Reduktion in der Metamorphose des Stechmückendarms. *Biol. Zentralbl.* **80,** 413–428.

ROBINSON, G. G. (1939) The mouthparts and their function in the female mosquito, *Anopheles maculipennis. Parasitology* **31,** 212–242.

ROCKWELL, E. M. and JOHNSON, P. (1952) The insect bite reaction. II. Evaluation of the allergic reaction. *J. Invest. Dermatol.* **19,** 137–155.

ROEDER, K. D. (Ed.) (1953) *Insect Physiology.* John Wiley & Sons, Inc., New York.

ROESSLER, P. (1960) Anlockung weiblicher Stechmücken (*Aedes aegypti* L., Culicidae) mit Duftstoffen. *Naturwissenschaften* **47,** 549–550.

ROESSLER, H. P. (1961) Versuche zur geruchlichen Anlockung weiblicher Stechmücken (*Aëdes aegypti* L., Culicidae). *Z. Vergl. Physiol.* **44,** 184–231.

ROGOFF, W. M. (1944) The anatomy and metamorphosis of the cephalic ganglia of the mosquito. *Cornell University Abstracts of Theses* 1943, 291–293.

ROSAY, B. (1959) Gross external morphology of embryos of *Culex tarsalis* Coquillett (Diptera: Culicidae). *Ann. Ent. Soc. Amer.* **52,** 481–484.

ROSAY, B. (1961) Anatomical indicators for assessing the age of mosquitoes: the teneral adult (Diptera: Culicidae). *Ann. Ent. Soc. Amer.* **54,** 526–529.

ROTH, L. M. (1948) A study of mosquito behavior. An experimental laboratory study of the sexual behaviour of *Aedes aegypti* (Linnaeus). *Amer. Midl. Nat.* **40,** 265–352.

ROTH, L. M. (1951) Loci of sensory end-organs used by mosquitoes (*Aedes aegypti* (L.) and *Anopheles quadrimaculatus* Say) in receiving host stimuli. *Ann. Ent. Soc. Amer.* **44,** 59–74.

ROTH, L. M. and WILLIS, E. R. (1952) Possible hygroreceptors in *Aedes aegypti* (L.) and *Blattella germanica* (L.) *J. Morph.* **91,** 1–14.

ROUBAUD, E. (1929) Cycle autogène d'attente et générations hivernales suractives inapparentes chez le moustique commun, *Culex pipiens. C. R. Acad. Sci., Paris* **188,** 735–738.

ROUBAUD, E. (1930) Sur l'existence de races biologiques génétiquement distinctes chez le moustique commun *Culex pipiens. C. R. Acad. Sci., Paris* **191,** 1386–1388.

ROUBAUD, E. (1932a) Des phénomènes d'histolyse larvaire post-nymphale et d'alimentation imaginal autotrophe chez le moustique commun (*Culex pipiens*). *C. R. Acad. Sci., Paris* **194,** 389–391.

ROUBAUD, E. (1932b) Recherches sur les variations trophiques et biologiques des peuplements de l'*Anopheles maculipennis. Bull. Soc. Pat. Exot.* **25,** 755–762.

ROUBAUD, E. (1933) Essai synthétique sur la vie du moustique commun (*Culex pipiens*). L'évolution humaine et les adaptations biologique du moustique. *Ann. Sci. Nat. (Zool.).* **16,** 5–168, 8 pl.

ROUBAUD, E. (1934) Observations sur la fécondité des Anophélines. *Bull. Soc. Pat. Exot.* **27,** 853–854.

ROUBAUD, E. and COLAS-BELCOUR, J. (1933) Observations sur la biologie de l'*Anopheles plumbeus,* II.—L'asthénobiose cyclique hivernale. *Bull. Soc. Pat. Exot.* **26,** 965–972.

ROY, D. N. (1931) On the ovulation of *A. stephensi. Indian J. Med. Res.* **19,** 629–634.

ROY, D. N. (1936) On the role of blood in ovulation in *Aedes aegypti,* Linn. *Bull. Ent. Res.* **27,** 423–429.

ROY, D. N. (1940) Influence of spermathecal stimulation on the physiological activities of *Anopheles subpictus. Nature, Lond.* **145,** 747–748.

ROZEBOOM, L. E. (1935) The relation of bacteria and bacterial filtrates to the development of mosquito larvae. *Amer. J. Hyg.* **21,** 167–179.

Rozeboom, L. E. (1936) The life cycle of laboratory-bred *Anopheles albimanus* Wiede-mann. *Ann. Ent. Soc. Amer.* **29**, 480–489.

Rudolfs, W. (1922) Chemotropism of mosquitoes. *Bull. N.J. Agr. Exp. Sta.* No. 367, 23 pp.

Rudolfs, W. (1923) Observations on the relations between atmospheric conditions and the behaviour of mosquitoes. *Bull. N.J. Agr. Exp. Sta.* No. 338, 32 pp.

Rudolfs, W. (1925) Relation between temperature, humidity and activity of house mosquitoes. *J. N.Y. Ent. Soc.* **33**, 163–169.

Rudolfs, W. and Lackey, J. B. (1929) Effect of food upon phototropism of mosquito larvae. *Amer. J. Hyg.* **10**, 245–252.

Russell, P. F. and Mohan, B. N. (1939) Experimental infections in *Anopheles stephensi* (type) from contrasting larva environments. *Amer. J. Hyg.* **30**, 73–79.

Russell, P. F. and Rao, T. R. (1942a) On the ecology of larvae of *Anopheles culicifacies* Giles, in borrow-pits. *Bull. Ent. Res.* **32**, 341–361, 1 pl.

Russell, P. F. and Rao, T. R. (1942b) On the swarming, mating and ovipositing behavior of *Anopheles culicifacies*. *Amer. J. Trop. Med.* **22**, 417–427.

Russell, P. F. and Rao, T. R. (1942c) Observations on longevity of *Anopheles culici-facies* imagines. *Amer. J. Trop. Med.* **22**, 517–533.

Salt, R. W. (1958) Application of nucleation theory to the freezing of supercooled insects. *J. Insect. Physiol.* **2**, 178–188.

Salt, R. W. (1961) Principles of insect cold-hardiness. *Annu. Rev. Ent.* **6**, 55–74.

Samtleben, B. (1929) Zur Kenntnis der Histologie und Metamorphose des Mittel-darms der Stechmückenlarven. *Zool. Anz.* **81**, 97–109.

Satô, S. (1950) Compound eyes of *Culex pipiens* var. *pallens* Coquillett. (Morphological studies on the compound eye in the mosquito No. I). *Sci. Rep. Tôhoku Univ. (Biol.).* **18**, 331–341.

Satô, S. (1951a) Development of the compound eye of *Culex pipiens* var. *pallens* Coquillett (Morphological studies on the compound eye in the mosquito, No. II). *Sci. Rep. Tôhoku Univ. (Biol.)* **19**, 23–28.

Satô, S. (1951b) Larval eyes of *Culex pipiens* var. *pallens* Coquillett. (Morphological studies on the larval eye in the mosquito No. 1). *Sci. Rep. Tôhoku Univ. (Biol.)* **19**, 29–32.

Satô, S. (1953a) Structure and development of the compound eye of *Aedes* (*Finlaya*) *japonicus* Theobald. (Morphological studies of the compound eye in the mosquito, No. III). *Sci. Rep. Tôhoku Univ. (Biol.)* **20**, 33–44.

Satô, S. (1953b) Structure and development of the compound eye of *Anopheles hyrcanus sinensis* Wiedemann. (Morphological studies on the compound eye in the mosquito, No. IV). *Sci. Rep. Tôhoku Univ. (Biol.)* **20**, 45–53.

Satô, S. (1957) On the dimensional characters of the compound eye of *Culex pipiens* var. *pallens* Coquillett. (Morphological studies on the compound eye in the mosquito, No. V). *Sci. Rep. Tôhoku Univ. (Biol.)* **23**, 83–90.

Satô, S. (1959) Structure and development of the compound eye of *Culex* (*Lutzia*) *vorax* Edwards. (Morphological studies on the compound eye in the mosquito, No. VI). *Sci. Rep. Tôhoku Univ. (Biol.)* **25**, 99–110, 2 pl.

Satô, S. (1960) Structure and development of the compound eye of *Armigeres* (*Armigeres*) *subalbatus* (Coquillett). (Morphological studies on the compound eye in the mosquito, No. VII). *Sci. Rep. Tôhoku Univ. (Biol.)* **26**, 227–238, 2 pl.

Satô, S., Katô, M. and Toriumi, M. (1957) Structural changes of the compound eye of *Culex pipiens* var. *pallens* Coquillett in the process to dark adaptation. *Sci. Rep. Tôhoku Univ. (Biol.)* **23**, 91–100, 1 pl.

SCHAERFFENBERG, B. and KUPKA, E. (1951) Untersuchungen über die geruchliche Orientierung blutsaugender Insekten. I. Über die Wirkung eines Blutduftstoffes auf *Stomoxys* und *Culex*. *Österreich. Zool. Z.* **3,** 410–424.

SCHAERFFENBERG, B. and KUPKA, E. (1959) Der attraktive Faktor des Blutes für blutsaugende Insekten. *Naturwissenschaften* **46,** 457–458.

SCHIEMENZ, H. (1957) Vergleichende funktionell-anatomische Untersuchungen der Kopfmuskulatur von *Theobaldia* und *Eristalis* (Dipt. Culicid. und Syrphid.). *Dtsch. Ent. Z.* **5,** 268–331.

SCHILDMACHER, H. (1950) Darmkanal und Verdauung bei Stechmückenlarven. *Biol. Zbl.* **69,** 390–438.

SCHREIBER, G. and GUEDES, A. S. (1961) Cytological aspects of the taxonomy of anophelines (subgenus *Nyssorhynchus*). *Bull. World Hlth Org.* **24,** 657–658.

SCHREMMER, F. (1950) Morphologische und funktionelle Analyse der Mundteile und des Pharynx der Larve von *Anopheles maculipennis* Meig. *Österreich. Zool. Z.* **2,** 173–222.

SCHUH, J. E. (1951) Some effects of colchicine on the metamorphosis of *Culex pipiens*. *Chromosoma* **4,** 456–469.

SCHWARTZ, P. H. (1961) Behavior of spermatozoa of *Aedes aegypti* (L.). *M. Sc. Thesis, University of Maryland*, 45 pp.

SEATON, D. R. and LUMSDEN, W. H. R. (1941) Observations on the effects of age, fertilization and light on biting by *Aedes aegypti* (L.) in a controlled microclimate. *Ann. Trop. Med. Parasit.* **35,** 23–36.

SEN, P. (1935) Observations on the emergence of anophelines. *Rec. Malar. Surv. India* **5,** 159–171.

SEN, P. (1957) Role of albuminoid ammonia and other factors in the breeding of *Anopheles sundaicus* (Rodenwaldt): a preliminary note. *Mosquito News* **17,** 102.

SEN, P. and DAS GUPTA, S. K. (1958) "Dyar's Law" in the determination of larval instars in mosquitoes. *Bull. Calcutta Sch. Trop. Med.* **6,** 69–70.

SENIOR-WHITE, R. (1926) Physical factors in mosquito ecology. *Bull. Ent. Res.* **16,** 187–248.

SENIOR-WHITE, R. (1928a) Algae and the food of anopheline larvae. *Indian J. Med. Res.* **15,** 969–988.

SENIOR-WHITE, R. (1928b) Physical factors in mosquito ecology. Part II. *Indian J. Med. Res.* **16,** 11–30, 2 pl.

SENIOR-WHITE, R. A. (1953) On the evening biting activity of three neotropical *Anopheles* in Trinidad, British West Indies. *Bull. Ent. Res.* **44,** 451–460.

SHALABY, A. M. (1959) Forced retention of eggs in *Culex* (*Barraudius*) *pusillus* Macq. (Diptera: Culicidae). *Indian J. Malar.* **13,** 199–208, 1 pl.

SHAMBAUGH, G. F. (1954) Protease stimulation by foods in adult *Aedes aegypti* Linn. *Ohio J. Sci.* **54,** 151–160.

SHANNON, R. C. (1931) On the classification of Brazilian Culicidae with special reference to those capable of harboring the yellow fever virus. *Proc. Ent. Soc. Wash.* **33,** 125–164, 7 pl.

SHANNON, R. C. (1935) Malaria studies in Greece. The reaction of anopheline mosquitoes to certain microclimatic factors. *Amer. J. Trop. Med.* **15,** 67–81.

SHANNON, R. C. and HADJINICALAO, J. (1941) Egg production of Greek anophelines in nature. *J. Econ. Ent.* **34,** 300–305.

SHANNON, R. C. and PUTNAM, P. (1934) The biology of *Stegomyia* under laboratory conditions. I. The analysis of factors which influence larval development. *Proc. Ent. Soc. Wash.* **36,** 185–216.

SHELLEY, W. B., HURLEY, H. J. and NICHOLS, A. C. (1953) Axillary odor: experimental study of the role of bacteria, apocrine sweat and deodorants. *Arch. Derm. Syph. N.Y.* **68**, 430–446.

SHIPITSINA, N. K. (1930) On the rôle of the organic colloids of water in the feeding of the larva of *Anopheles maculipennis. Bull. Inst. Rech. Biol. Univ. Perm.* **7**, 171–194.

SHIPITSINA, N. K. (1935) Grandeur maximum et minimum des particules pouvent être avalées par les larves d'*Anopheles maculipennis messeae. Med. Parasit., Moscow* **4**, 381–389.

SHIPITSINA, N. K. (1941) The influence of the density of the powdery pellicle on the filtration of food by the *Anopheles* larva. *Med. Parasit., Moscow* **10**, 396–401.

SHIPITSINA, N. K. (1959) Effect of the shortening of daytime on the initial date of diapause in *Anopheles maculipennis* Mg. *Med. Parasit., Moscow* **28**, 4–17 (In Russian with English summary).

SHISHLIAEVA-MATOVA, Z. S. (1942) Comparative study of Culicinae salivary glands of the Samarkand District. Report I. Histology and comparative morphology of mosquito salivary glands. *Med. Parasit., Moscow* **11** (6), 61–66.

SHLENOVA, M. F. (1938) Vitesse de la digestion du sang par la femelle de l'*Anopheles maculipennis messeae* aux températures effectives constantes. *Med. Parasit., Moscow* **7**, 716–735. (In Russian with French summary.)

SHLENOVA, M. F. (1959) The biology of the principal species of *Aedes* in the forest zone of the European part of the USSR. *Med. Parasit., Moscow* **28**, 193–298. (In Russian with English summary).

SHUTE, G. T. (1958) The mating plug in *Anopheles gambiae. Trans. R. Soc. Trop. Med. Hyg.* **52**, 305.

SHUTE, P. G. (1929) The effect of severe frost on larvae of *Culicella morsitans* (Diptera, Culicidae). *Entomologist* **62**, 243–244.

SHUTE, P. G. (1933a) The life-history and habits of British mosquitoes in relation to their control by antilarval operations. *J. Trop. Med. Hyg.* **36**, 83–88.

SHUTE, P. G. (1933b) A simple method of obtaining eggs of mosquitoes. *Ann. Trop. Med. Parasit.* **27**, 469–470.

SHUTE, P. G. (1935) Agglutination of the red blood-corpuscles of man, animals and birds by the salivary glands of *Anopheles maculipennis. J. Trop. Med. Hyg.* **38**, 277–278.

SHUTE, P. G. (1936) A study of laboratory-bred *Anopheles maculipennis* var. *atroparvus,* with special reference to egg laying. *Ann. Trop. Med. Parasit.* **30**, 11–16.

SHUTE, P. G. (1951) *Culex molestus.* In Mattingly *et al.* (1951), pp. 380–382.

SIMATCHKOVA, M. S. (1936) The factors influencing the distribution of the mosquitoes *A. maculipennis* in the diurnal resting places. *Med. Parasitol., Moscow* **5**, 547–565.

SINGH, K. R. P. (1957) The effect of osmotic pressure on the growth and development of *Aedes aegypti* larvae. *J. Anim. Morph. Physiol.* **4**, 48–53.

SINGH, K. R. P. and BROWN, A. W. A. (1957) Nutritional requirements of *Aedes aegypti* L. *J. Insect Physiol.* **1**, 199–220.

SINGH, K. R. P. and MICKS, D. W. (1957) Synthesis of amino acids in *Aedes aegypti* L. *Mosquito News* **17**, 248–251.

SIPPELL, W. L. and BROWN, A. W. A. (1953) Studies of the responses of the female *Aedes* mosquito. Part V. The role of visual factors. *Bull. Ent. Res.* **43**, 567–574, 1 pl.

SLIFER, E. H. and BRESCIA, V. T. (1960) Permeable sense organs on the antenna of the yellow fever mosquito, *Aedes aegypti* (Linnaeus). *Ent. News* **71**, 221–225, 1 pl.

SMART, M. R. and BROWN, A. W. A. (1956) Studies on the responses of the female *Aedes* mosquito. Part. VII. The effect of skin temperature, hue and moisture on the attractiveness of the human hand. *Bull. Ent. Res.* **47**, 80–100, 1 pl.

SMITH, A. (1958) Outdoor cattle feeding and resting of *A. gambiae* Giles and *A. pharoensis* Theo. in the Pare-Taveta area of East Africa. *E. Afr. Med. J.* **35**, 559–567.

SMITH, J. B. (1901) Some notes on the larval habits of *Culex pungens*. *Ent. News* **12**, 153–157.

SMITH, J. B. (1902) Life-history of *Aedes smithii* Coq. *J. N.Y. Ent. Soc.* **10**, 10–15.

SMITH, J. B. (1904) *Report of the New Jersey State Agriculture Experiment Station upon the Mosquitoes Occurring within the State, their Habits, Life History, etc.* MacQuellish & Quigley, Trenton, N.J.

SMITH-WHITE, S. and WOODHILL, A. R. (1955) The nature and significance of non-reciprocal fertility in *Aedes scutellaris* and other mosquitoes. *Proc. Linn. Soc. N.S.W.* **79**, 163–176.

SNODGRASS, R. E. (1944) The feeding apparatus of biting and sucking insects affecting man and animals. *Smithson. Misc. Coll.* **104** (7), 113 pp.

SNODGRASS, R. E. (1957) A revised interpretation of the external reproductive organs of male insects. *Smithson. Misc. Coll.* **135**, (6) iii+60 pp.

SNODGRASS, R. E. (1959) The anatomical life of the mosquito. *Smithson. Misc. Coll.* **139**, (8) iii+87 pp.

SOTOVALTA, O. (1947) The flight-tone (wing-stroke frequency) of insects. *Acta Ent. Fenn.* **4**, 1–117.

SPEERT, H. (1948) Local action of sex hormones. *Physiol. Rev.* **28**, 23–50.

SPIELMAN, A. (1957) The inheritance of autogeny in the *Culex pipiens* complex of mosquitoes. *Amer. J. Hyg.* **65**, 404–425.

STEIN, W. H. and MOORE, S. (1954) The free amino acids of human blood plasma. *J. Biol. Chem.* **211**, 915–926.

STICH, H. and GRELL, M. (1955) Incorporation of phosphorus-32 into the Malpighian tubes during the metamorphosis of *Culex pipiens*. *Nature, Lond.* **176**, 930–931.

STOBBART, R. H. (1959) Studies on the exchange and regulation of sodium in the larva of *Aedes aegypti* (L.). I. The steady-state exchange. *J. Exp. Biol.* **36**, 641–653.

STOBBART, R. H. (1960) Studies on the exchange and regulation of sodium in the larva of *Aedes aegypti* (L.). II. The net transport and fluxes associated with it. *J. Exp. Biol.* **37**, 594–608.

STOHLER, H. (1957) Analyse des Infektionsverlaufes von *Plasmodium gallinaceum* im Darme von *Aedes aegypti*. *Acta. Trop., Basel* **14**, 302–352.

STONE, A. (1961) A synoptic catalog of the mosquitoes of the world, supplement I (Diptera, Culicidae). *Proc. Ent. Soc. Wash.* **63**, 29–52.

STONE, A., KNIGHT, K. L. and STARCKE, H. (1959) *A Synoptic Catalog of the Mosquitoes of the World (Diptera, Culicidae)*. Thomas Say Foundation vol. 6, Entomological Society of America.

STONE, W. S. and REYNOLDS, F. H. K. (1939) Hibernation of anopheline eggs in the tropics. *Science* **90**, 371–372.

SUOMALAINEN, E. (1950) Parthenogenesis in animals. *Advanc. Genet.* **3**, 193–253.

SURTEES, G. (1959) Functional and morphological adaptations of the larval mouth-parts in the sub-family Culicinae (Diptera) with a review of some related studies by Montschadsky. *Proc. R. Ent. Soc. Lond.* (A). **34**, 7–16.

SUTTON, E. (1942) Salivary gland type chromosomes in mosquitoes. *Proc. Nat. Acad. Sci., Wash.* **28**, 268–272.

SUZUKI, K. (1960) Perception of movement in compound eyes studied by optomotor reaction of mosquitoes. *J. Fac. Sci. Hokkaido Univ. (Zool.)* **14**, 349–380.

SUZUKI, K. (1961) The colour sense of a mosquito, *Culex pipiens pallens* Coquillett. *Jap. J. Zool.* **13**, 185–197.

SWELLENGREBEL, N. H. (1929) La dissociation des fonctions sexuelles et nutritives (dissociation gonotrophique) d'*Anopheles maculipennis* comme cause du paludisme dans les pays-bas et ses rapports avec 'l'infection domicilaire'. *Ann. Inst. Past. Paris* **43**, 1370–1389.

SWELLENGREBEL, N. H. and DE BUCK, A. (1938) *Malaria in the Netherlands.* Scheltema and Holkema, Amsterdam.

TAKAHASHI, R. (1924) Insects living in hot springs. *Zool. Mag., Tokyo* **36**, 475–481. (In Japanese) (Cited from *Rev. Appl. Ent.* (B) (1925) **13**, 27).

TATE, P. and VINCENT, M. (1936) The biology of autogenous and anautogenous races of *Culex pipiens* L. (Diptera: Culicidae). *Parasitology* **28**, 115–145.

TEESDALE, C. (1955) Studies on the bionomics of *Aedes aegypti* (L.) in its natural habitats in a coastal region of Kenya. *Bull. Ent. Res.* **46**, 711–742, 1 pl.

TELFORD, A. D. (1957) The pasture *Aedes* of central and northern California. The egg stage: gross embryology and resistance to desiccation. *Ann. Ent. Soc. Amer.* **50**, 537–543.

TELFORD, A. D. (1958) The pasture *Aedes* of central and northern California. Seasonal history. *Ann. Ent. Soc. Amer.* **51**, 360–365.

TERZIAN, L. A., IRREVERRE, F. and STAHLER, N. (1957) A study of nitrogen and uric acid patterns in the excreta and body tissues of adult *Aedes aegypti. J. Insect Physiol.* **1**, 221–228.

TERZIAN, L. A. and STAHLER, N. (1949) The effects of larval population density on some laboratory characteristics of *Anopheles quadrimaculatus* Say. *J. Parasit.* **35**, 487–495.

TERZIAN, L. A. and STAHLER, N. (1958) A study of some effects of gamma radiation on the adults and eggs of *Aedes aegypti. Biol. Bull. Wood's Hole* **115**, 536–550.

THAYER, D. W. and TERZIAN, L. A. (1962) The free amino acids of the ageing female *Aedes aegypti* mosquito. *J. Insect Physiol.* **8**, 133–143.

THEOBALD, F. V. (1901) *A Monograph of the Culicidae or Mosquitoes,* vol. 1. British Museum (Natural History), London.

VAN THIEL, P. H. (1928) La nourriture des larves de l'*Anopheles maculipennis* en rapport avec le problème de l'existence de la variété *atroparvus. Bull. Soc. Pat. Exot.* **21**, 551–574.

VAN THIEL, P. H. (1937) Quelle sont les excitations incitant l'*Anopheles maculipennis atroparvus* à visiter et à piquer l'homme ou le bétail. *Bull. Soc. Pat. Exot.* **30**, 193–203.

VAN THIEL, P. H. (1939) On zoophilism and anthropophilism of *Anopheles* biotypes and species. *Riv. Malariol.* **18**, 95–124.

VAN THIEL, P. H. (1947) Attraction exercée sur *Anopheles maculipennis atroparvus* par l'acide carbonique dans un olfactomètre. *Acta Trop., Basel* **4**, 10–20.

VAN THIEL, P. H. and WEURMAN, C. (1947) L'attraction exercée sur *Anopheles maculipennis atroparvus* par l'acide carbonique dans l'appareil de choix II. *Acta Trop., Basel* **4**, 1–9.

THOMAS, H. D. (1943) Preliminary studies on the physiology of *Aedes aegypti*. I. The hatching of eggs under sterile conditions. *J. Parasit.* **29**, 324–327.

THOMAS, I. M. (1950) The reactions of mosquito larvae to regular repetitions of shadows as stimuli. *Aust. J. Sci. Res.* (B) **3**, 113–123.

THOMAS, T. C. E. (1951) Biting activity of *Anopheles gambiae. Brit. Med. J.* **2**, 1402.

THOMPSON M. T. (1905) Alimentary canal of the mosquito. *Proc. Boston Soc. Nat. Hist.* **32**, 145–202, 6 pl.

THOMPSON, R. P. and BROWN, A. W. A. (1955) The attractiveness of human sweat to mosquitoes and the role of carbon dioxide. *Mosquito News* **15**, 80–84.

THOMSEN, M. (1951) Weismann's ring and related organs in larvae of Diptera. *K. Danske Vidensk. Selsk.* **6**, 1–32, 14 pl.

THOMSON, R. C. M. See MUIRHEAD-THOMSON, R. C.

TISCHNER, H. (1953) Über den Gehörsinn von Stechmücken. *Acustica* **3**, 335–343.

TISCHNER, H. (1954) Das Hören der Stechmücken. *Attempto (Nachrichten für die Freunde der Tübinger Universität).* Heft **4**, 23–26.

TISCHNER, H. (1955) Gehörsinn und Fluggeräusch bei Stechmücken. *Umschau* **55**, 368–370.

TISCHNER, H. and SCHIEF, A. (1955) Fluggeräusch und Schallwahrnehmung bei *Aedes aegypti* L. (Culicidae). *Zool. Anz.,* suppl. **18**, 453–460.

TRAGER, W. (1937) Cell size in relation to the growth and metamorphosis of the mosquito, *Aedes aegypti. J. Exp. Zool.* **76**, 467–489.

TRAGER, W. (1948) Biotin and fat-soluble materials with biotin activity in the nutrition of mosquito larvae. *J. Biol. Chem.* **176**, 1211–1223.

TRAVIS, B. V. (1953) Laboratory studies on the hatching of marsh-mosquito eggs. *Mosquito News* **13**, 190–198.

TREHERNE, J. E. (1954) The exchange of labelled sodium in the larva of *Aedes aegypti* L. *J. Exp. Biol.* **31**, 386–401.

TREMBLEY, H. L. (1951) Pyloric spines in mosquitoes. *J. Nat. Malar. Soc.* **10**, 213–215.

TREMBLEY, H. L. (1952) The distribution of certain liquids in the oesophageal diverticula and stomach of mosquitoes. *Amer. J. Trop. Med. Hyg.* **1**, 693–710.

TRENSZ, F. (1933) Etude expérimentale sur la fonction des chambres à air de l'oeuf d'*Anopheles maculipennis. Arch. Inst. Pasteur Algér.* **11**, 192–197, 1 pl.

TRENSZ, F. (1934) De l'influence des rayons solaires sur le cycle évolutif de *Aedes mariae. C.R. Soc. Biol., Paris* **115**, 1108–1110.

TULLOCH, G. S. and GOLDMAN, M. (1942) The Malpighian tubules of *Aedes aegypti* L. (Diptera, Culicidae). *Bull. Brooklyn Ent. Soc.* **37**, 52–56, 1 pl.

TULLOCH, G. S. and SHAPIRO, J. E. (1951) Electron micrographs of antennal hairs of mosquitoes. *Bull. Brooklyn Ent. Soc.* **46**, 76–78.

TWOHY, D. W. and ROZEBOOM, L. E. (1957) A comparison of food reserves in autogenous and anautogenous *Culex pipiens* populations. *Amer. J. Hyg.* **65**, 316–324.

VANDEHEY, R. C. and CRAIG, G. B. (1958) Multiple fertilization demonstrated in *Aedes aegypti. Bull. Ent. Soc. Amer.* **4**, 102.

VERMEIL, C. (1953) De la reproduction par autogénèse chez *Aedes* (O.) *detritus* Haliday. *Bull. Soc. Pat. Exot.* **46**, 971–973.

VINOGRADOVA, E. B. (1960) An experimental investigation of the ecological factors inducing imaginal diapause in bloodsucking mosquitoes (Diptera, Culicidae). *Ent. Rev.* **39**, 210–219.

VINOGRADOVA, YE.B (1961) The biological isolation of subspecies of *Culex pipiens* L. (Diptera, Culicidae). *Ent. Rev.* **49**, 29–35.

VINOGRADSKAYA, O. N. (1941) The spiracle index of *Anopheles. Med. Parasit., Moscow* **10**, 401–403. (In Russian; cited from *Rev. Appl. Ent.* (B) (1943) **31**, 188).

VINOGRADSKAYA, O. N. (1942) Body temperature in *Anopheles maculipennis messeae* Fall. *Zool. Zh.* **21**, 187–195. (In Russian with English summary).

VINOGRADSKAYA, O. N. (1945) Resistance to dryness and moisture requirements in different species of *Anopheles*. *Med. Parasit., Moscow* **14**, 28–37. (In Russian; cited from *Rev. Appl. Ent.* (B) (1946) **34**, 179–180).

VINOGRADSKAYA, O. N. (1948) Functional adaptations of the abdominal spiracles in mosquitoes (Fam. Culicidae, Diptera). *Dokl. Akad. Nauk S.S.SR.* **59**, 1225–1227. (In Russian; cited from *Rev. Appl. Ent.* (B) (1949) **37**, 27).

VINOGRADSKAYA, O. N. (1950) The spiracles of *Anopheles* and their variations depending on the xerophily and hygrophily of the individual species. *Ent. Obozr.* **31**, 151–154. (In Russian; cited from *Rev. Appl. Ent.* (1953) (B) **41**, 84).

VINOGRADSKAYA, O. N. (1953) The participation of the tracheal system in the evaporation of water in *Anopheles maculipennis messeae* Fall. and the seasonal variation in the spiracle index in species of the subfamily Culicinae (Diptera, Culicidae). *Ent. Obozr.* **33**, 157–160. (In Russian; cited from *Rev. Appl. Ent.* (B) (1955) **43**, 106).

VISWANATHAN, D. K., RAO, T. R. and RAO, T. S. R. (1945) The behaviour of *Anopheles fluviatilis*. Part. IV. Experiments on the behaviour of gravid females. *J. Malar. Inst. India* **6**, 243–245.

VOGEL, R. (1921) Kritische und ergänzende Mitteilungen zur Anatomie des Stechapparats der culiciden und tabaniden. *Zool. Jb.* **42**, 259–282.

WALLIS, D. I. (1961) Response of the labellar hairs of the blowfly, *Phormia regina* Meigen, to protein. *Nature, Lond.* **191**, 917–918.

WALLIS, R. C. (1954a) A study of oviposition activity of mosquitoes. *Amer. J. Hyg.* **60**, 135–168.

WALLIS, R. C. (1954b) The effect of population density and of NaCl concentrations in test series in laboratory experiments with ovipositing *Aedes aegypti*. *Mosquito News* **14**, 200–204.

WALLIS, R. C. (1954c) Observations on oviposition of two *Aedes* mosquitoes (Diptera Culicidae). *Ann. Ent. Soc. Amer.* **47**, 393–396.

WALLIS, R. C. (1955) A study of the oviposition activity of three species of *Anopheles* in the laboratory. *Amer. J. Trop. Med. Hyg.* **4**, 557–563.

WATERHOUSE, D. F. (1953) The occurrence and significance of the peritrophic membrane, with special reference to adult Lepidoptera and Diptera. *Aust. J. Zool.* **1**, 299–318, 2 pl.

WEINER, J. S. and HELLMANN, K. (1960) The sweat glands. *Biol. Rev.* **35**, 141–186.

WEITZ, B. (1960) Feeding habits of bloodsucking arthropods. *Exp. Parasit.* **9**, 63–82.

WELLINGTON, W. G. (1945) The effect of ground temperature inversions upon the flight activity of *Culex* sp. (Diptera, Culicidae). *Canad. Ent.* **76**, 223.

WENK, P. (1961) Die Muskulatur der Mandibel einiger blutsaugender Culiciden. *Zool. Anz.* **167**, 254–259.

WESENBERG-LUND, C. (1921) Contributions to the biology of the Danish Culicidae. *K. Danske Vidensk. Selsk.* **7**, 1–210, 21 pl.

WEST, A. S. and HUDSON, A. (1959) Reactions to insect bites. *Proc. N.J. Mosq. Ext. Ass.* **46**, 140–148.

WEYER, F. (1934) Der Einfluss der Larvalernährung auf die Fortpflanzungsphysiologie verschiedener Stechmücken. *Arch. Schiffs-u. Tropenhyg.* **38**, 394–398.

WHARTON, R. H. (1953a) The habits of adult mosquitoes in Malaya. III. Feeding preferences of anophelines. *Ann. Trop. Med. Parasit.* **47**, 272–284.

WHARTON, R. H. (1953b) The habits of adult mosquitoes in Malaya. IV. Swarming of anophelines in nature. *Ann. Trop. Med. Parasit.* **47**, 285–290.

WHARTON, R. H. (1959) Age determination in *Mansonioides* mosquitoes. *Nature, Lond.* **811**, 830.

WHEELER, R. E. and JONES, J. C. (1960) The mechanics of copulation in *Aedes aegypti* (L.) mosquitoes. *Anat. Rec.* **138**, 388.

WHITE, M. J. D. (1954) *Animal Cytology and Evolution.* Cambridge University Press, 2nd ed.

WHITE, R. H. (1961) Analysis of the development of the compound eye in the mosquito, *Aedes aegypti. J. Exp. Zool.* **148**, 223–239.

WIGGLESWORTH, V. B. (1929) Delayed metamorphosis in a predaceous mosquito larva and a possible practical application. *Nature, Lond.* **123**, 17.

WIGGLESWORTH, V. B. (1930) The formation of the peritrophic membrane in insects, with special reference to the larvae of mosquitoes. *Quart. J. Micr. Sci.* **73**, 593–616.

WIGGLESWORTH, V. B. (1932) On the function of the so-called 'rectal glands' of insects. *Quart. J. Micr. Sci.* **75**, 131–150.

WIGGLESWORTH, V. B. (1933a) The effect of salts on the anal gills of the mosquito larva. *J. Exp. Biol.* **10**, 1–15.

WIGGLESWORTH, V. B. (1933b) The function of the anal gills of the mosquito larva. *J. Exp. Biol.* **10**, 16–26.

WIGGLESWORTH, V. B. (1933c) The adaptation of mosquito larvae to salt water. *J. Exp. Biol.* **10**, 27–37.

WIGGLESWORTH, V. B. (1938a) The regulation of osmotic pressure and chloride concentration in the haemolymph of mosquito larvae. *J. Exp. Biol.* **15**, 235–247.

WIGGLESWORTH, V. B. (1938b) The absorption of fluid from the tracheal system of mosquito larvae at hatching and moulting. *J. Exp. Biol.* **15**, 248–254.

WIGGLESWORTH, V. B. (1942) The storage of protein, fat, glycogen and uric acid in the fat body and other tissues of mosquito larvae. *J. Exp. Biol.* **19**, 56–77.

WIGGLESWORTH, V. B. (1943) The fate of haemoglobin in *Rhodnius prolixus* (Hemiptera) and other blood-sucking arthropods. *Proc. Roy. Soc.* (B) **131**, 313–339.

WIGGLESWORTH, V. B. (1949) The physiology of mosquitoes, pp. 284–301. (In BOYD, M. F. (ed.) *Malariology,* vol. 1, Saunders, Philadelphia and London).

WILLIAMS, C. A. (1956) Digestion of serum proteins by *Aedes aegypti. Proc. Fourteenth int. Congr. Ent.*, 1953, p. 278.

WILLIAMS, C. M. (1960) The juvenile hormone. *Acta Endocrinol.,* Suppl. 50, 189–191.

WILLIAMSON, K. B. (1928) Mosquito breeding and malaria in relation to the nitrogen cycle. *Bull. Ent. Res.* **18**, 433–439.

WILLIS, E. R. (1947) The olfactory responses of female mosquitoes. *J. Econ. Ent.* **40**, 769–778.

WILLIS, E. R. and ROTH, L. M. (1952) Reactions of *Aedes aegypti* (L.) to carbon dioxide. *J. Exp. Zool.* **121**, 149–179.

WISHART, G. and RIORDAN, D. F. (1959) Flight responses to various sounds by adult males of *Aedes aegypti* (L.) (Diptera: Culicidae). *Canad. Ent.* **91**, 181–191.

WOKE, P. A. (1937a) Effects of various blood fractions on egg production of *Aedes aegypti* Linn. *Amer. J. Hyg.* **25**, 372–380.

WOKE, P. A. (1937b) Comparative effects of the blood of man and of canary on egg-production of *Culex pipiens* Linn. *J. Parasit.* **23**, 311–313.

WOKE, P. A. (1937c) Comparative effects of the blood of different species of vertebrates on egg-production of *Aedes aegypti* Linn. *Amer. J. Trop. Med.* **17**, 729–745.

WOKE, P. A. (1955) Deferred oviposition in *Aedes aegypti* (Linnaeus) (Diptera: Culicidae). *Ann. Ent. Soc. Amer.* **48**, 39–46.

WOKE, P. A., ALLY, M. S. and ROSENBERGER, C. R. (1956) The numbers of eggs developed related to the quantities of human blood ingested in *Aedes aegypti* (L.) (Diptera: Culicidae). *Ann. Ent. Soc. Amer.* **49**, 435–441.

WOOD, R. J. (1961) Oviposition in DDT-resistant and susceptible strains of *Aedes aegypti* (L.) in relation to light preference. *Bull. Ent. Res.* **52**, 541–560.

WOODHILL, A. R. (1936) Observations and experiments on *Aedes concolor*, Tayl. (Dipt. Culic.). *Bull. Ent. Res.* **27**, 633–648.

WOODHILL, A. R. (1941) The development of *Aedes* (*Pseudoskusea*) *concolor* Taylor in relation to small quantities of salts in solution and to the temperature of the water. *Proc. Linn. Soc. N.S.W.* **66**, 396–400.

WOOLLEY, T. A. (1943) The metamorphosis of the nervous system of *Aedes dorsalis* Meigen (Diptera: Culicidae). *Ann. Ent. Soc. Amer.* **36**, 432–447.

WRIGHT, R. H. (1958) The olfactory guidance of flying insects. *Canad. Ent.* **90**, 81–89.

WRIGHT, W. R. (1927) On the effects of exposure to raised temperatures upon the larvae of certain British mosquitoes. *Bull. Ent. Res.* **18**, 91–94.

WYKES, G. R. (1952) An investigation of the sugars present in the nectar of flowers of various species. *New Phytol.* **51**, 210–215.

YAGUZHINSKAYA, L. V. (1940) Présence d'une membrane péritrophique dans l'estomac de la femelle adulte d'*Anopheles maculipennis*. *Med. Parasit., Moscow* **9**, 601–603. (In Russian with French summary).

YAGUZHINSKAYA, L. V. (1954) New data on the physiology and anatomy of the dipteran heart. (Structure and function of the heart of *Anopheles maculipennis* Mgn.). *Byull. Mosk. Obshch. Ispyatelej Prirody. Otd. Biol.* **59**, 41–50. (In Russian).

YEOLI, M. and MER, G. G. (1938) The relation of blood feeds to the maturation of ova in *Anopheles elutus*. *Trans. R. Soc. Trop. Med. Hyg.* **31**, 437–444.

YORKE, W. and MACFIE, J. W. S. (1924) The action of the salivary secretion of mosquitoes and *Glossina tachinoides* on human blood. *Ann. Trop. Med. Parasit.* **18**, 103–108.

YOUNG, C. J. (1922) Notes on the bionomics of *Stegomyia calopus*, Meigen, in Brazil. Part I. *Ann. Trop. Med. Parasit.* **16**, 389–406.

ZALUTSKAYA, L. I. (1959) Comparative data on the biology of *Anopheles minimus* and *Anopheles vagus* in the vicinity of Tay-Nguen (Democratic Republic of Vietnam). *Med. Parasit., Moscow* **28**, 548–553. (In Russian with English summary. Cited from Gillies, 1961).

DE ZULUETA, J. (1950) Comparative oviposition experiments with caged mosquitoes. *Amer. J. Hyg.* **52**, 133–142.

DE ZULUETA, J. and BATES, M. (1948) Laboratory experiments with selection of oviposition site by *Anopheles darlingi*. *Amer. J. Hyg.* **48**, 350–360.

AUTHOR INDEX

LANG, S. in BERG *et al.* (1948) 231

LANG, W. D. (1920) 55

LARSEN, E. B. (1948) 245, 251

LARSEN, J. R. (1958) 179; *et al.* (1959) 172, 178–181

LAURENCE, B. R. (1959) 304; (1960) 296, 304

LAVEN, H. (1955) 21, 23; (1956) 24; (1957a) 23; (1957b) 23; (1959) 23; *et al.* (1956) 112; in KRISHNAMURTHY *et al.* (1961) 175; in KITZMILLER *et al.* (1958) 298; in MATTINGLY *et al.* (1951) 290

LAVOIPIERRE, M. M. J. (1958a) 121, 184, 237, 269; (1958b) 269; (1961) 122; in GOLBERG *et al.* (1945) 48

LEA, A. O. *et al.* (1956) 45; *et al.* (1958) 45–48, 152, 161; in DIMOND *et al.* (1956) 158–160; in DIMOND *et al.* (1958) 160; unpublished, 156, 157

LEES, A. D. (1955) 221, 232

LEESON, H. S. (1931) 237

LEFTWICH, A. W. (1954) 219

LENGY, J. I. in FEIR *et al.* (1961) 213, 214

LEOPOLD, R. S. in DECOURSEY *et al.* (1953) 183

LE PRINCE, J. A. *et al.* (1916) 263, 288

LEWIS, D. J. (1933) 120, 268; (1939) 303; (1949) 54, 55

LICHTENSTEIN, E. P. (1948) 49

LIEB, F. in JETTMAR *et al.* (1949) 74

LILES, J. N. *et al.* (1960) 121

LO, S. C. in HO *et al.* (1945) 301

LOVE, G. J. *et al.* (1955) 227–230; *et al.* (1957) 119; in PLATT *et al.* (1958) 250

LUM, P. T. M. (1961a) 164, 297, 298; (1961b) 164, 297, 299; in VAN HANDEL *et al.* (1962) 156; in HORSFALL *et al.* (1957) 31, 223; in HORSFALL *et al.* (1958) 221

LUMSDEN, W. H. R. (1947) 267, 268; (1951) 260; (1952) 247, 251; in GORDON *et al.* (1939) 131, 138; in SEATON *et al.* (1941) 268

LUND, H. O. (1942) 305

MACAN, T. T. (1950) 173; (1961) 69, 303

MCCLELLAND, G. A. H. (1958) 306; (1959) 268; (1960a) 268; (1960b) 22, 281; (1962) 22

MCDANIEL, I. N. *et al.* (1957) 299

MACDONALD, G. (1952a) 122, 125; (1952b) 122; (1957) 122

MACDONALD, W. W. (1956) 169, 268, 269; (1960) 303; *et al.* (1960) 28, 128, 220

MACFIE, J. W. S. (1915) 183; (1917) 54, 55; in YORKE *et al.* (1924) 146

MCGREGOR, I. A. in BERTRAM *et al.* (1956) 288

MACGREGOR, M. E. (1921) 69; (1929) 69; (1932) 116

MACKENNA, R. M. B. *et al.* (1950) 278

MCKIEL, J. A. (1959) 147–150; *et al.* (1960) 148; *et al.* (1961a) 147, 148; *et al.* (1961b) 149; in HUDSON *et al.* (1958) 148

MCKINLEY, E. B. *et al.* (1930) 149

MAGER, J. in AVI-DOR *et al.* (1958) 156

MAJID, A. in AFRIDI *et al.* (1940) 120

MANEFIELD, T. (1951) 308

MARCOVITCH, S. (1960) 73

MARKOVICH, N. Ya. (1941) 175

MARKS, E. N. (1954) 80, 81; (1958) 198, 295

MARSHALL, J. F. (1938) 26, 31, 185; *et al.* (1932) 85, 86; *et al.* (1935) 132; *et al.* (1936) 175

MARTINI, E. *et al.* (1933) 253; in HUNDERTMARK *et al.* (1938) 255

WATTAL, B. L. in BHATIA *et al.* (1957) 145

WEBSTER, A. P. in DECOURSEY *et al.* (1952) 183; in DECOURSEY *et al.* (1953) 183

WEINER, J. S. *et al.* (1960) 278

WEITZ, B. (1960) 290

WELLINGTON, W. G. (1945) 250

WENK, P. (1961) 131

WESENBERG-LUND, C. (1921) 54

WEST, A. S. *et al.* (1959) 149; in ALLEN *et al.* (1962) 149; in McKIEL *et al.* (1961a) 147,
    148; in McKIEL *et al.* (1961b) 149; in HUDSON *et al.* (1958) 148

WEURMAN, C. in VAN THIEL *et al.* (1947) 278, 289

WEYER, F. (1934) 175

WHARTON, R. H. (1953a) 290; (1953b) 297; (1959) 189

WHEATLEY, V. R. in MACKENNA *et al.* (1950) 278

WHEELER, R. E. *et al.* (1960) 296, 297

WHELCHEL, J. G. in LOVE *et al.* (1955) 227–230; in LOVE *et al.* (1957) 119

WHITE, M. J. D. (1954) 24

WHITE, R. H. (1961) 92, 94

WIGGLESWORTH, V. B. (1929) 73; (1930) 40; (1932) 161; (1933a) 57, 59; (1933b) 51,
    54, 57, 64, 65; (1933c) 51, 70; (1938a) 58, 62–64, 70, 71; (1938b) 32, 82, 83; (1942)
    41, 43, 44, 49–52; (1943) 112, 153; (1949) 70

WILLIAMS, C. A. (1956) 153, 154

WILLIAMS, C. M. (1960) 74

WILLIAMS, E. L. in PLATT *et al.* (1958) 250

WILLIAMSON, K. B. (1928) 69

WILLIS, E. R. (1947) 276, 277; *et al.* (1952) 275, 285–287; in ROTH *et al.* (1952) 196,
    197, 199, 216, 217, 285–287

WISHART, G. *et al.* (1959) 293, 294

WITHERSPOON, J. P. in PLATT *et al.* (1957) 120, 253–255

WOKE, P. A. (1937a) 158; (1937b) 161; (1937c) 161; (1955) 183, 184; *et al.* (1956) 185,
    186

WOOD, R. J. (1961) 305

WOODHILL, A. R. (1936) 69; (1941) 71; in SMITH-WHITE *et al.* (1955) 24

WOOLLEY, T. A. (1943) 91, 103

WORMALL, A. in MACKENNA *et al.* (1950) 278

WRIGHT, R. H. (1958) 265, 282

WRIGHT, W. R. (1927) 119

WYKES, G. R. (1952) 155

YAGUZHINSKAYA, L. V. (1940) 134; (1954) 109–111

YATES, W. W. in GJULLIN *et al.* (1950) 220, 222, 227

YEOLI, M. *et al.* (1938) 158

YORKE, W. *et al.* (1924) 146

YOUNG, C. J. (1922) 223

YOUNG, M. D. in BURGESS *et al.* (1944) 268

ZALUTSKAYA, L. I. (1959) 125

ZARO, J. A. in DARSIE *et al.* (1945) 150

ZUBAREVA, S. P. in DANILOVA *et al.* (1932) 73

DE ZULUETA, J. (1950) 305, 308; *et al.* (1948) 305, 306

ZWEIG, G. in ILTIS *et al.* (1962) 30

SUBJECT INDEX

References to tables are given in *italics* and to figures in **bold** type.

Abdominal muscles, **50,** 99, *104,* 107
Absorption,
  of digestion products, 43, **44,** 136, 154
Accessory glands, 164, **165,** 168
Accessory gland secretion, 164, 297–299
Accessory hearts, 110, **111**
Acclimatization,
  to pressure, 256
  to temperature, 125–127
Activation, 265, 270, 273, 276, 277
Activation centre, 16, 19, 20
Adenosine-5'-phosphate, 142, *143,* 144
Aedeagus, 164, **165,** 166
Aestivation,
  of adults, 236, 237
  of eggs, 220
Age,
  estimation of, 188–190
  at time of biting, 247, 248, 268
  composition, *124,* 125
Agglutinin, 145, 146, 149
Air sacs, 53
Alarm response, 125, 126, 238–241
Alighting, 270, 273, 274, 276, 291
Alimentary canal,
  adult, 132, **133,** 134–136
  air in, 85, **86**
  cytogenetics of, 95, 103, *104,* 105,
    106, 107
  larval, 38, **39,** 40–42
  metamorphosis, 94, 95, **96,** 97, 98
Allergy, 148, 150
Allometric growth, 90, 91
Amino acids,
  essential, 45, *46,* 47, 158, *159*
  free, 113
  in excreta, 162, *163*
  in haemolymph, 112
  level in tissues, 113
  requirements of larva, 45, *46,* 47, 49

requirements of adult, 158, *159,* 160,
  161
response to, 279, *280*
Amnion, **5,** 6, 9
Amniotic fold, **7, 8,** 9
Ampulla, 168, 182, 188
Amputation,
  of flagella, 205, 209
  of sense organs, 285–287
Anal canal, 106
  adult, 134
  larval, **39,** 41, **57**
  metamorphosis, 97, 105
Anal papillae,
  growth, 12, 72
  physiology, 54, 58, 59
  structure, 54, **57,** 58
Anal ring, 97, 98, **106**
Antennae, 196–213
  amputation of, 205, 209, 264, 265,
    285–287
  buds, 87, **88, 89**
  endoskeleton, **199**
  fibrillae, 107, 205, 245, 296
  pulsating organ, 110, **111**
  resonance frequency, 205, 206, 207
  sensilla, 198, 199, 200
  structure, 196–204
Anterior imaginal ring, 39, 95, 96, **106**
Anthropophilic species, 289
Antibiotics, 49
Antibodies, 148, 156
Anticoagulin, 145, 146, 150
Aorta, 109–111, 176, 177
Appetitive behaviour, 291
Apposition image, 193
Artificial insemination, 299
Atmospheric pressure, 255, 256
Attraction to host, 288–291
Attraction to water, 304

373

SPECIES INDEX

References to tables are given in *italics* and to figures in **bold** type.